Contaminated Land and Groundwater: Future Directions

Geological Society Engineering Geology Special Publications
Series Editor M. E. Barton

It is recommended that reference to all or part of this book should be made in one of the following ways:

Lerner, D. N. & Walton, N. R. G. (eds) 1998. *Contaminated Land and Groundwater: Future Directions*. Geological Society, London, Engineering Geology Special Publications, **14**.

Lindsay, P., Bell, F. G. & Hytiris, N. 1998. Contamination of sediments in the Forth Estuary, Scotland. *In*: Lerner, D. N. & Walton, N. R. G. (eds) *Contaminated Land and Groundwater: Future Directions*. Geological Society, London, Engineering Geology Special Publications, **14**, 179–187.

Geological Society Engineering Geology Special Publication No. 14

Contaminated Land and Groundwater: Future Directions

EDITED BY

D. N. Lerner
Department of Civil and Environmental Engineering,
University of Bradford, West Yorkshire
BD7 1DP, UK

N. R. G. Walton
Department of Geology, University of Portsmouth,
Burnaby Building, Burnaby Road, Portsmouth
PO1 3QL, UK

1998
Published by
The Geological Society
London

THE GEOLOGICAL SOCIETY

The Society was founded in 1807 as The Geological Society of London and is the oldest geological society in the world. It received its Royal Charter in 1825 for the purpose of 'investigating the mineral structure of the Earth'. The Society is Britain's national society for geology with a membership of around 8000. It has countrywide coverage and approximately 1000 members reside overseas. The Society is responsible for all aspects of the geological sciences including professional matters. The Society has its own publishing house, which produces the Society's international journals, books and maps, and which acts as the European distributor for publications of the American Association of Petroleum Geologists, SEPM and the Geological Society of America.

Fellowship is open to those holding a recognized honours degree in geology or cognate subject and who have at least two years' relevant postgraduate experience, or who have not less than six years' relevant experience in geology or a cognate subject. A Fellow who has not less than five years' relevant postgraduate experience in the practice of geology may apply for validation and, subject to approval, may be able to use the designatory letters C Geol (Chartered Geologist).

Further information about the Society is available from the Membership Manager, The Geological Society, Burlington House, Piccadilly, London W1V 0JU, UK. The Society is a Registered Charity, No. 210161.

Published by The Geological Society from:
The Geological Society Publishing House
Unit 7 Brassmill Enterprise Centre
Brassmill Lane
Bath BA1 3JN
UK
(*Orders*: Tel. 01225 445046
        Fax 01225 442836)

First published 1998

The publishers make no representation, express or implied, with regard to the accuracy of the information contained in this book and cannot accept any legal responsibility for any errors or omissions that may be made.

British Library Cataloguing in Publication Data
A catalogue record for this book is available from the British Library.

ISBN 1–86239–001–0
ISSN 0267–9914

Typeset by Aarontype Ltd, Unit 47, Easton Business Centre, Felix Road, Bristol BS5 0HE, UK.

Printed by The Alden Press, Osney Mead, Oxford, UK.

Distributors

USA
AAPG Bookstore
PO Box 979
Tulsa
OK 74101-0979
USA
(*Orders*: Tel. (918) 584-2555
        Fax (918) 560-2652)

Australia
Australian Mineral Foundation
63 Conyngham Street
Glenside
South Australia 5065
Australia
(*Orders*: Tel. (08) 379-0444
        Fax (08) 379-4634)

India
Affiliated East-West Press PVT Ltd
G-1/16 Ansari Road
New Delhi 110 002
India
(*Orders:* Tel. (11) 327-9113
        Fax (11) 326-0538)

Japan
Kanda Book Trading Co.
Tanikawa Building
3-2 Kanda Surugadai
Chiyoda-Ku
Tokyo 101
Japan
(*Orders*: Tel. (03) 3255-3497
        Fax (03) 3255-3495)

Contents

Section 5: Research on pollutant behaviour

Preface

Contaminated land and groundwater are major environmental issues in all industrialized countries, and will become so throughout the world in the next century. The threat of both health and environmental liabilities drives land holders to investigate, and sometimes restore, their sites. However, the lack of good technical and cost effective solutions hampers restoration. The currently dominant technology of *dig and dump* is clearly unsustainable in the long term, with its transfer of contaminant loads into valuable landfill space combined with all the associated traffic hazards.

The future handling of these problems must be more sophisticated, and is likely to include:

- better and cheaper site investigation tools, to give more confidence and higher precision to our understanding of individual sites
- risk assessment techniques which are not only practical to use but also reliable, to move away from the currently simple standards-based decisions towards more realistic risk-based assessments of priorities
- alternative restoration techniques, including the acceptance of natural attenuation, and the development of ways to overcome the long time constants which are caused by diffusion in heterogeneous geological environments
- research-based understanding of pollutant behaviour, in order to derive better models and hence better site investigation, risk assessment, and restoration techniques

This book is based on the papers presented to the Geological Society conference *Contaminated Land and Groundwater: Future Directions* which was convened jointly by the Engineering and Hydrogeological Groups. The meeting was hosted by the University of Portsmouth in September 1996. Selected papers from the meeting have been refereed and revised, and some new papers have been commissioned. They cover many of the issues listed above with a number dealing with risk and economically based approaches. Notable absences are new restoration technologies, although several deal with natural attenuation of contaminants. Overall, the book emphasizes policy, decision making, and contaminant behaviour, but includes site investigation and case studies from the field. We hope it will remain a valuable resource for both practitioners and researchers into the next century.

David Lerner   Nick Walton
Bradford   Portsmouth

Acknowledgements

This volume is only possible though the generous support of many individuals and organizations to whom the editors extend their thanks. The sponsors of the *Contaminated Land and Groundwater: Future Directions* conference were:

- Environment Agency
- Scott Wilson Kirkpatrick
- Southern Science
- University of Portsmouth
- Portsmouth City Council

The national and local committees comprised:

Organizing Committee

Chair	David Lerner	University of Bradford
Local Chair	Nick Walton	University of Portsmouth
Treasurer	Neil Moseley	ENTEC UK Ltd
Secretary	Carol Bamsey	Hyder Environmental
Exhibition	David Giles	University of Portsmouth
Publicity	Paul Ashley	Parsons Engineering Science
Workshops	Steve Moncaster	Golder Associates (UK) Ltd
Engineering Group	Martin Culshaw	British Geological Survey

Local Organization

Mrs L. Jackson	University of Portsmouth
Mr P. W. McDowell	University of Portsmouth
Ms D. Moody	Portsmouth City Council
Mrs J. Woodford	University of Portsmouth

The referees of the papers in this volume were:

A. Al-Tabbaa	Dick Flavin	J. Mather
Paul Ashley	C. Ferguson	Brian Morris
Stephen Banwart	M. Fermor	C. Nathanail
Paul Bardos	Steven Foster	M. Ramsey
J. Barker	D. C. Gooddy	Mike Rivett
R. Bewley	Paul Hardisty	C. G. Shields
Richard Boak	Bob Harris	Steve Thornton
M. Carey	Sue Herbert	Peter Tucker
Martin Chapple	Stefan Jefferis	Nick Walton
Stella Christie	P. Kennedy	R. Watkinson
L. Coates	A. Lawrence	Chris White
D. Cox	Stephen Leharne	G. Williams
Martin Culshaw	David Lerner	
Jane Dottridge	Doug Mackay	

And not least, our thanks go to Janet Holland (University of Bradford) who handled all the paperwork of the preprints, refereeing and this volume with customary good humour.

SECTION 1

CLEANUP OF CONTAMINATED LAND AND GROUNDWATER

Is cleanup of VOC-contaminated groundwater feasible?

D. M. Mackay

Department of Earth Sciences, University of Waterloo, Waterloo, Ontario, Canada N2L 3G1

Abstract. VOCs are the organic contaminants most widely detected in public supply wells. Due to the complexity of VOC behaviour in the subsurface and the disappointing performance of many past attempts at site remediation, it appears that for many VOC-contaminated sites complete remediation of the subsurface may be practically infeasible for the foreseeable future. The contaminants do not reside solely in the easily extractable groundwater, but also in less readily treated non-aqueous phase liquid phases, sorbed phases and dissolved phases within relatively lower permeability media. Thus complete remediation is not directed solely at 'groundwater', *per se*, but at all locations of subsurface contaminant mass. New technologies under investigation may improve prospects for complete remediation, but the problems yet to be solved are many. Thus there has been a justified shift of attention to approaches to limit the migration of plumes and thereby control the risks they pose. These migration control approaches return the attention solely to groundwater, but specifically at that passing through a selected cross-section of the subsurface. With these and other technologies under development, there may soon be a range of tools available for remediation which will match the range of remediation goals necessitated by the site-specific complexities of VOC contamination.

The complexity of subsurface VOC contamination

Volatile organic chemicals (VOCs) are the most commonly detected organic contaminants in water supply wells in the United States (Westrick 1990; Mackay & Smith 1993). Although only preliminary attempts have been made to summarize information from other countries, the evidence compiled to date indicates that VOCs are prevalent groundwater contaminants worldwide (e.g. Mackay & Smith 1993; Mackay & Rivett 1993). In the US, chlorinated hydrocarbon compounds are by far the most commonly detected of the VOCs; petroleum hydrocarbons are, by comparison, rarely detected in public supply wells (Westrick 1990), presumably due largely to *in situ* biodegradation (Hadley & Armstrong 1991). The chlorinated hydrocarbons most commonly detected include perchloroethene (PCE), trichloroethene (TCE) and 1,1,1-trichloroethane (TCA), and carbon tetrachloride (CT), all of which have been widely used as industrial solvents. Also detected are 1,2-dichloroethane (1,2-DCA), c-1,2-dichlorethene (cDCE), 1,1-dichloroethene (1,1-DCE) and chloroethene (also known as vinyl chloride, VC), which in many cases appear to have been produced by biotic or abiotic transformations of PCE, TCE or TCA in the subsurface (e.g. Westrick 1990; McCarty & Semprini 1994), and chloroform (trichloromethane, TCM) and dichloromethane (DCM or methylene chloride) which may be produced by *in situ* transformations of carbon tetrachloride (e.g. McCarty & Semprini 1994).

In their pure form at ambient temperatures, many of the VOCs are liquids, often called NAPLs (non-aqueous-phase liquids), which are sparingly soluble in water. The petroleum hydrocarbons are referred to as LNAPLs because they are less dense ('lighter') than water whereas the chlorinated solvents are referred to as DNAPLs because they are denser than water. In the following, although we focus on DNAPLs as the VOCs least amenable to remediation, many of the general issues apply to remediation of LNAPLs as well. When released to the subsurface in sufficient quantities, the majority of the chlorinated solvent mass may migrate as a DNAPL. Depending on the amount and rate of release and the hydrogeological conditions, the DNAPLs may penetrate downwards through the unsaturated zone and into or through saturated strata. This is known to occur in granular as well as fractured media, and vertical penetration into and even through deposits that would generally be considered competent aquitards is indicated by a variety of anecdotal evidence (Feenstra *et al.* 1996).

Plumes of dissolved VOCs are produced, in part, as the DNAPL within the saturated zone is dissolved by the groundwater passing by. In the context of groundwater remediation, this latter point is very important since a very concentrated reservoir of the contaminants, i.e. the DNAPL, may exist in the deep unsaturated zone and even in the saturated zone itself, below the reach of excavation and other direct source remediation efforts. Such deep DNAPL in effect becomes the most significant portion of the source for long-term production of the groundwater contaminant plume. Because the VOCs are sparingly soluble and because of limitations to the

MACKAY, D. M. 1998. Is cleanup of VOC-contaminated groundwater feasible? *In*: LERNER, D. N. & WALTON, N. R. G. (eds) 1998. *Contaminated Land and Groundwater: Future Directions*. Geological Society, London, Engineering Geology Special Publications, **14**, 3–11.

mass transfer processes involved in DNAPL dissolution in the subsurface, the times for complete dissolution of typical subsurface DNAPL 'sources' by natural groundwater flow in porous (granular) media are often estimated to be decades or centuries (Johnson & Pankow 1992; Feenstra & Guiger 1996). Unfortunately, because of geological heterogeneities, the distribution of DNAPLs in the subsurface is typically very complex (e.g. Mackay & Cherry 1989; Feenstra *et al.* 1996). Since even 'large' releases of DNAPL may often be a very small fraction of the total volume of subsurface media within which they reside, the locations of DNAPL are typically virtually impossible to determine with common monitoring methods and sampling densities (Feenstra & Cherry 1996).

The plumes that emanate from DNAPL sources, like all plumes, follow the preferential paths of highest hydraulic conductivity, but also invade adjacent regions of lower conductivity by advection and/or diffusion. In granular media, the lower conductivity regions may be lenses within the generally more permeable medium or bounding layers such as aquitards or even the capillary fringe and zone of water-table fluctuation. In fractured media wherein the matrix itself is porous, the matrix comprises the lower permeability zone into which the contaminant may invade. Since chlorinated solvents have been in widespread use since World War II, many VOC plumes have been migrating uncontrolled for decades. Although dissolved VOCs migrate at an average velocity which is less than the average velocity of the groundwater, due to sorptive interactions with the geological media along the path, this 'retardation' due to sorption is often relatively minor for the constituents most commonly detected in water supply wells (e.g. see Mackay (1984) for some examples of field-determined retardation factors). Thus, there are many examples in the United States of chlorinated VOC plumes in sand and gravel aquifers that are kilometres in length and contain billions of litres of contaminated water (Mackay & Cherry 1989; Harman *et al.* 1993). Furthermore, contaminants have invaded the lower permeability media within or adjacent to the permeable paths of these older plumes. Although not always the case, sorption is sometimes more significant in the lower permeability media, which means that in such cases the lower permeability zones have an extra capacity for the contaminant as compared to the permeable paths on a volumetric basis. However, when the total mass of contaminant residing within the plume is estimated on the basis of monitoring data, rarely does the estimate exceed a few thousand litres. Although such estimates typically do not account for sorbed contaminants, this nevertheless means that, in many cases even years after the onset of the contamination, the majority of the VOC mass in the subsurface remains within the subsurface DNAPL-invaded zone (Mackay & Cherry 1989; Harman *et al.* 1996; Feenstra *et al.* 1996).

Thus, a VOC groundwater problem should almost always be considered to be composed of two parts, the subsurface source zone and the plume, which have very different amounts and distributions of contaminant mass (Mackay & Cherry 1989). In the early years of efforts to remediate VOC-contaminated subsurface zones, this distinction regarding mass distribution was not realized and, further, neither was the importance of low permeability zones. As described below, these misconceptions led to extremely unrealistic expectations regarding the efficiency and rapidity of subsurface remediation. Now, given more detailed understanding of the nature of the problem and the processes controlling the removal or *in situ* destruction of contaminant mass, a new set of expectations has developed, in large part more reasonable, but not without its own, albeit new, set of potential misconceptions. To answer the question 'Is cleanup of VOC-contaminated groundwater feasible?', we need to examine in some detail this historical development of expectations and remediation technologies and, as we will see, more carefully define the question.

'Complete' remediation by pump and treat?

By far the most common method applied to date for control or remediation of contaminated groundwater is the pump-and-treat method (P&T) in which contaminated groundwater is extracted, treated in above-ground facilities and disposed, reinfiltrated or reinjected. In the very early days of its implementation, the expectations were that the problem would be solved if little more than the volume of the plume (the contaminated 'pore volume') were extracted; thus the systems were designed with advection and perhaps dispersion in mind, but without consideration of LNAPL or DNAPL source zones or the contaminant mass residing in low permeability zones or sorbed phases. Time frames for completion of remediation were often expected to be in the range of 1–10 years, but such expectations were rarely met. Instead, the progress of P&T generally appeared to follow a trend of relatively rapid decrease in extracted concentration as or after the first pore volume was removed, until a concentration was reached which was generally above (often far above) the cleanup goals; additional pumping appeared to achieve little, if any, subsequent reduction in extracted concentration. Furthermore, if pumping were ceased, concentrations in the extractable groundwater would often 'rebound' to higher levels (e.g. Feenstra & Cherry 1996).

It is now generally agreed that such results arise from three basic limits to remediation by P&T, in order of general importance: (1) the subsurface DNAPL source zones that dissolve only very slowly; (2) the presence of contaminants within impermeable regions that 'bleed' contaminants back into the more permeable zones once

P&T has reduced the concentrations therein; and (3) the sorbed contaminant mass that also 'bleeds' slowly back into the groundwater (desorption having been found to be much more of a rate-limited process than originally envisioned). Phenomena that had previously been lumped into the rather vague term 'rebound' can now be subdivided a bit more clearly into 'regrowth' or 'regeneration' of plumes caused by continued emanation of contaminant mass from subsurface source zones after source control efforts are ceased (e.g. cessation of P&T downgradient of source zones) and 'rebound' of concentrations within existing plumes when the velocity of the water in the permeable strata is reduced (e.g. by cessation or lessening of P&T rates) caused, in essence, by less dilution of the flux of contaminant mass diffusing from low permeability zones or sorbed phases.

The importance of plume regrowth or rebound, and thus the effectiveness of P&T itself, clearly depends on the situation. There have been numerous reviews of the effectiveness of P&T in the US, the most comprehensive of which was conducted by a committee empanelled by the National Research Council (NRC 1994; MacDonald & Kavanaugh 1994). The committee reviewed data from 77 sites at which P&T systems were in operation. At 69 of the sites, cleanup goals had not been reached despite years of pumping although it was acknowledged that the goals might conceivably be reached in the future at some of those sites. The report stated (NRC 1994, p. 4) that 'the apparent success of remediation at the remaining eight sites suggests that in special circumstances, cleanup in a relatively short time period (less than a decade) may be possible.'

Thus, despite the generally negative reputation that P&T has gained in many circles, there is, in fact, evidence that goals for 'complete' cleanup (i.e. no further action required) can be met in selected cases with this technology. The NRC committee (NRC 1994) concluded that the relative ease of complete cleanup of contaminated aquifers by P&T could be viewed as a function of the nature of the contamination and the complexity of the hydrogeological environment in which the contamination existed or was migrating. Table 1 is drawn from that study (table ES-1 in NRC 1994). The easiest to remediate sites have a rating of 1 in this table; the most difficult a rating of 4. Of the 8 out of 77 sites reviewed by the committee which reached cleanup goals, one had a rating of 1 (small gasoline leak at a service station), four had a rating of 2 and three had a rating of 3 (all of which were gasoline leaks). None of the 42 sites with a rating of 4 had reached cleanup goals. Where complete cleanup was not achieved or perhaps achievable in a reasonable time frame, it was often noted that P&T was effective at plume migration control, i.e. preventing further expansion of the extent of contamination, and sometimes achieved reduction or removal of the plume, although the source zone remained.

Overall, then, the reviews of P&T performance have generally concluded that: (1) where contaminant characteristics and hydrogeology are not simple, P&T generally is ineffective for 'complete' remediation (removal of all or sufficient contaminant mass so that no problem re-emerges after cessation of P&T), (2) when 'complete' remediation is an elusive goal, P&T can be effective for plume migration control, and therefore for

Table 1. *Relative ease of cleanup of contaminated subsurface media as a function of the nature of the contamination and the complexity of the hydrogeological conditions, adapted from NRC (1994). The relative ease of cleanup is ranked from 1 (easiest) to 4 (most difficult)*

Complexity of hydrogeological conditions	Nature of the contamination					
	Mobile, dissolved (degrades/ volatilizes)	Mobile, dissolved	Strongly sorbed, dissolved (degrades/ volatilizes)	Strongly sorbed, dissolved	Separate phase LNAPL	Separate phase DNAPL
Homogeneous, single layer	1	1–2	2	2–3	2–3	3
Homogeneous, multiple layers	1	1–2	2	2–3	2–3	3
Heterogeneous, single layer	2	2	3	3	3	4
Heterogeneous, multiple layers	2	2	3	3	3	4
Fractured	3	3	3	3	4	4

risk management, by protecting supply wells or other points of potential or real risk further downgradient, and (3) if the source zone is insignificant or can be isolated (either by impermeable barriers or hydraulic control), P&T can in some circumstances achieve significant reduction or complete removal of the plume.

Regarding the latter case, when source zones are insignificant or isolated, the success of P&T for remediation of the plume is now known to be controlled by: (1) the magnitude and heterogeneity of hydraulic conductivity; (2) the magnitude and heterogeneity of sorption; (3) the composition and properties of the contaminated groundwater; and (4) the rates and products of *in situ* transformations. This summary draws from a wide variety of research and practical results, and is a consistent extension of the ideas presented in Table 1. The third factor refers to a variety of issues including the presence of chemicals that could promote or impede biodegradation, the presence of chemicals, colloids or microparticles that could facilitate the mobility of target contaminants (reduce their partitioning to the immobile geological medium), etc. The fourth factor refers to abiotic and biologically mediated transformations of the target contaminants, which could result in products that are less or more mobile and less or more toxic than the parents. For example, 1,1,1-trichloroethane (1,1,1-TCA) abiotically transforms in the subsurface to 1,1-dichloroethene (1,1-DCE) and acetic acid. Although the rate is low and 1,1-DCE the minor product (e.g. Vogel & McCarty 1987), it appears that the *in situ* production of 1,1-DCE in this fashion may be the major limitation to achievement of cleanup goals at some P&T sites (e.g. Harman *et al.* 1993), largely because the cleanup standard for 1,1-DCE is typically considerably below that for 1,1,1-TCA. Similarly, at some sites PCE and TCE are found to have degraded, at least partially, to 1,2-DCE (and lesser amounts of the other dichloroethenes) and vinyl chloride; the products are generally more mobile but have lower cleanup standards than the parents (e.g. McCarty & Semprini 1994) so the net effect of the transformations on the progress of P&T is likely to be site-specific.

In summary, 'complete' remediation of VOC contamination can be achieved in some cases by P&T, generally when the subsurface source zone contains little or no NAPL mass, the hydrogeology is simple and especially if the contaminants are degradable nontoxic products. If source zones contain significant NAPL mass, 'complete' remediation of source and plume by P&T is unlikely since the NAPL mass is so slowly dissolved by the flow of groundwater. However, if the source can be isolated, removed or destroyed *in situ* (i.e. prevented from replenishing the plume), 'complete' remediation of plumes by P&T is possible within reasonable time frames under some circumstances. This fact has of course fuelled considerable interest in source isolation, removal and *in situ* destruction.

Source isolation, removal and *in situ* destruction

Cherry *et al.* (1996) have reviewed the state-of-the-art in isolation, removal and *in situ* destruction of subsurface contaminant sources, focusing on the special case of DNAPLs. Some salient points of their discussion are summarized here.

Source isolation

Source isolation (or containment) implies that measures have been taken to isolate the subsurface source from contact with the general flow of groundwater downgradient from the source. Pump and treat can achieve this goal if an extraction well or array of wells near the source captures all mass flux from the source. Impermeable barriers may also be installed to reduce or eliminate mass flux from the source to the plume. The success of both approaches depends either on the accurate location of the subsurface source zones, a matter already noted to be quite difficult in typically heterogeneous geological media, or on the overdesign of the isolation system to account for the uncertainty in subsurface source location. There are real examples of the practical success of source zone isolation (e.g. Harman *et al.* 1993; Feenstra & Cherry 1996). However, the costs of continuous P&T and the costs and in some cases infeasiblity of impermeable enclosures may limit the application of these approaches, especially as alternatives become accepted.

Source removal or *in situ* destruction

In the context of complete remediation, the ultimate practical goal of source removal or *in situ* destruction must be to reduce the subsurface source mass to a sufficient extent that there is no subsequent regrowth of a plume exceeding cleanup criteria. This is a very tall order if current thinking regarding the efficacy of source mass reduction is correct. For example, Cherry *et al.* (1996) suggest that greater than 99% removal of DNAPL mass may often be required to avoid regeneration of plumes. These kinds of estimates are based on various general assumptions, of course, and additional work is certainly warranted to allow more site- and contaminant-specific estimation of the fractional source mass removal required to prevent plume regeneration. As an extreme case, for example, it is likely that there are hydrogeological situations in which a few litres of DNAPL could be spilled and, after some time period, no plume of regulatory concern would exist (e.g. it could be so narrow that it was highly diluted by sampling or extraction wells). Nevertheless, it is clear that for many, if not most, cases in which significant quantities of

DNAPL exist in subsurface source zones, efforts that achieve less than 90% source reduction will not achieve the basic objective of preventing regrowth of the plume. Such efforts certainly will reduce the length of time that the remaining source will persist under natural conditions or remediation by P&T, but many believe that this may be of little or no practical significance (e.g. if the persistence is reduced from many to a few centuries). So, at least in the context of attempting to achieve complete site remediation within reasonable time frames, source mass reductions on the order of 90% or greater appear to be required for cases involving significant subsurface source zones.

A variety of source removal technologies are under investigation including extraction of NAPL, soil vapour extraction (SVE), combined SVE and air sparging, surfactant flushing, solvent flushing and steam flushing. NAPL extraction has obvious advantages but is incapable of achieving high per cent removal because of the development of residual NAPL saturation, which will not flow out of the formation. All the other removal technologies suffer from essentially the same problems as P&T in that they are limited by heterogeneities and, generally, diffusive mass transfer; thus they often achieve considerable mass removal in the initial stages but their mass removal declines dramatically thereafter. In practice, this reduction in mass removal rate is often assumed to indicate that nearly complete source removal has occurred, even though the actual initial mass of the subsurface source is unknown. However, controlled field tests of the removal technologies, in which the subsurface mass is accurately known, often are less encouraging.

The most successful evaluations of subsurface source removal have occurred within sheet pile cells installed to isolate existing DNAPL or to allow the release of specific masses of DNAPL. In one such instance, for example, removal of target DNAPL constituents in excess of 90% has been reported for alcohol flushing (Rao 1995); considering the total DNAPL mass (which contained a variety of constituents, not all identified) less than 90% was removed. In this instance, the majority of the removal apparently occurred within a flush of several pore volumes. However, it is generally recognized that longer flushing would be required for equivalent removal when flow was more affected by natural heterogeneities (and not constrained by sheet pile cells). More importantly, since a practical source removal effort would have to address the entire subsurface source, whose location is imprecisely known at best, the total volume of alcohol required for nearly complete source removal would typically be quite large and perhaps prohibitively expensive unless treatment and recycling prove feasible.

Similarly, a variety of technologies for *in situ* source destruction are under investigation. For example, the use of strong oxidants such as potassium permanganate has achieved very high per cent removals of certain DNAPLs (TCE and PCE) in laboratory tests and field tests within sheet pile cells (Gonullu *et al.* 1994; Truax *et al.* 1994; Cherry *et al.* 1996). However, the investigators pointed out that in practice the technology would be limited by uncertainty regarding DNAPL location, media heterogeneities, etc.

For reasons such as these, it has been argued that the prospects for practical use of source removal or *in situ* source destruction technologies for complete source remediation are currently very limited. With more research the prospects may improve for one or more of the technologies. On the other hand, it has been argued that source mass reduction efforts, even if incomplete, may be warranted if they result in a significant reduction of mass flux from the source zone to the plume, thereby making plume migration control efforts (discussed below) more feasible. This possibility requires careful reassessment as more becomes known about both the practical capabilities of source mass reduction and the limitations of plume migration control.

Plume migration control

For the range of reasons outlined above, it has become clear that aggressive attempts at complete remediation may not be successful or may be successful in some instances only at great cost or over very long time periods. Thus in the US there has been a rise in interest in the prospects for risk management by plume migration control. The goal of such efforts is to ensure that the contaminants do not reach points at which they may pose a risk. Figure 1 illustrates the three main approaches under investigation or use for plume migration control: pump and treat, intrinsic (bio)remediation, and semi-passive remediation. Each is discussed briefly below. In Fig. 1 the outer downgradient boundary illustrates the extent of migration that would be expected at some future time if no migration control method was in effect. If that boundary were predicted or known to encompass points posing unacceptable risk, then a migration control technology would be warranted. Note that no source removal or *in situ* destruction is required in principle. Instead, the control technology need only address the contaminant flux through a cross-section of the plume. For that reason, these technologies treat only groundwater, not the mass that resides in DNAPL or sorbed form upgradient. This treatment can occur above-ground (as in P&T) or *in situ* (as in the other technologies).

Pump and treat

Pump and treat is a proven method for plume migration control. The obvious disadvantages of P&T are the need

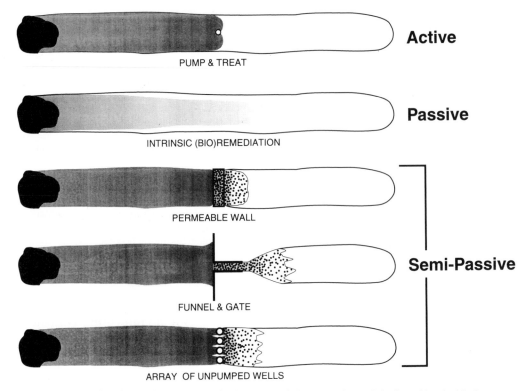

Fig. 1. Alternatives for plume migration control. The source of the contaminants is indicated by the black area. The contaminants within the plume are indicated by the grey shading. The downgradient boundary of the plume indicates the extent to which the contaminants would have migrated at the hypothesized time without any form of plume migration control. In the intrinsic (bio)remediation case, the contaminants degrade *in situ*, making the plume more narrow and shorter than expected in the absence of the intrinsic remediation. The semi-passive examples illustrated here release amendments into the groundwater (symbolized by the solid dots) which stimulate contaminant degradation reactions in the aquifer downgradient of the semi-passive systems.

and cost of continued operations and maintenance. Less obvious disadvantages include the fact that P&T inevitably involves extraction of some uncontaminated water, thereby wasting more of the natural resource and increasing the costs of extraction and treatment beyond what is theoretically required of a perfect capture system. For these and other reasons, there is considerable interest in evaluating and improving the reliability of other plume migration control approaches.

Intrinsic (bio)remediation

Intrinsic (bio)remediation (also termed natural attenuation) refers to natural abiotic or biotic processes reducing or eliminating contaminants along the migration pathway, thereby reducing or eliminating the risks they pose at points further along the pathway. In recent years there has been an explosion of interest in this topic, generally focused on the effect of biologically mediated reactions. From the efforts to date, it appears that many cases of groundwater contamination may be properly addressed by reliance on intrinsic bioremediation, with monitoring programmes in place to confirm that the health of the public and/or the environment remains protected. The example most often used is petroleum hydrocarbon contamination, since many of the constituents of regulatory concern have been proven to be biodegradable under a variety of geochemical conditions. Indeed, as mentioned previously, petroleum hydrocarbons are relatively infrequently detected above standards in public supply wells. Considering their widespread use and previously common releases from storage facilities, it does appear that in many cases the subsurface environment is quite capable of bioremediating the contaminants within relatively short transport distances from the sources. However, when the petroleum hydrocarbon source contains apparently nondegradable or slowly degradable constituents of known or potential public health concern, such as some gasoline additives (e.g. methyl tert-butyl ether, ethylene dibromide, etc.), adequate plume migration control may not be achieved solely by intrinsic bioremediation.

For chlorinated VOC contamination, it should be obvious by their widespread presence in public supply wells over the years that intrinsic bioremediation cannot be a very effective migration control in many, or perhaps even most, cases. Recent studies have identified some cases in which intrinsic bioremediation has apparently reduced the concentrations of certain chlorinated VOCs and their degradation products to below cleanup standards by the time a point of risk is reached; the most well-known example is a plume of TCE, c-DCE and VC in Michigan (e.g. Semprini *et al.* 1995). Although the findings are of considerable interest, so also are the remaining unknowns, including what synthetic organic chemicals, if any, are serving as the primary substrate for the anaerobic transformations, whether they persist and migrate at concentrations that pose risks, and whether the apparent treatment efficiency for the chlorinated VOCs will remain steady over time.

There are certainly many documented cases in which the same intrinsic biological reactions worsen the problem by transforming PCE and TCE into c-DCE and VC, which subsequently persist and present more of a public health risk. Furthermore, even if complete bioremediation of some constituents is certain, there may in many mixed-contaminant cases be other constituents that remain unaffected by the *in situ* reactions. Thus it is clear that while intrinsic bioremediation should be capitalized on whenever possible, much research remains to be done to determine under what conditions intrinsic reactions may be relied upon for long-term public health or environmental protection.

Semi-passive remediation

When intrinsic bioremediation may not be adequate and intervention is warranted, the 'semi-passive' approaches offer potential advantages over the conventional active approaches such as P&T. The term 'semi-passive' is used because the technologies are designed to operate relatively maintenance-free for considerable periods of time after emplacement or regeneration/replacement. Assuming that target contaminants are in fact reduced to required levels *in situ* by the semi-passive approaches, then an obvious advantage is that no above-ground treatment or disposal is required. Furthermore, operations and maintenance costs should be lower for semi-passive than P&T or other active technologies and monitoring requirements may be reduced. Because of these and other potential advantages, there is a considerable amount of effort under way to understand the strengths and limitations of semi-passive remediation approaches.

Figure 1 illustrates three semi-passive approaches: permeable barriers, funnel and gate systems, and rows or arrays of unpumped wells. Each of these is under active investigation and therefore we do not yet understand in detail the advantages, disadvantages and uncertainties of each of the approaches. In each approach, the engineered system can function as an *in situ* treatment reactor (i.e. containing reactive media which cause desired reactions to occur within the system) and/or as a source of amendments to stimulate/support treatment reactions downgradient of the barrier. Examples of reactive media under investigation or use in practice for plume migration control include activated carbon for capture of strongly sorbing contaminants and zero-valent iron (e.g. Gillham & O'Hannesin 1991, 1994) for *in situ* destruction of a wide range of halogenated VOCs. Examples of amendments under investigation or use are oxygen (e.g. Bianchi-Mosquera *et al.* 1994; Kao & Borden 1994; Byerley *et al.* 1996) for stimulation of aerobic degradation of BTEX or other degradable contaminants, nitrate (see review by Reinhard 1994) for degradation of petroleum derived hydrocarbons under nitrate-reducing conditions, and acetate (Devlin & Barker 1994) to provide a substrate to drive anaerobic degradation of certain halogenated VOCs.

Permeable barriers must be at least as wide and deep as the plume to be treated, which in many cases, especially where contamination is deep, may be infeasible. Funnel-and-gate systems must be installed in the same cross-section, which again may be infeasible in many cases, but the cross-section is captured and forced to flow through a narrower zone (the 'gate'). The gate may have the same functions as a barrier wall but in some cases be more efficient, less expensive to install and use, and easier to monitor. Note that in permeable granular media, the 'funnel' would be constructed from impermeable material (Starr & Cherry 1994); in fractured or other media with limited preferential flow paths, the 'funnel' might be constructed as an artificial permeable flow path intersecting all the naturally present preferential paths carrying contaminants and thus direct them to the 'gate' (J. Barker, University of Waterloo, pers. comm). Arrays of unpumped wells may function in essence as discontinuous permeable barrier walls (Wilson & Mackay 1995); the array of wells screens must be at least as large as the plume cross-section and the fraction of the plume which actually flows through the individual wells is a function of the well diameter and interwell spacing. Arrays of unpumped wells may be an attractive alternative to permeable barrier walls or funnel-and-gate systems in some cases because they potentially can be installed to any depth that can be monitored and they allow periodic replacement of the reactive or reaction-stimulating media. However, if complete or nearly complete remediation of the plume flux is required, close interwell spacing appears to be necessary, which may be difficult and/or expensive. On the other hand, if the goal is only partial treatment to reduce the contaminant load left for subsequent intrinsic remediation, arrays of wells may offer considerable promise (e.g. Kao & Borden 1994; Byerley *et al.* 1996). In the latter approach, it may be possible to reduce the total distance contaminants migrate at concentrations posing risks. The same goal of partial treatment could of course be reached with permeable barriers or funnel-and-gate systems, but the construction of either may not be justified in such cases.

These semi-passive technologies are in various stages of development, with the permeable barrier approach currently furthest along and, indeed, already in application for plume control at some contaminated sites (e.g. Gillham 1996; Gillham *et al.* 1996). Considerably more research is necessary to understand the advantages and particularly the limitations of these approaches. Modelling and field trials are needed to evaluate the appropriateness of the alternatives for the wide variety of hydrogeological environments of concern. Modelling, laboratory studies and field trials are needed to investigate reactive media and media or devices that can serve as long-term, preferably passive sources of remediation-inducing amendments. In many cases we have found and no doubt will continue to find that models and fundamental understanding of the processes controlling the efficacy of semi-passive remediation approaches are inadequate, either because there has been no previous need to consider some of the processes in detail or because the prior focus has been on inappropriate spatial or temporal scales. This is a fascinating research challenge for the future.

Summary and conclusions

At VOC-contaminated sites, and perhaps most contaminated sites, it is often the case that only a small fraction of the total contaminant mass residing in the subsurface is dissolved in groundwater that is readily extractable by wells. Rather, a large fraction of the mass is often present in the form of a non-aqueous phase liquid (NAPL), and lesser mass fractions are present in the dissolved phase in zones bypassed by the majority of groundwater flow and in the sorbed phase throughout the contaminated zone. In the past, attempts at 'complete' remediation of the subsurface have often failed because the limitations imposed by the actual distribution of contaminant mass were not understood or anticipated. Because these limitations are now much more well-known, there is general agreement that the prospects for 'complete' remediation of VOC-contaminated sites are very limited for the foreseeable future, except in a limited number of relatively simple cases. Here we refer to remediation as 'complete' if there is no further action required to ensure groundwater concentrations of the contaminants do not exceed criteria such as drinking water standards upon cessation of treatment.

On the other hand, there are proven tools (e.g. pump-and-treat remediation) and others under development which can achieve the objective of risk reduction or elimination by limiting the migration of existing plumes. These migration control approaches return the attention solely to groundwater within mobile strata, fractures, etc. (i.e. that relatively easily extractable by wells), but specifically at that passing through a selected cross-section of the subsurface. Such technologies may require new regulatory approaches, but, if accepted, augment the range of tools that are available for addressing groundwater problems. With these and other technologies under development, there may soon be a range of tools available for remediation that will match the range of remediation goals that many think are necessitated by the site-specific complexities of VOC contamination.

References

BIANCHI-MOSQUERA, G. C., ALLEN-KING, R. M. & MACKAY, D. M. 1994. Enhanced degradation of dissolved benzene and toluene using a solid oxygen-releasing compound. *Ground Water Monitoring and Remediation*, Winter, 120–128.

BYERLEY, B. T, CHAPMAN, S. W., SMYTH, D. J. A. & MACKAY, D. M. 1996. A pilot test of passive oxygen release for enhancement of in-situ bioremediation of BTEX-contaminated ground water. (manuscript in submission).

CHERRY, J. A., FEENSTRA, S. & MACKAY, D. M. 1996. Alternative goals and approaches for groundwater remediation. *In*: CHERRY, J. & PANKOW, J. (eds) *Dense Chlorinated Solvents and Other DNAPLs in Groundwater*. Waterloo, Waterloo Educational Services, Guelph, Ontario, 475–506.

DEVLIN, J. F. & BARKER, J. F. 1994. A semi-passive nutrient injection scheme for enhanced in-situ bioremediation. *Ground Water*, **32**(3), 374–380.

FEENSTRA, S. & CHERRY, J. A. 1996. Diagnosis and assessment of DNAPL sites. *In*: PANKOW, J. F. & CHERRY, J. A. (eds) *Dense Chlorinated Solvents and Other DNAPLs in Groundwater*. Waterloo, Portland, OR, 395–473.

—— & GUIGER, N. 1996. Dissolution of dense non-aqueous phase liquids (DNAPLs) in the subsurface. *In*: PANKOW, J. F. & CHERRY, J. A. (eds) *Dense Chlorinated Solvents and Other DNAPLs in Groundwater*. Waterloo, Portland, OR, 203–232.

——, CHERRY, J. A. & PARKER, B. L. 1996. Conceptual models for the behavior of dense non-aqueous phase liquids (DNAPLs) in the subsurface. *In*: PANKOW, J. F. & CHERRY, J. A. (eds) *Dense Chlorinated Solvents and Other DNAPLs in Groundwater*. Waterloo, Portland, OR, 53–88.

GILLHAM, R. W. 1996. Metal-enhanced degradation of halocarbons: technology development and implemenatation. *In*: *Groundwater and Subsurface Remediation: Research and Strategies and In-Situ Technologies*. Springer, Germany, 159–169.

—— & O'HANNESIN, S. F. 1991. Metal-catalyzed abiotic degradation of halogenated organic compounds. *Ground Water*, **29**(5), 749.

—— & ——1994. Enhanced degradation of halogenated aliphatics by zero-valent iron. *Ground Water*, **32**(6), 958–967.

——, ——, ORTH, S. W. & VOGAN, J. L. 1996. Field applications of metal enhanced dehalogenation of chlorinated organic contaminants (manuscript in submission).

GONULLU, T., FARQUHAR, G., TRUAX, C., SCNHARR, M. & STICKNEY, B. 1994. Studies on the use of permanganate to oxidize chlorinated solvents in soil (manuscript in submission).

HADLEY, P. W. & ARMSTRONG, R. 1991. Where's the benzene? – Examining California ground-water quality surveys. *Ground Water*, **29**(1), 35–40.

HARMAN, J., MACKAY, D. M. & CHERRY, J. A. 1993. *Goals and Effectiveness of Pump and Treat Remediation: A Review of Selected Case Studies of Large Plumes of Chlorinated Solvents or Pesticides in Sandy Aquifers.* Final Report (Volumes I and II). Sponsored by US Air Force via USEPARS. Kerr Environmental Research Laboratory, Ada, Oklahoma; original available from University of Waterloo; peer-reviewed version now in press as an EPA technical report.

JOHNSON, R. L. & PANKOW, J. F. 1992. Dissolution of dense chlorinated solvents in groundwater. 2. Source functions for pools of solvent. *Environmental Science and Technology*, **26**, 896–901.

KAO, C. M. & BORDEN, R. C. 1994. Enhanced aerobic bio-remediation of a gasoline contaminated aquifer by oxygen-releasing barriers. *In*: HINCHEE, R. E., ALLEMAN, B. C., HOEPPEL, R. E. & MILLER, R. N. (eds) *Hydrocarbon Bioremediation*. Lewis, Boca Raton, FL. 262–266,

MCCARTY, P. L. & SEMPRINI, L. 1994. Ground-water treatment for chlorinated solvents. *In*: NORRIS, R. L. *et al.* (eds) *Handbook of Bioremediation*. CRC, Boca Raton, FL, 87–116,

MACDONALD, J. A. & KAVANAUGH, M. C. 1994. Restoring contaminated groundwater: an achievable goal? *Environmental Science and Technology*, **28**(8), 362A–368A.

MACKAY, D. M. & CHERRY, J. A. 1989. Groundwater contamination: limits of pump-and-treat remediation. *Environmental Science and Technology*, **23**(6), 630–636.

—— & RIVETT, M. O. 1993. *Groundwater Contamination by VOCs Worldwide*. Paper presented at Association of Groundwater Scientists and Engineers (AGWSE) Convention, Kansas City, October.

—— & SMITH, L. A. 1993. Organic contaminants. *In*: ALLEY, W. M. (ed.) *Regional Ground-Water Quality*. Van Nostrand Reinhold, NY, 323–343.

NRC 1994. *Alternatives for Groundwater Cleanup*. National Academy of Sciences, National Academy, Washington, DC.

RAO, P. S. C. 1995. Presented at 'In-situ field tests for site characterization and remediation'. National Ground Water Association Annual Meeting, Indianapolis, IN, 28–30 October.

REINHARD, M. 1994. In-situ bioremediation technologies for petroleum derived hydrocarbons based on alternate electron acceptors (other than molecular oxygen). *In*: NORRIS R. L. *et al.* (eds) *Handbook of Bioremediation*. CRC, Boca Raton, FL, 131–148.

SEMPRINI, L., KITINIDIS, P. K. KAMPBELL, D. H. & WILSON, J. T. 1995. Anaerobic transformation of chlorinated aliphatic hydrocarbons in a sand aquifer based on spatial chemical distributions. *Water Resources Research*, **31**(4), 1051–1062.

STARR, R. C. & CHERRY, J. A. 1994. Passive in situ remediation of contaminated groundwater: the funnel and gate system. *Ground Water*, **32**(3), 465–476.

TRUAX, C., FARQUHAR, G., SCHNARR, G. M. & STICKNEY, B. 1994. Field experiments using permanganate to oxidize trichloroethylene and perchloroethylene spilled into soil (in submission).

VOGEL, T. M. & MCCARTY, P. L. 1987. Rate of abiotic formation of 1,1-dichloroethylene from 1,1,1-trichloro-ethane in groundwater. *J. Contaminant Hydrology*, **1**, 299–308.

WESTRICK, J. J. 1990. National surveys of volatile organic compounds in ground and surface waters. *In*: RAM, N. M., CHRISTMAN, R. F. & CANTOR, K. P. (eds) *Significance and Treatment of Volatile Organic Compounds in Water Supplies*. Lewis, Chelsea, MI, 103–138.

WILSON, R. D. & MACKAY, D. M. 1995. A method for passive release of solutes from an unpumped well. *Ground Water*, **33**(6), 936–945.

Capillary influences on the operation and effectiveness of LNAPL interceptor trenches

Martin C. Chapple,[1] Louis F. Vittorio, Jr.,[1] William A. Tucker[2] & Melissa G. Richey[3]

[1] Earth Resource Engineering Group, 85 Old Dublin Pike, Doylestown, PA 18901, USA
[2] Ellis Environmental Group, 611 NW 60th Street, Gainesville, FL 32607, USA
[3] Star Enterprise, 3800 Pickett Road, Fairfax, VA 22031, USA

Abstract. Interceptor trenches are commonly used to recover light non-aqueous-phase liquids (LNAPL) from the subsurface and are particularly effective in the recovery of floating hydrocarbons. Interceptor trenches function by creating a zone of high permeability within the aquifer either as an open excavation (where the formation permits) or filled with a suitable backfill (typically gravel) that retains the high permeability and effective porosity required of a collection system.

Numerous texts suggest that placement of an impermeable membrane is required on the downgradient side of the trench to prevent captured LNAPL from exiting the trench on its downgradient side. Installation of such a liner can be difficult if not impossible under certain soil conditions. Simple calculations show that the membrane may not be necessary due to the hydraulic conditions created by installing the trench. Using these calculations in the preliminary design will result in an effective trench installation and correspondingly reduce installation and operation costs.

LNAPL has been shown to migrate primarily near the top of the capillary fringe in porous media. Since the high permeability and effective porosity of the trench backfill do not support a capillary fringe of similar magnitude, LNAPL rests essentially on the water table in the trench. The zone of capillary saturation on the downgradient side inhibits LNAPL migration from the trench into the native soil. Provided that recovery of the LNAPL is maintained and the thickness of LNAPL in the trench is less than the capillary fringe height in the native soil, the LNAPL will remain hydraulically trapped.

To demonstrate this condition, a review of some of the methods used to calculate the capillary fringe height was performed. To verify the magnitude of the calculated capillary fringe height and its effects on LNAPL retention within a trench, a simple laboratory-scale simulation was undertaken.

Introduction and background

Installation of an interceptor trench is a simple and commonly used method to recover and prevent the migration of LNAPL (EPA 1988; Domenico & Schwartz 1991). The trench creates a linear zone of high permeability into which formation fluids (LNAPL and/or water) flow which are removed by skimming and or pumping. Trenches can be operated either passively, where only LNAPL is removed by skimming, or actively, where water removal is also performed to enhance the flow of formation fluids into the trench. A common practice for passive systems is the installation of a downgradient membrane, suspended below the water table, to prevent the re-entry of the LNAPL into the formation along the downgradient trench wall.

The existence, movement and thickness of LNAPL in the subsurface has been the subject of numerous studies. Prior to the work of Farr *et al.* (1990) and Lenhard & Parker (1990), hydrogeologists generally assumed the

LNAPL to occupy a layer directly above the water capillary fringe (Blake & Hall 1984; Hall *et al.* 1984). The more recent work has shown both hydrocarbon (as LNAPL) and water coexisting in the pore space between the water/hydrocarbon interface to a point slightly above the hydrocarbon/air interface with the majority of the pore space being occupied by water.

As described by Kemblowski & Chiang (1990), monitor wells exaggerate the hydrocarbon thicknesses present in the formation. This exaggerated thickness is due to the difference in capillary pressure between the formation and the well construction material. Mobile LNAPL present in the pores within the capillary zone exits the formation and enters the well bore, which, due to the presence of coarser material, and space of the well bore, has a much smaller capillary fringe than the formation. LNAPL will remain trapped by the formation capillary pressure and can only re-enter the formation if (1) the LNAPL layer reaches equilibrium in the well (LNAPL enters and exits through a continuous layer), or

CHAPPLE, M. C., VITTORIO, L F. JR, TUCKER, W. A. & RICHEY, M. G. 1998. Capillary influences on the operation and effectiveness of LNAPL interceptor trenches. *In:* LERNER, D. N. & WALTON, N. R. G. (eds) 1998. *Contaminated Land and Groundwater: Future Directions.* Geological Society, London, Engineering Geology Special Publications, **14**, 13–18.

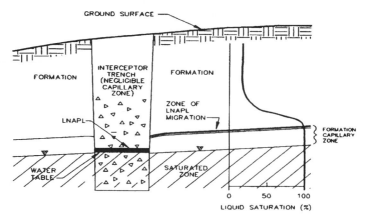

Fig. 1. Effects of trench installation on the capillary zone.

(2) rapid water level rises occur and the top of the LNAPL layer in the well bore rises above the corresponding capillary fringe height in the formation adjacent to the well (allowing the LNAPL to flow out).

A trench creates a similar environment to a monitor well by creating a discontinuity in the capillary zone (Fig. 1). LNAPL within a trench will remain similarly trapped unless either of the two conditions described above is met. If the design purpose of the trench is to intercept and recover LNAPL (and not dissolved constituents), then passive skimming that maintains an LNAPL thickness below the capillary fringe height should be sufficient to trap the LNAPL.

To evaluate the effectiveness of capillary capture in passive recovery trenches, several simple experiments were performed under laboratory conditions. The purpose was to provide an empirical demonstration of the validity of the concepts discussed above.

Methods

Both theoretical and practical methods were employed during the study. First, the theoretical water capillary fringe height was calculated based on equations presented in the literature. Second, bench-scale simulations of capillary fringe heights and their influence on the flow patterns of LNAPL and water under a modest hydraulic gradient in and around an interceptor trench were performed in a $1.3 \times 1 \times 0.3$ m acetate aquarium tank.

Estimation of capillary fringe height

Several semi-empirical methods are available to estimate the capillary fringe height. One class of methods is based on a statistical description of the porous medium and usually requires permeability and porosity values.

Another class of methods is based on a phenomenological description of the medium (e.g. a bundle of capillary tubes of various diameters). The latter methods rely on an estimate of pore size, which is practically impossible to measure. Therefore, the pore size is usually estimated from particle size distribution analyses. For illustration, calculations of capillary fringe height in the interceptor trench model are presented using an exemplary equation for each of these two classes of estimation methods.

The first class (statistical) is represented by an equation presented by van Dam (1967):

$$h_c = \frac{\beta \sigma}{\rho g} \sqrt{\frac{\phi}{k}} \qquad (1)$$

where h_c = capillary fringe height (cm),
     β = wettability constant = 0.4,
     σ = surface tension of water = 72.8 dyne cm^{-1},
     ρ = density of water = 1 g cm^{-3},
     g = acceleration due to gravity = 980 cm s^{-2},
     ϕ = porosity,
     k = intrinsic permeability (cm^2) = $10^{-5} \, Kw$,
     Kw = hydraulic conductivity (cm s^{-1}).

More complex variations of this equation replace the wettability constant with the J-Leverett function (see Bear 1972, equation 9.2.11).

The second class (phenomenological) is represented by (Bear 1972, equation 9.4.9):

$$h_c = \frac{0.45(1 - \phi)}{d_{10}\phi} \qquad (2)$$

where d_{10} is the effective particle diameter (cm).

Necessary parameters for equations (1) and (2) were obtained as follows. The grain size for the sand was taken from the sieve analysis performed by The Morie

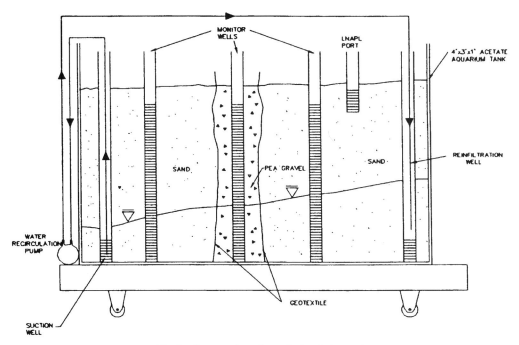

Fig. 2. Cross-section of trench simulation tank.

Company ($d_{10} = 0.5$ mm). Porosity of the sand was estimated by performing a drawdown test whereby a known volume of water was removed from the tank and divided by the total volume of sand dewatered to establish a porosity of 29%. An approximate value of hydraulic conductivity (K) for the material was calculated using Darcy's Law: $Q = KiA$.

Values for flow rate ($Q = 0.86 \, \text{m}^3 \, \text{day}^{-1}$), gradient ($i = 0.027$), and the saturated cross-sectional area of the tank ($A = 0.093 \, \text{m}^2$) were measured with the saturated hydraulic conductivity value for the sand calculated to be $349 \, \text{m day}^{-1}$. This value is in agreement with published data for similar material presented in Freeze & Cherry (1990) and Kruseman & de Ridder (1991).

Tests were performed to establish the effectiveness of the capillary barrier outside the interceptor trench by evaluating what thickness of LNAPL could be harboured in the trench before LNAPL was able to flow out of the trench and into the surrounding sand.

The simulated trench was constructed using an aquarium tank. The construction of the tank is shown in Fig. 2. Two outer layers were formed from medium-grained sand (Morie 00N sand), to represent a sandy formation. The middle layer was formed from pea gravel and was designed to be representative of interceptor trench backfill material. Due to the unconsolidated nature of the materials, a layer of filter fabric was installed between the sand and pea gravel layers to prevent mixing of the materials during the fluid addition

and removal necessary as part of the testing. Monitor wells (each formed out of a PVC screen split longitudinally) were installed adjacent to the tank walls in all three sections of the tank. The wells were used to establish fluid elevations and the presence of LNAPL.

LNAPL was added through a port situated above the capillary zone on the designated upgradient side of the trench. A discharge tube connected to a low flow Grundfos pump was placed in a downgradient well to allow removal of water. During the testing, the water was reinfiltrated in an upgradient well, creating a gradient across the trench and promoting LNAPL flow towards the trench. To simulate passive operation no water was removed from the trench at any time.

All simulations were performed with downgradient pumping and upgradient reinfiltration, resulting in a gradient across the trench of 0.027. Progressively larger amounts of LNAPL were then added and allowed to percolate through the sand to establish its migration pattern. The LNAPL selected was a bright red lamp oil with an approximate density of $0.8 \, \text{g cm}^{-3}$. The colour allowed the spread and migration of the oil in the sand to be closely monitored and photo-documented.

Water-table fluctuations occurred in the tank due to pump shutdowns and evaporational losses and water replacement. However, the fluctuations were not dissimilar to those expected under field conditions.

Addition of LNAPL continued until several centimetres were observed in the trench. To complete the experiment, LNAPL was added directly to the trench until it was forced out into the sand on the down-gradient side.

Results and discussion

Capillary fringe height

Calculation of the capillary fringe height was performed using the equations presented in the previous section. In addition, the capillary rise was measured directly by observing the saturated extent of the sand (which was clearly visible through the tank) above the water level in the observation wells.

For the experimental conditions, $Kw = 349 \, \text{m day}^{-1} = 0.376 \, \text{cm s}^{-1}$; $k = 3.76 \times 10^{-6} \, \text{cm}^2$; $\phi = 0.29$; and $d_{10} = 0.05 \, \text{cm}$. Applying these values in van Dam's equation [Equation (1)] yields a capillary fringe height of 8.2 cm, while Bear's equation [Equation (2)] estimates a capillary fringe height of 22 cm. Considering that the sand in the experiment was not compacted as much as most natural formations, the method based on permeability (Equation (1), indicating a capillary rise of 8 cm) is believed to be more reliable because the measured permeability reflects the actual extent of compaction and its effect on the pore sizes.

Equation (2), on the other hand, is derived from natural soil profiles that are well compacted, producing smaller average pore sizes at a given particle diameter than the pore size/particle diameter relationship that exists in the sand in the tank. Thus Equation (2) overestimates capillary rise in the experimental porous medium because it implicitly considers compaction and underestimates pore size in the sand. This discrepancy does not undermine use of this equation in natural porous media, but does illustrate why the statistical methods, represented by Equation (1), are more realistic in the context of the experiment.

This conclusion is supported by the use of a semi-empirical relationship between particle size and hydraulic conductivity to evaluate results of this experiment. Both the Kozeny–Carmen equation and the Hazen relationship (Freeze & Cherry 1991, equations 8.47 and 8.50) underestimate the hydraulic conductivity observed in the experiment, indicating that pore sizes are larger in the experimental porous medium than they would be in a natural sediment of the same particle sizes.

Capillary fringe heights were also measured against the tank walls. The difference between the piezometric surface in the monitoring wells and the top of the visibly saturated sand in the tank was considered approximately equal to the capillary fringe height. During the measurements, it was realized that the effects of the flat surfaces of the tank (which increases the pore throat size) would lower the capillary fringe height. This proved to be the case: the height of the visible zone of capillary saturation against the sides of the tank was somewhat lower than the height of the calculated capillary zone height for the sand, averaging 7 cm, which is consistent with Equation (1). However, it was noted that larger voids were present adjacent to the tank walls (due to the media resting against a flat surface rather than interlocking with other sand grains) where the zone of visible saturation extended up from the piezometric surface only 4 or 5 cm. The sides of the tank were therefore expected to be 'first breakthrough points'. Based on the presence of these voids, oil thicknesses of 4–8 cm above the corrected piezometric surface in the trench (corresponding to a total oil thickness of 20–40 cm in the trench) were expected to create breakthrough.

LNAPL addition

Addition of the oil to the tank resulted in a downward and outward migration from the point of addition (Fig. 3). At the observed capillary zone, it began to migrate towards the trench. As more oil was added it was observed to penetrate somewhat deeper into the capillary zone. Oil was first observed in the trench approximately 90 min after introduction (Fig. 4).

Over a period of a few weeks, additional oil was added, increasing the thickness in both the upgradient well and the trench until the upper level of the oil in the trench was close to the oil impacted layer in the sand (Fig. 5). The distribution of the oil indicated only a relatively thin (<25 mm) layer of oil in the sand upgradient of the trench. However, the oil accumulated to almost 20 cm in the monitor wells and trench.

Fig. 3. Oil migration following addition to the tank. Note that migration occurs near the top of the capillary fringe. The actual piezometric surface is marked in pen on the side of the tank.

Fig. 4. Arrival of oil in the trench. Note the elevation difference between the oil in the trench and the oil migrating in the sand.

Fig. 6. Breakthrough to downgradient side of trench. Note the thin film of oil in the well on the left side of the tank and the oil thickness in the trench required to cause breakthrough to occur.

Fig. 5. Oil accumulations in trench and monitor wells. (Note: this photo was taken on the opposite side of the trench to Figs 3 and 4).

Forced breakthrough

To complete the study, oil was periodically added directly to the trench, increasing the LNAPL thickness and forcing breakthrough into the sand and the monitor wells on the downgradient side of the trench (Fig. 6). The thickness of oil observed in the trench to create breakthrough differed on the two sides of the tank, being considerably less on one side (20 cm) than the other (25 cm). This corresponded to in-trench oil thicknesses residing above the corrected piezometric surface in the trench of 4 cm and 5 cm.

The observed capillary fringe height for the sand adjacent to the tank walls (which should approximate the thickness of oil residing above the corrected piezometric surface in the trench required to create breakthrough) averaged 7 cm but was noticeably lower (4–5 cm) where the sand was not well packed.

Breakthrough actually occurred with 20–25 cm of oil accumulation in the trench, which is what was expected based on observations of the capillary fringe against the tank walls but only approximately 70% of the thickness required to cause breakthrough based on the calculations.

However, to put the results in context, it should be noted that the study evaluated what in real life would be considered a highly porous (0.29) and conductive ($350\,\text{m day}^{-1}$) sand. Typically, interceptor trenches are selected for finer grained and lower permeability environments, with correspondingly higher capillary fringe heights. In addition, effective and continuous recovery of LNAPLs (which keeps the LNAPL thickness down) is one of the primary functions of a trench and would be ongoing in a trench considered to be operating correctly.

It was noted that the hydraulic gradient, which remained at approximately 0.03 across the trench throughout the testing, did not appear to be a critical parameter in causing the breakthrough. The study showed that LNAPL did not exit the trench under this gradient even with considerable LNAPL thicknesses. During the monitoring and evaluation of trench systems, the analysis of hydraulic gradients around a trench may therefore only be useful in monitoring the movement of dissolved compounds. Monitoring of a trench system's effectiveness at capturing LNAPL and preventing its migration would best be served by ensuring that the LNAPL recovery system is operational and that the thickness in the trench remains below the calculated critical thickness for the formation soil.

Conclusions

A model simulating the hydraulic effects of an interceptor trench was constructed in an acetate tank. Medium-grained sands were used to represent formation materials and pea gravel was used to mimic trench backfill materials. Oil added to the unsaturated zone on one side of the tank behaved as expected by migrating in a thin layer within the uppermost portion of the saturated capillary zone and accumulating in much greater thicknesses in wells and the trench, where the capillary zone was much lower.

Oil that entered the interceptor trench became trapped due to the difference in capillary fringe height between the formation and the coarser trench backfill material and was unable to enter the corresponding formation on the opposite side of the trench. During the study, a total of 20–25 cm of oil accumulated in the trench before the capillary zone was breached allowing oil to 'cross' the trench. Although the accumulation required to breach the capillary barrier was closer to the observed capillary fringe rather than that predicted by the equations, the study results demonstrate that even in a highly permeable and porous sand, significant thicknesses of oil can be allowed to develop in a trench without compromising its effectiveness in preventing LNAPL migration. It should also be noted that in a real situation, LNAPL would be recovered continuously, keeping oil thicknesses to a minimum. Finally, interceptor trenches are normally installed in fine-grained soils, whose capillary fringe heights are greater, requiring greater thicknesses of LNAPL to allow breakthrough to occur.

Analysis of hydraulic gradients around a trench system can only be used to establish the effectiveness of that system in preventing migration of dissolved compounds. The results of the study demonstrate that LNAPL remained trapped, even though a constant hydraulic gradient (0.03) and flow of water was maintained across the trench system. In field setting, therefore, gradient data indicating water flow through a trench does not mean that LNAPL is not being retained by the trench. The thickness of accumulated hydrocarbon in the trench must also be considered.

In summary, the results demonstrate that simple soil parameters can be used to help design effective interceptor trenches without their overdesign. Numerous trench systems that have been installed to recover oils, or other LNAPLs, have had impermeable liners installed on the downgradient side to prevent losses into the formation that would have been prevented by natural soil conditions and the LNAPL recovery system. In addition, there are no doubt trenches installed without membranes, from which large quantities of water are unnecessarily removed (requiring processing under the appropriate statutes) to ensure that hydraulic control is maintained in order to prevent LNAPLs from escaping from the trench. Finally, care should be taken when judging the effectiveness of certain trench systems at retaining LNAPLs based on monitoring data that indicates a loss of hydraulic control. As has been shown, hydraulic gradient data alone are very misleading in establishing anything other than the movement of dissolved compounds.

Acknowledgements. Thanks are due to S. Mason, M. Rapoport and V. Williams for their help, input and enthusiasm in constructing the tank, T.J. for the graphics, and to M. Yost for helping out with funding it. Thanks are also due to Groundwater Systems, Inc. for supplying the materials.

References

BEAR, J. 1972. *Dynamics of Fluids in Porous Media.* Dover.

BLAKE, S. B. & HALL, R. A. 1984. Monitoring petroleum spills with wells: some problems and solutions. *Proc. of Fourth National Symposium on Aquifer Restoration and Ground Water Monitoring,* NWWA.

DOMENICO, P. A. & SCHWARTZ, F. W. 1991. *Physical and Chemical Hydrogeology.* John Wiley, Chichester.

EPA 1988. *Cleanup of Releases from Petroleum USTs: Selected Technologies.* Document no. EPA/530/UST-88/001, US Environmental Protection Agency

FARR, A. M., HOUGHTALEN, R. J. & MCWHORTER, D. B. 1990. Volume estimation of light nonaqueous phase liquids in porous media. *Ground Water,* **28**(1), 48–56.

FREEZE, R. A. & CHERRY, J. 1990. *Groundwater.* Prentice-Hall.

HALL, R. A., BLAKE, S. B. & CHAMPLIN, S. C., JR. 1984. Determination of hydrocarbon thickness in sediments using borehole data. *Proc. of Fourth National Symposium on Aquifer Restoration and Ground Water Monitoring,* NWWA.

KEMBLOWSKI, M. W. & CHIANG, C. Y. 1990. Hydrocarbon thickness fluctuations in monitoring wells. *Ground Water,* **28**(2), 244–252.

KRUSEMAN, G. P. & DE RIDDER, N. A. 1991. *Analysis and Evaluation of Pumping Test Data.* International Institute for Land Reclamation and Improvement, Wageningen, The Netherlands.

LENHARD, R. J. & PARKER, J. C. 1990. Estimation of free hydrocarbon volume from fluid levels in monitoring wells. *Ground Water,* **28**(1), 57–67.

VAN DAM, J. 1967. The migration of hydrocarbons in a water bearing stratum. *Proc. of the Symposium on the Joint Problems of the Oil and Water Industries.* Elsevier.

Lime stabilization of inorganic contaminants in clays

S. Glendinning, C. D. F. Rogers & D. I. Boardman

Department of Civil and Building Engineering, Loughborough, Leicestershire LE11 3TU, UK

Abstract. The legacy of industrial operations over the past 200 years are contaminated natural clays and clay-based sediments. There is an urgent need for economic methods to stabilize these materials since the problem is widespread. Chemical fixation or encapsulation of inorganic contaminants using lime provides one potential solution that has yet to be adequately explored.

This paper aims to review the methods of chemical stabilization of inorganic contaminants using pozzolanas, and in particular discuss the interaction of clays with both metal ions and lime. The parallels between cement, lime–fly ash and lime–clay stabilization reactions are examined to determine the potential for contaminant stabilization using lime and suggest the mechanisms upon which success would rely. The factors affecting the lime stabilization process are discussed. Methods of incorporation of lime in practice are thereafter discussed, covering deep mixing as well as surface mixing *in situ* and mixing *ex situ*. Specific research required to prove the potential of lime is then discussed.

The paper concludes that lime stabilization provides a potentially valuable and economic means of treating both natural clays and (often very wet) clay-rich sediments. This is achieved via both enhanced contaminant adsorption and precipitation of metal ions under conditions of high pH, and binding in of the contaminants with the reaction products of the pozzolanic reaction between lime and clay. However, the fundamental nature of the clay/sediment is altered by the lime–clay reactions, most notably in the context of future potential for ion mobility by an immediate increase followed by a progressive decrease in coefficient of permeability. The degree to which inorganic contaminants become associated with the reaction products and the permanency of this association under conditions of seepage (i.e. resistance to leaching) need to be researched in detail before confidence in the technique can be engendered.

Introduction

The legacy of contamination

Public awareness of the adverse effects of contamination on the environment has grown considerably over the last decade, partly due to the active involvement of environmental groups. This has produced pressure upon government bodies to act urgently by introducing new legislation to control waste disposal. With increasing demands for environmental responsibility, the European Community has set strict controls on the content and quantity of waste that can be disposed of at sea or applied to land. The economic consequence of this has been greatly increased costs for industries producing toxic wastes as by-products of their production processes, and for governments or other bodies who are responsible for cleaning up contaminated sites for future development or public use (derelict industrial sites, docks, canals, etc.). Two of the major categories of material that need to be dealt with are clay-based sediments deposited under water and clays that contain inorganic contaminants, the remediation of which forms the basis of this paper.

The major source of contamination derives from industrial processes. The composition of the contamination varies enormously from one industrial process to another. Typical sources of such contamination are copper, lead and zinc smelting industries, duplicating and photographic equipment manufacturing industries, pharmaceutical industries and sewage treatment works. Whilst industries are now closely controlled and produce waste materials that are both identifiable and are treated, this has not always been the case. By studying the waste materials (known as waste streams or sludges) produced by modern processes, good indications of the contamination of the environment caused by past industrial processes can be obtained. Examples of heavy metals that can become released into the environment are given in Table 1. These contribute to the contamination of sediments in rivers, canals, lakes and reservoirs following transport via air and/or water,

GLENDINNING, S., ROGERS, C. D. F. & BOARDMAN, D. I. 1998. Lime stabilization of inorganic contaminants in clays. *In:* LERNER, D. N. & WALTON, N. R. G. (eds) 1998. *Contaminated Land and Groundwater: Future Directions.* Geological Society, London, Engineering Geology Special Publications, **14**, 19–28.

Table 1. *The composition of particular industrial waste streams and sludges (after Landreth, 1982)*

Sludge description	Annual production (tonnes, wet)	% Solids	Density $(Mg\,m^{-3})$	pH	Constituents $>10\,g\,kg^{-1}$ (dry)	Constituents 0.1–$10\,g\,kg^{-1}$ (dry)	Constituents 1–$100\,mg\,kg^{-1}$ (dry)
Electroplating sludge	50	32	1.27	7.6	Ca, Cr, Cu, Fe, SO_4, Cl, Si	Be, Cd, Pb, Mg, Mn, Ni, Zn	As, Hg
Nickel–cadmium battery sludge	100	40	1.25	12.3	Ca, Ni, Cl, Si	Cd, Cr, Cu, Fe, Pb, Mg, Zn	As, Hg
Pigment production	17 000	25	1.17	8.4	Ca, Cr, Fe, Pb, Mg, SO_4, Cl, Si	As, Cd, Cu, Mn, Ni, Zn	Hg
Chlorine production brine	3 000	59	1.57	9.5	Ca, SO_4, Cl, Si	Cu, Fe, Mg, Mn, Ni, Zn, Hg	As, Cd, Cr, Pb
Glass etching sludge	2 000	47	1.41	8.3	Ca, SO_4, Cl, Si	Cu, Fe, Pb, Mg, Mn, Ni, Zn	As, Cd, Cr, Hg

and to land by these routes or by direct contact. Although controls on material handling and disposal now in place reduce the risk of contamination to an acceptably small level, the degree of control until relatively recently has been minimal and much contamination occurred by this route. Although this paper deals only with the contaminated environment, the technology put forward could potentially be adapted to treat the waste sludges directly in combination with the addition of a pozzolana (Lutz & Minehan 1986).

Similarly, heavy and radioactive metal contamination of land is a major global problem. Land can become contaminated both at the surface and sub-surface as a result of the legacy of industrial processes. Indeed metal contamination can result from sources as apparently innocuous as fly ash and colliery spoil heaps. Such contamination is again symptomatic of the early periods of the century when industrial processes and waste control were not firmly regulated by government bodies. In Europe alone there are just under one million known or potentially contaminated land sites requiring remediation.

Alternative remediation technologies

Due to the variability of contaminant composition in clays and sediments it is difficult to find a single treatment which fulfils all the requirements for safe long-term disposal. Prior to disposal of contaminated materials such as excavated clays and dredged sediments, assurance is necessary that toxic elements will in some way be contained within the waste disposal facility boundaries forever, or at least that losses will be kept sufficiently low that no harmful effects occur to the environment. Methods of disposal currently available and under research include spreading on land, dewatering and landfill disposal, encapsulation and burial, and stabilization and disposal on land or in landfill sites. There are intermediate processes which can be used to

increase the physical, chemical and cost effectiveness of the primary disposal methods, such as precipitating toxic metal species from the waste materials by altering the pH of the solutions. Toxic metals also tend to attenuate preferentially on small mineral particles. Thus it is possible to remove a large quantity of certain contaminants by removing specific particle sizes as a means of pre-treatment. A summary of the alternative remediation technologies is illustrated in Fig. 1.

Stabilization techniques generally involve mixing the contaminated material with a chemical additive such as lime or cement. The combination of a high pH and the production of cementitious compounds create a solidified mass that can reduce the mobility of toxic elements in the waste. Stabilization methods tend to cost less than other treatments, but their application can be limited due to the contaminant composition and the limitations of the fixation processes. For example, both the solids content and the form of the toxic species present in the contaminated material influence their suitability. The environment is similarly important since, if water can permeate through the contaminated deposit, certain species will become mobile. In addition, the presence of some contaminants can also impede the creation of the cementitious products that are associated with solidification and stabilization methods.

The need for economic solutions

The problems, in terms of numbers of sites and varieties of contamination, are as serious worldwide as they are in Europe. While in certain European countries the government has to pay for remediation of sites if the industrial polluter cannot pay or cannot be made to pay, the USA has firmly embraced the philosophy that the polluters must pay for the clean-up of contamination. In order for these industries to remain competitive with industries in countries where pollution control is not so rigorous and/or to reduce the burden on governments,

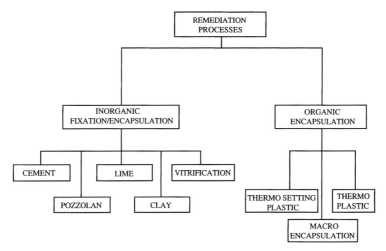

Fig. 1. Fixation remediation technologies.

there is a need to develop economical treatment and disposal techniques. Thus any technique that is simple to operate, can deal with large amounts of contaminated materials and does not require large quantities of expensive materials is of major importance.

Chemical stabilization using lime would satisfy these criteria. Furthermore, the addition of lime to clay soils has proved to be of great benefit in improving their engineering properties, making the material physically as well as chemically stable. Supplies of lime, more so than cement, are relatively high around the world making lime an almost universally viable option. There is consequently a need to investigate lime stabilization of contaminated clays and clay-based sediments, and in particular to discover whether the longevity requirement of ion immobility can be satisfied.

Aims of the paper

The paper aims to confirm the potential of lime stabilization for the treatment of inorganic contamination of clays and sediments from technical and practical view points. This is to be achieved primarily via a study of the chemical processes and the literature on associated remediation techniques as there is little literature concerned with the use specifically of lime in this context. The clay–contaminant and clay–lime reaction processes in isolation are presented in order that fundamental chemical reactions might be appreciated. Chemical stabilization, notably using cement and fly ash, is examined to determine the primary stabilization mechanisms that occur. Parallels with lime–clay–contaminant interaction are drawn and its potential is assessed in the light of the factors that influence the interaction. Practical application of lime treatment is then examined to establish alternative means of lime

incorporation, intimate mixing being necessary to effect the stabilization sought. Conclusions are thereafter drawn on the future directions for lime stabilization, and specifically on the research required to prove the efficacy of the process.

Interaction between clay minerals, contaminants and lime

Clay–contaminant reaction

The mineral structure of soils is of great significance when considering chemical fixation techniques. Mineral structure is dictated in the early stages of rock formation by temperature, pressure and chemical environment. Subsequent physical weathering of the rock reduces particle size and causes chemical decomposition which leads to the creation of a complex mixture of minerals in the form of clay and primary mineral particles (e.g. quartz sand). As the chemical decomposition is affected by both climate and surface geological features, so the resulting mineral structures in clays vary considerably. Hence the degree of chemical fixation will also vary.

Physically, clay minerals are defined as those particles in a soil system smaller than $2\,\mu m$. However, in structural chemistry terms they may be defined as substances which combine aluminium octahedrally co-ordinated with oxygen, and silicon tetrahedrally co-ordinated with oxygen. During the formation process isomorphous substitution must also have occurred, during which quantities of the metals present in the primary mineral structure were displaced by other elements of a lower valence, or charge, including magnesium and iron (II). This displacement creates a measurable charge deficit within the mineral structure causing the attraction of cations, usually in the form of positively charged metals. The charge deficit is responsible for the majority of a clay's cation exchange capacity.

The special orientation of the tetrahedral and octahedral stacking units and the level of charge imbalance results in an extremely large variety of different clay minerals.

Indeed, not all clays with an apparent charge deficit have exchangeable ions between the sheet structure. This apparent deficit can be attributed to clay surface behaviour and is the mechanism which describes cation surface adsorption. Figure 2 shows the basic structures for a dioctahedral smectite and kaolinite. In the smectitic structure isomorphous substitution can occur in both the octahedral and tetrahedral sheets, resulting in varying charge location. Dioctahedral smectite, montmorillonite, has the general formula: $M_{x+y}^+(Al_{2-x}Mg_x)(Si_{4-y})O_{10}(OH)_2$. In contrast, kaolinite, which has the ideal formula $Si_4Al_{10}(OH)_8$, does not display this effect. The variable surface charge exhibited by kaolinite is due to fracture edge sites and the presence of hydroxylated species on the clay surface. The nature of the charge on these hydroxylated surfaces

is pH dependent. Dragun (1988) states that at low pH the equilibrium equality [Equation (1)] predominates, resulting in a high proportion of positive charge sites on the clay surface and hence the attraction of anions. At high pH, however, equilibrium Equation (2) predominates, resulting in a high proportion of negative charge sites on the clay surface and hence the attraction of cations.

$$XOH + H^+ \rightarrow XOH_2^+ \qquad (1)$$

$$XOH \rightarrow H^+ + XO^- \qquad (2)$$

where X is mineral structure.

Thus under normal conditions metal attraction to clays occurs to a degree that is dependent upon the mineralogy and facility for cation exchange. At high pH, however, these metals can be caused to be retained by the clay within its structure.

The clay–lime reaction

The addition of lime, either in the form of quicklime $(CaO_{(s)})$ or as hydrated lime $(Ca(OH)_2)$, to a soil system initiates a two-stage reaction. During the first stage, the

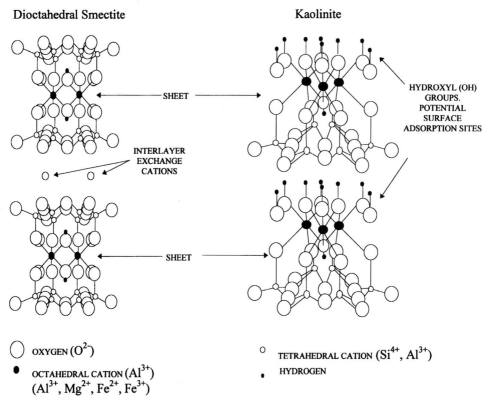

Dioctahedral Smectite

Kaolinite

SHEET

HYDROXYL (OH) GROUPS. POTENTIAL SURFACE ADSORPTION SITES

INTERLAYER EXCHANGE CATIONS

SHEET

○ OXYGEN (O^{2-})

● OCTAHEDRAL CATION (Al^{3+}) $(Al^{3+}, Mg^{2+}, Fe^{2+}, Fe^{3+})$

○ TETRAHEDRAL CATION (Si^{4+}, Al^{3+})

• HYDROGEN

Fig. 2. Clay mineral structure.

quicklime initially reacts with water in the soil system according to the following equation:

$$CaO_{(s)} + H_2O_{(l)} \rightarrow Ca(OH)_2 + heat \qquad (3)$$

This reaction is highly exothermic, producing approximately $17 \times 10^9 \, J \, kg^{-1}$ of quicklime. Indeed quicklime is sometimes used purely as a de-watering agent due to the benefits of dehydration by reaction and by steam generation. There is a decrease in the plasticity of the clay associated with the first-stage reaction, which is caused by the flocculation of the clay particles. There is also an increase in strength caused both by the dehydration and by the change in the fundamental nature of the clay particles. This *modification* of the clay occurs immediately in a well mixed system and is due to the exchange of cations such as sodium and hydrogen in the clay mineral for calcium ions.

The second stage of the reaction process, termed *stabilization*, occurs in the longer term and is the result of pozzolanic reactions. Sherwood (1993) defines a pozzolana as a material that is capable of reacting in the presence of water, at ordinary temperatures, to produce cementitious compounds. In basic terms, the addition of lime to a clay creates a highly alkaline environment and promotes the dissolution from the clay of silica and alumina, particularly at the edge sites of the clay plates, permitting the formation of calcium silicate hydrate and calcium aluminate hydrate gels. These gels crystallize with time to create cementitious products that are similar in composition to those of cement paste. The second-stage reaction results in a continued reduction in a clay's plasticity and a markedly increased shear strength. Ultimately in the context of treatment of contaminated land the most significant physical change, however, is related to potential changes in the permeability of the material since they could lead to either an in increase or decrease in contaminant migration due to leaching. In the short term it would be expected that the permeability would increase, the degree of increase depending on the mixing, mellowing, compaction and curing conditions during lime treatment. However, in the longer term this tendency can reverse as the gels form and crystallize in the pore spaces between the flocs (El-Rawi & Awad 1981).

Principles of chemical stabilization

Introduction

There are several different reaction processes that combine to facilitate chemical stabilization of inorganic contaminants in clays. The primary aim is to stabilize the association of the contaminants with the clays such that they are not free to leach out (or become mobile). The initial association between metal contaminants and clays occurs via a process of cation exchange. This takes place in accordance with the Lyotropic series, as a result of which ions having a higher valency state and an appropriately small diameter are substituted for lower valency metal ions on the exchange sites of the clay minerals. This natural substitution causes temporary stability, but the metal ions could become disassociated by future cation exchange or by other chemical processes. In addition the quantity of contaminant rendered immobile by cation exchange is limited. Thus some means of both creating further association of the free metal ions causing contamination and preventing disassociation needs to be sought. There are broadly three ways in which such stability can be brought about.

The first is to increase the pH of the environment in order to bring about enhanced surface adsorption. The mechanism is explained above in the discussion of Equation (2). This process remains successful as long as the pH remains high, but its effectiveness is dependent on a specific mineral structure and would reduce if the pH reduced with time. Assurance of continued high pH is likely to pose a problem, however, since natural groundwater tends towards acidity rather than alkalinity in general and thus an artificial means of maintaining a high pH would need to be provided. In addition there is a further consideration that must be made since the process of cation exchange results in the displacement of the host metal ions from the clay. For example, it is probable that following the penetration of metal ions through a clay barrier lining a landfill site, cation exchange on the exchange of sites of the clay mineral would take place to a significant degree. This would in turn result in the displaced lower valency sodium ions creating a plume of metal pollution leading away from the site. The consequences of sodium pollution might not prove as severe as those of the escaping metal ions, but nevertheless they could form a subsequent problem that would need to be addressed.

Griffin & Shimp (1976) noted this behaviour whilst investigating the attenuation of metals from landfill leachate on kaolinite (1:1 lattice type clay mineral), montmorillonite (2:1 expanding lattice), and illite (2:1 non-expanding lattice, mica type). During column leaching of landfill leachate through these clays, elution of calcium (Ca), and to a lesser degree iron (Fe) and manganese (Mn) was observed. The elution of Ca was attributed to Ca being the predominant exchangeable cation present on the clays. However, the elution of Mn was not attributed to cation exchangeable metals. Griffin *et al.* (1976) state that Mn is three times more abundant on the surface of kaolinite than on the surface of montmorillonite and that this difference corresponds to the increased elution from the kaolinite columns. Thus the potential for elution of metals from clays is not purely dependent on cation exchange. However on addition of lime to a soil system this is likely to be the main mechanism for release of metals from the treated material.

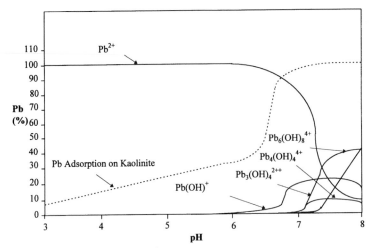

Fig. 3. Distribution of Pb(II) species in 4×10^{-4} M Pb(NO$_3$)$_2$ and uptake by 0.1 g kaolinite from 60 ml of solution (Griffin & Shimp 1976).

The second mechanism is similarly pH dependent and relies upon the precipitation of salts from solution. As well as increasing the surface adsorption of ions, increasing the concentration of hydroxyl (OH$^-$) ions in solution can ultimately result in the formation of metal complexes and, potentially, precipitation of metal salts will occur. This mechanism is clearly of significance when considered along with the lime soil stabilization reaction. Griffin & Shimp (1976) considered the precipitation reactions of lead (Pb) from a landfill leachate along with Pb adsorption on the surface of kaolinite. They showed that species other than Pb^{2+} are relatively insignificant at pH values less than 6. It is clear that at values above pH 6 apparent increased adsorption of Pb coincided with the formation of hydroxyl Pb species. Precipitation was found to be an important mechanism for Pb removal and the effect is clearly depicted in Fig. 3. Precipitation of specific metal salts under conditions of high pH thus provides an important means of reducing the mobility of metal ions as long as the pH remains high. Reversal of precipitation would occur if the pH reduces, however, thus presenting the same potential long-term limitation as that of surface adsorption.

The third means of improvement consequently produces the most important potential change in properties, since it provides a long-term stabilizing process which acts subsequently to adsorption and salt precipitation. This reaction process is that of cementation via the clay–lime reactions described above. Dissolution of alumina and silica and subsequent crystallization of calcium aluminate hydrate and calcium silicate hydrate gels produces a very strong and stiff, yet brittle, cemented structure. The cemented mass is thought to be stable, that is the reactions are considered non-reversible under conditions of subsequently reduced pH. The principle

of contaminant stabilization, or lock up, is that the contaminants would become physically and chemically bound into the cemented structure. According to this principle the cemented structure, which essentially binds the flocculated particles (containing the adsorbed contaminant ions) together, would incorporate the precipitated salts (held as an amorphous mass in the pore spaces between the flocs) since the gels would form around them. It is unclear whether the cementation reactions would be inhibited by the presence of the contaminant ions in the soil structure, and in particular whether the gel crystallization process would result in a continuous cemented structure being formed. This is because little published research directly concerning clay–lime–contaminant reaction processes is available. However direct parallels have been researched in the form of cement stabilization and lime–fly ash stabilization of contaminated sludges (as have waste materials including cement kiln dust, waste lime tailings and clays from the manufacture of brick; see Stanczyk *et al.* 1982). Both have been used successfully and, since they are based upon the same pozzolanic reactions (the silica and alumina being provided by the cement and fly ash respectively), their success is encouraging.

Cement stabilization

Betteker *et al.* (1986) carried out extensive research into the solidification/stabilization of contaminated dredged material, including the addition of Type 1 Portland cement and two proprietary pozzolamic additives. The technologies were assessed for both physical and chemical stabilization. The cement-based and pozzolanic-based additives were used to convert contaminated sediment into a solidified mass, as discussed above. A polymer was added to determine its effect on the leaching of selected organic compounds. Physical stabilization was assessed by measuring the changes in unconfined compressive strength, while leaching tests were used to evaluate the chemical stabilization. Leachates were analysed for polyaromatic hydrocarbons (PAHs), polychlorinated biphenyls (PCBs), arsenic, zinc, cadmium and lead.

This research concluded that physical stabilization of contaminated dredged material is a viable option, but no single process formulation proved to be effective in providing chemical stabilization for all contaminants as a group. Portland cement proved to be the most effective at treating arsenic, while more than half of the PCBs could not be detected in the leachate of Portland cement solidified sediment. Those PCBs that did leach were measured at less than one part per billion. Zinc, cadmium and lead were contained most effectively by the proprietary pozzolanic additive with no detectable concentrations of the metals in any of the leachates. The polymer additive was the most effective at containing the PAHs, more than half of the PAHs being completely immobilized. Those PAHs that were not totally immobilized were found in concentrations four to five orders of magnitude lower in the leachates than in the untreated sediment. This indicates that some organic contaminants can be treated by solidification processes as well as inorganic contaminants, and highlights the fact that every waste to be treated should be assessed independently to design the most appropriate stabilization mix. Landreth (1982) carried out similar investigations, producing similar conclusions.

Lime–fly ash stabilization

By far the most researched pozzolana used in stabilization processes has been fly ash. Weng & Huang (1994) investigated a specific fly ash with cement for treating industrial wastewaters. The chemical composition of the fly ash used was dominated by silicates (SiO_2, 44%) and aluminates (Al_2O_3, 31%), with smaller amounts of iron, calcium, magnesium, potassium and titanium oxides. The addition of cement created a high pH, thus resulting in the formation of calcium silicates and aluminates. As with the clay–lime reaction, this cementitious reaction bound the particles together producing a solidified matrix. Weng & Huang (1994) also stated that the high proportion of silica, alumina and iron oxide implied that the fly ash will be a good metal adsorbent, at least for Zn (II) and Cd (II). Although fly ash has a relatively low metal adsorption capacity relative to activated carbon, it can be obtained cheaply in large quantities and used as a neutralizing agent in the treatment process due to its alkaline nature.

Landreth (1982) evaluated the containment efficiency and physical properties of four different solidification/stabilization processes when applied to common industrial wastes. The four treatment processes included a patented lime and fly ash additive. The chemical success of the treatments was monitored via column tests, whilst durability was assessed using compression, freeze–thaw, permeability and Atterberg limit tests. Landreth stated that the lime–fly ash treatment achieved a variable degree of success, containing electroplating sludge to a relatively high degree but losing contaminants to a higher degree than the control columns for the untreated nickel–cadmium battery and glass-etching sludges.

Some of these effects could be predicted. If the principal fixation mechanism is adsorption, then generally at high pH cations are preferentially retained whereas at low pH anions are preferentially retained. Hence in the case of chlorine production sludge, it is no surprise that Cl^- and SO_4^- ions are mobile at high pH. However, in complex mixtures of pozzolanic material, organic and inorganic contaminants, the chemistry is not so predictable. This highlights the site-dependency, or sludge-dependency, of the success with which fixation can be achieved.

Potential of lime stabilization

It is known that the addition of lime to a clay produces an immediate effect by ion exchange or adsorption, calcium ions generally replacing sodium or potassium ions on the exchange sites. The lime also creates a high pH environment, resulting not only in the dissolution of silicates and aluminates but also potentially the increased adsorption of contaminant metals and the precipitation of certain metal solids. In conjunction with potential long-term reduction in permeability due to the formation of cementitious compounds, it is clear that lime has the potential to reduce contaminant migration, providing chemical fixation. This is considered crucial to the fixation process since it is uncertain whether conditions of high pH can be maintained in a natural (often slightly acidic) groundwater environment, thus questioning the degree of permanency of the adsorption and precipitation reactions. In this respect, some encouragement that the pH is maintained in the long term is provided by Biczysko (1996) as a result of his long-term studies of road pavement subgrade stabilization. It is apparent from the above discussion that a structured programme of research is necessary to prove the efficacy of the reactions in the presence of contaminants and the long-term stability of the reaction products under prolonged leaching. These are discussed below once practical means of application have been examined.

Practical application of lime stabilization

Practical site considerations

Both the method of incorporation of the lime and the form of the lime used depend upon the material to be treated. Several treatment scenarios can be envisaged, although they can broadly be categorized into the following:

- stiff (typically heavily overconsolidated) natural clays that have become contaminated via pollution plumes migrating through them or via surface contamination caused by uncontrolled tipping in and around old industrial sites
- soft, wet (typically normally or lightly overconsolidated) alluvial deposits that have become contaminated in the same way
- very soft, very wet sediments in the base of canals, docks, rivers, flooded quarry sites or lakes that have become contaminated via polluted water, whether as a result of accidental or intended discharge, over a long period of time
- stockpiled contaminated dredgings or tailings that have been deposited on land in inadequately designed landfill sites

These materials differ considerably not only in water content, but also in situation, and the future intended use of the site and material must be considered. This in turn will dictate the potential future problems, if any, that the contaminated materials pose. For example, a contaminated natural clay would generally be expected either to be built upon at some future date or to be used for food production (crops, grazing, etc.). In both cases release of the contaminant upwards would pose a danger and some form of surface capping would be required. In addition the likely effects of groundwater flow causing lateral migration would need to be assessed in terms of future contamination of adjacent sites or water courses. Any surface capping would need to be deep enough and be afforded protection to avoid subsequent excavation (e.g. for utilities, foundations, land drains, etc.) causing penetration and future contaminant release. If lateral movement of contaminants at depth poses a potential hazard, then some means of deep treatment must be sought to provide a continuous barrier, or curtain. This would be equally applicable to contaminated natural clays and alluvial soils, and to stockpiled dredgings or tailings. In the case of polluted sediments that currently exist under water, some means is required of treatment by dredging and stabilization *ex situ* prior to replacement or disposal, or possibly even treatment *in situ*.

Water content is an important consideration in any treatment process, both as a result of the degree of mixing of the lime (or lime–additive mix) that can be achieved and the subsequent compaction of the lime-treated clay. Intimate mixing is usually possible given the correct plant, and lime in the correct form. Lime can be provided in the following three basic forms:

- quicklime, which is calcium oxide (CaO)
- hydrated lime or slaked lime, calcium hydroxide ($Ca(OH)_2$)
- lime slurry, which is a solution of slaked lime in water

Thus the water content of the material to be treated, and hence the clay–lime mix, can be adjusted. Quicklime, being strongly hydrophilic and reacting exothermically with water, will dry out a material, whereas hydrated lime will effect no significant change and lime slurry will cause a water content increase.

Surface clay–lime mixing

The usual procedure for surface clay–lime mixing involves spreading the powdered quicklime or hydrated lime onto the surface and mixing to a depth of 200–400 mm using a purpose-built rotavator. Water content changes during mixing can be made by direct injection of water into the hood of the rotavator. Lime slurry spreading onto the surface of a material to be treated is less successful due to its propensity to flow, and thus achieve a non-uniform distribution. Hydrated lime spreading and incorporation of larger quantities of water via the mixing hood would probably provide a better option than slurry spreading. It was traditional practice to allow the clay–lime mix to stand for a period of typically 24 h, either in a stockpile or for single layer treatment *in situ*, in order that complete lime distribution could occur. This process, known as mellowing, was considered vital for full modification of the clay minerals. Current thinking, however, suggests that immediate water content adjustment (where necessary) and compaction is more beneficial in achieving a long-term strength gain.

Compaction of the clay–lime mix is important to achieve the intimacy of contact of the modified clay particles necessary for the full benefits of the reaction to be achieved. In addition a minimum air void content should be aimed for since this will again aid the reaction process. For these reasons the water content should be slightly higher than the optimum water content determined for the clay–lime mix and an appropriate level of compaction should be applied to achieve a dry density close to the maximum achievable. Immediate compaction would undoubtedly be beneficial for contaminated soil treatment, as long as thorough mixing is possible, since the pozzolanic reaction bonds that form at an early stage would assist with contaminant retention.

Deep clay–lime mixing

An alternative treatment *in situ* for deep deposits is to form lime columns, which are cylindrical columns of lime mixed with clay typically 0.5–1.0 m in diameter. The technique was developed in Sweden (Broms & Boman 1976) for stiffening and strengthening soft, wet clayey soils. A lime content of typically 10% is used, the lime being incorporated through the stem of an auger that is first driven into the ground to an appropriate depth. The direction of rotation of the auger is reversed as the lime is fed into the soil, causing mixing and a degree of compaction. Such a technique could provide a suitable containment measure if contiguous lime columns were to be constructed around the edge of a contaminated mass, such as a dredge tip. Care would be needed in design to ensure intimate mixing, as high a compacted density and thus as low a permeability as possible in the constructed columns. This would necessitate a programme of laboratory testing and field trials to prove its efficacy, but nevertheless has considerable potential. Indeed the technique could be used to create an underlying clay–lime blanket *in situ* by constructing a series of contiguous piles over the whole site, but only feeding lime into (say) the lowermost one metre of the internal columns. This would have the additional effect of excavation and recompaction of the contaminated soil above the base clay–lime mix layer, although such disturbance is unlikely to cause any significant problems. Construction of a surface clay–lime mixed layer would complete the barrier, although such a layer would need to be designed to cope with significant settlements.

Treatment *ex situ*

In certain cases treatment *in situ* is unlikely to prove a viable option. Treatment underwater (e.g. canal base treatment without canal dewatering) is theoretically possible, but the combined effects of heating of quicklime during hydration (quicklime would be needed for water content reduction) and potential contamination of the water by lime would render the technique unacceptable in environmental terms. In such cases excavation/dredging, treatment *ex situ* and replacement in compacted layers would be necessary (e.g. Boardman & MacLean 1996). This would permit a considerable degree of control over the process.

Conclusions and future directions

Lime stabilization has considerable potential as an economic means of treating clay-based soils containing inorganic contaminants. The processes that combine to reduce future contaminant mobility are as follows:

- cation exchange on the clay minerals
- increased metal adsorption as a result of creation of a high pH environment
- precipitation of salts in the high pH environment
- binding in of contaminants as a result of the pozzolanic cementing reactions

The success of the process will necessarily be soil/sediment specific since different contaminants react with lime in different ways. For example, certain metal ions are released, rather than adsorbed, as a result of lime treatment. Nevertheless the technique could prove to be of considerable practical benefit since the subsequent clay stabilization reactions are considered to provide a stable cemented matrix.

Incorporation of the lime in practice could be effected by both *in situ* and *ex situ* techniques. Traditional clay–lime mixing techniques can be adopted for exposed deposits, although for deeper deposits the problems of temporarily stockpiling treated material (which would reduce the overall effectiveness of the process) or untreated material could prove logistically and environmentally unacceptable. Lime columns provide a solution for both global treatment of a deep deposit or creation of a barrier. Lime treatment *ex situ* provides a further alternative for dredged material or in cases where treatment *in situ* is otherwise impractical.

For practical application, there are other considerations of importance. Mixing lime with a clay-based soil/sediment and subsequent compaction results in an altered material nature and an immediate increase in permeability. The onset of stabilization reactions causes a progressive reduction in permeability, but the time dependency of the process results in a material that may have a greater potential for leaching in the short term. The mobility of ions is reduced by the addition of lime and thus leaching under conditions of seepage flow might not prove to be a problem in practice as long as the pH remains high. Sustained leaching with acidic water could alter the pH balance, however. The rapidity of the pozzolanic reactions is thus important in this respect since it would be important to reduce the length of time that the material is vulnerable to leaching. It remains unclear whether the presence of inorganic contaminants in a clay affects the pozzolanic reactions. In the same way it is uncertain whether a certain set of chemical conditions could affect the permanency of the lime stabilization reaction products. It is currently thought that organics in significant quantities can inhibit the pozzolanic reactions and it is known that the presence of excess sulphates under certain conditions will result in the formation of ettringite and thaumasite, thus not allowing the pozzolanic reactions to create a strong, dense cemented structure. Although the reaction products, once formed, are considered to be stable (Transportation Research Board, 1987), attack under adverse conditions has not apparently been fully studied.

In order to address some of the above concerns a programme of research is under way at Loughborough University to study the mobility of metal ions once incorporated into clay minerals as a result of the action of lime. Batch leaching tests are being carried out as a means of determining performance under accelerated leaching conditions (Glendinning & Boardman 1996). Additional research is required to study the effect of chemical conditions on the reaction products and to extend the work of El-Rawi & Awad (1981) on the permeability of lime-treated soils. Practical areas requiring study include the effectiveness of lime columns to create a dense, intimately mixed material. Arising from the above work, recommendations for site-specific testing to determine the potential of lime treatment would thereafter need to be developed.

References

BETTEKER, J. M., SHERRARD, J. H. & LUDWIG, D. D. 1986. Solidification/stabilisation of contaminated dredged material. *Mid Atlantic Industrial Waste 18th Conference*, VA, 253–273.

BICZYSKO, S. 1996. Long-term performance of lime stabilised road subgrade. *In*: ROGERS, C. D. F., GLENDINNING, S. & DIXON, N. (eds) *Lime Stabilisation*. Thomas Telford, London, 62–74.

BOARDMAN, D. I. & MACLEAN, J. A. 1996. Lime treatment of metal contaminated sludges. *In*: ROGERS, C. D. F., GLENDINNING, S. & DIXON, N. (eds) *Lime Stabilisation*. Thomas Telford, London, 115–126.

BROMS, B. B. & BOMAN, P. 1976. Stabilisation of deep cuts with lime columns. *6th European Conference on Soil Mechanics and Foundation Engineering*, Vienna, 207–210.

DRAGUN, J. 1988. *The Soil Chemistry of Hazardous Materials*. Hazardous Materials Control Research Institute, Silver Spring, MD.

EL-RAWI, N. M. & AWAD, A. A. 1981. Permeability of lime stabilised soils. *Transportation Engineering Journal*, January, 25–35.

GLENDINNING, S. & BOARDMAN, D. I. 1996. Lime treatment of metal contaminated clay soils. *32nd Annual Conf. of the Geological Society*, University of Portsmouth, 249–258.

GRIFFIN, R. A. & SHIMP, N. F. 1976. Effect of pH on exchange-adsorption or precipitation of lead from landfill leachates by clay minerals. *Environmental Science and Technology*, **10**(13), 1256–1261.

——, ——, STEEL, J. D., RUCH, R. R., WHITE, W. A. & HUGHES, G. M. 1976. Attenuation of pollutants in municipal landfill leachate by passage through clay. *Environmental Science and Technology*, **10**(13), 1262–1268.

LANDRETH, R. E. 1982. *Physical properties and leach testing of solidified/stabilised industrial wastes*. Report Number EPA-600/2-82-099, US Environmental Protection Agency, Cincinnati, OH.

LUTZ, E. J. & MINEHAN, L. J. 1986. Laboratory study to determine longterm stability of pozzolanically stabilised waste. *Proc. of HAZPRO '86*, Baltimore, April 1986. Puduan, USA, 295–303.

SHERWOOD, P. A. 1993. *Soil Stabilisation with Cement and Lime*. Transportation Research Laboratory, State-of-the-Art Review, HMSO, London.

STANCZYK, T. F., SENEFELDER, B. C. & CLARKE, J. H. 1982. *Solidification/Stabilisation Processes Appropriate to Hazardous Chemicals and Waste Spills*. Hazardous Material Spills, Milwaukee, WI, 79–84.

TRANSPORTATION RESEARCH BOARD 1987. *Lime Stabilisation State-of-the-Art Report: Reactions, Properties, Design and Construction*. National Research Council, Washington DC.

WENG, C. H. & HUANG, C. P. 1994. Treatment of metal industrial wastewater by fly ash and cement fixation. *Journal of Environmental Engineering*, **120**(6), 1470–1487.

The legacy of contaminated land in Portsmouth: its identification and remediation within a socio-political context

N. R. G. Walton[1] & A. Higgins[2]

[1] Department of Geology, University of Portsmouth, Burnaby Road, Portsmouth PO1 3QL, UK
[2] Environmental Health Service, Portsmouth City Council, Portsmouth PO1 2AL, UK

Abstract. The unique situation of Portsmouth with regards to the historical development of large areas of filled and contaminated land is described together with the methodologies which have been developed over the past decade for identifying, investigating and remediating such lands. This happened under the impetus of both Portsmouth City Council's specific strategy for contaminated land and the increasing volume of environmental guidance which has recently been released prior to the introduction of copious new government legislation.

Three typical case histories are presented which show how different approaches to risk evaluation have evolved during the 1990s and demonstrate how Portsmouth has applied these evolving methodologies in a pragmatic way in an attempt to optimize environmental improvements and financial returns whilst minimizing both public and political risks.

Historical background

The development of Portsmouth as Britain's premier naval port and Royal Dockyard over the past few hundred years and its subsequent recent decline as the Royal Navy (RN) has contracted, has had a profound effect on the island city of Portsmouth. During the expansionary phases, which saw the dockyard develop into the largest industrial complex in the world, there were two pressing problems: the need for more land on an island of limited extent and the need to dispose of increasing volumes of waste materials.

Portsmouth, in common with other island and coastal cities, chose the most obvious and practical solution to these two problems by filling the low-lying marshy coastal fringes and creeks of Portsea Island with a wide variety of dockyard, industrial and municipal waste materials (Fig. 1). Although some landfilling took place in the 16th and 17th centuries, major landfill and reclamation did not become significant until mid-Victorian times, when the last major expansion of both the dockyard area and the city itself took place.

Towards the end of the 19th century, both waste and lack of open spaces were becoming major public issues and so Portsmouth Corporation purchased and operated two 'refuse destructors' (early incinerators) in an attempt to resolve the growing waste problem. These two incinerators operated from about 1906 to 1935, and their residual ash and clinker were distributed by tramways over, and into, substantial creek/mudflat areas on the eastern side of Portsea Island. Wartime rubble was used to cap many of these fills, although later filling with municipal wastes sometimes occurred to raise the ground to more suitable levels. Post-war municipal waste filling continued into the Salterns area on the east of the Island and also into the marshy ground at the head of Portsmouth Harbour to the northwest of Portsea Island (Fig. 1).

Municipal filling continues in this area into the large Paulsgrove landfill which, it is estimated, will be full by the end of this century. Part of this extensive landfill, which commenced in the 1960s, was redeveloped as the Port Solent Marina Village in the 1980s (Fig. 2), demonstrating the high demand for development land in the Portsmouth area. All housing in the marina development was constructed on clean, compacted chalk, whilst the commercial area is situated on the landfill (Privett 1990). Because of this, all buildings were required to incorporate comprehensive gas protection measures which include impermeable membranes, active and passive vent systems and an integrated network of gas detection sensors. The marina lagoon was excavated out of the edge of the landfill and is now separated from it by a gas and leachate barrier. The large car park has a gas permeable surface and essential gas venting structures have been incorporated as an attractive feature to both the buildings and landscaped areas.

Interestingly, the waste problems experienced at the end of the last century have re-appeared at the turn of this new century as the local waste incinerators were forced to close down at the end of 1996 because of new European Union (EU) promulgated stack emission controls, leaving Portsmouth and southeast Hampshire with a sizeable waste problem to solve. However, with or without incineration, additional land filling will continue to be required into an ever-diminishing land resource area and

WALTON, N. R. G. & HIGGINS, A. 1998. The legacy of contaminated land in Portsmouth: its identification and remediation within a socio-political context. *In:* LERNER, D. N. & WALTON, N. R. G. (eds) 1998. *Contaminated Land and Groundwater: Future Directions.* Geological Society, London, Engineering Geology Special Publications, **14**, 29–36.

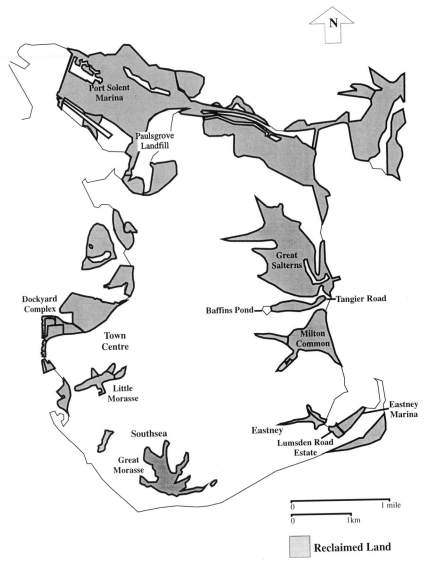

Fig. 1. Portsea Island showing historical reclamation sites.

expansionary pressures will continue to demand safe developments on previously filled land.

Therefore Portsmouth has developed its own contaminated land strategy over the past ten years, partly as a response to the lack of green field sites for development and also as a result of specific problems that have occurred during this period. The most prominent of these have been the development of the Eastney Marina and housing site on an old Navy landfill, the development of the Port Solent commercial complex and marina on a gassing landfill, and near-surface contamination

problems that led to the offers of rehousing to residents on the Lumsden Road estate which had been built on an old Navy waste tip adjacent to the Eastney Marina (Figs 1 and 3).

These all had a significant impact on the awareness of elected politicians to the contaminated land issue and paved the way for the acceptance of a pro-active approach to contaminated land which involved the search for, and identification of, contaminated sites, followed by their investigation and remediation where appropriate. This has been funded through the Department of the

Fig. 2. Aerial view of Port Solent Marina showing (from the left) houses built on compacted chalk, lagoon excavated out of the landfill commercial area and car parks on the landfill and the remaining undeveloped filled land area with grass covering to the right of the picture.

Fig. 3. Aerial view of Eastney Lake showing the infilled 'Glory Hole' and the Lumsden Road housing estate in the centre, with the new marina excavated from the fill to the top of the picture.

Environment's (DoE) supplementary credit approval programme, concentrating primarily on council-owned sites in the first instance. This has resulted in a capital expenditure of approximately £3.3 million over the past five years.

This paper reviews three representative periods of landfilling in Portsmouth and discusses the specific contamination problems raised and solutions found to remediate the situation under the City Council's contaminated land strategy and highlights the importance of the legal, financial and socio-political contexts when dealing with contaminated land issues.

Contaminated lands from different ages

Three quite different areas of landfill on the eastern coastline of Portsea Island have been chosen as representative study areas, each posing different land contamination problems and requiring different remediation methodologies

The Glory Hole, Eastney

The Glory Hole was an arm of Eastney Lake in the extreme southeast corner of Portsea Island, which was bunded off and infilled by the Royal Navy between approximately 1914 and 1960 (Figs 1 and 3). A wide variety of naval scrap and waste materials were dumped into this muddy creek, including asbestos from boiler and armaments lagging, lead from submarine and other batteries, mercury from electrical switchgear, zinc and cadmium plated metal objects and a host of other, mainly solid, materials. No records of the wastes deposited are available.

The approximately 2 ha site was covered over with several centimetres of topsoil and given over to the

building of naval married quarters which were constructed on the site between 1955 and 1965. Some of these homes were subsequently declared surplus to RN requirements and were leased to the City Council for council tenancy during the mid-1980s.

During the course of nearby excavations to construct a new marina in the late 1980s, substantial contamination was found which alerted both the Ministry of Defence (MOD) and Portsmouth City Council to the problems likely to be present in the ground under the neighbouring married quarters. A series of subsequent site investigations showed significant quantities of asbestos and various toxic heavy metals close to the surface, under the grass cover, although the MOD declared, at the time, that health risks were minimal. The City Council, following the receipt of further soil investigation results from a potential purchaser in August 1991 (a typical results summary is given in Table 1), decided the site was unfit for family habitation and immediately offered to rehouse families elsewhere. This decision ensured 'Lumsden Road' a place in contaminated land history (Fig. 4).

A quantitative risk assessment was subsequently undertaken using the United States Environmental Protection Agency (US-EPA) risk assessment guidance model (Anon 1989), which confirmed near-surface lead and asbestos contamination to be the major hazards of significance. The remedial solution proposed by the new owners of the land was to close-crop the turf cover, emplace a 25-mm polypropylene geogrid mesh, and recover with 50–75 mm of clean topsoil prior to re-turfing. The aim of the geogrid was to enable the grass roots to interlock so that it becomes virtually impossible for children to pull up the grass and get at the underlying soil. This methodology allows the contaminants to remain effectively encapsulated in the soil below. However, since there is no significant usable underlying groundwater, the site being sandwiched between the seashore and the tidal lake, this relatively cheap and simple solution reduced the principal exposure pathway

Table 1. *Summary results of selected significant contaminant concentrations found in the surface soils at the Lumsden Road (Glory Hole) site*

Chemical determined	Detected range ($mg\,kg^{-1}$)	Arithmetic mean ($mg\,kg^{-1}$)	ICRCL (gardens) threshold trigger ($mg\,kg^{-1}$)
Arsenic	<3–700	13	10
Cadmium	<1–17	1	3
Copper	<6–10 000	230	130
Lead	<20–96 000	1400	500
Mercury	<1–590	7	3
Zinc	11–11 000	440	300
PAH	<50–150	88	50
Asbestos	10–1000	36	10

Fig. 4. The Lumsden Road housing estate boarded-up and sealed-off in 1992 after the tenants had been re-housed and prior to remediation work beginning.

to within acceptable levels and the revamped housing estate is now a desirable private residential estate with sea views (Fig. 3).

Milton Common

Milton Common is a substantial area of filled land on the eastern shore of Portsea Island (Fig. 1). It was created by post-war municipal tipping into mudflats behind a chalk bund which sealed off the tidal mudflats from Langstone Harbour. Most of the fill that created the present Milton Common open space consists of municipal wastes tipped between 1962 and 1970.

Areas of poor and dying vegetation, occasional smells and an underground fire all pointed to the presence of landfill gas emissions. Preliminary investigations conducted by both the University of Portsmouth and the City Council proved significant gas emissions with concentrations of methane of up to 80% in some 20 identified hot-spots across the site. Because of the presence of housing within 50 m of the site on two sides, a full site investigation was undertaken under the Council's strategy to investigate land in its ownership, to define contamination levels in the groundwater, soil and soil gas (Parkman 1994). The results showed modest levels of contaminants present in the soil at depth, and also in the groundwater, but clearly identified

the substantial amounts of gas being given off across the common as the major hazard from this site, with an unacceptably high risk factor due to the proximity of local houses.

Remediation measures included the digging of a perimeter trench around the site through the fill into the underlying natural clay, lining it with a geotextile and backfilling with clean gravel against an impermeable polypropylene membrane on the housing side thereby allowing water and gas free access to the trench. The trench was fitted every 150 m with 3-m-high vent stacks topped with cowls to draw up and disperse the gas into the atmosphere. Unfortunately, in the southwestern area, the depth to clay was so great across the old main creek channel, that a bentonite slurry wall 8 m deep and keyed into the underlying clay was required to prevent gas migration off-site to the nearby (20 m) houses (Fig. 5).

The original clay and soil covering could have been simply repaired at the identified hot-spots. However this covering, placed in the 1970s, was not an engineered cap and, due to fill settlement, was generally in poor condition. Simple repairs would therefore only have encouraged gas migration to other weak spots, necessitating further works in the future. Therefore a proprietary vent cap system was chosen involving removal of some 100 mm of surface vegetation and soil, and then placement of a geotextile overlain by 100 mm of coarse sand followed by the plastic vent cap. This was then

Fig. 5. Emplacement of the bentonite slurry gas cut-off wall across the deepest part of the old creek at Milton Common.

overlain by 100 mm of coarse gravel and a further geotextile, before being finished off with clean soil, thereby dissipating the gas over a much wider area and allowing diffusion escape through different permeability zones (Fig. 6).

A novel feature of this work was the combination of the trenching work down the western edge of the site with the construction of a new cycle way, which is part of the City Council's plan to encircle Portsea Island with a continuous cycle path by the turn of the century.

Tangier Road/Little Salterns

This is another site on the eastern coast of Portsea Island (Fig. 1). It was originally dammed off from the sea in the 17th century to produce a series of salt ponds (Salterns) for the production of sea salt. Sea salt production rapidly declined in Victorian times as mined rock salt became more cheaply available, and the Council purchased the land for municipal filling and commenced tipping at the turn of the century.

A municipal refuse destructor operated on the Baffins site between approximately 1906 and 1935 and the residual ash and clinker were spread out into the salterns ponds to raise their levels to above maximum high-tide levels. Additional rubble and waste material were added both during and after the war and, in response to local complaints about flies and smells, the entire site was sometimes sprayed with creosote at the end of the working day. The site was finally covered over with a few centimetres of topsoil before being used as allotments and, subsequently, open playing fields.

In 1994, a proposal to build a new school on the site prompted a site investigation to discover the precise nature, depth and extent of contaminants in the ground. A thorough site investigation (30 m grid spacing of site investigation holes to 3 m depth) was followed by a full risk assessment based upon exposure pathways for the identified principal contaminants of lead, arsenic and polynuclear aromatic hydrocarbons (PAH). The result of the quantitative risk assessment model (Anon 1989) determined that the exposure hazard presented an unacceptable risk to school children, and so the proposed new school was located elsewhere.

Remediation works for the playing fields then involved the laying of a geotextile drainage fabric and a 75-mm sand capillary break layer capped with 75 mm

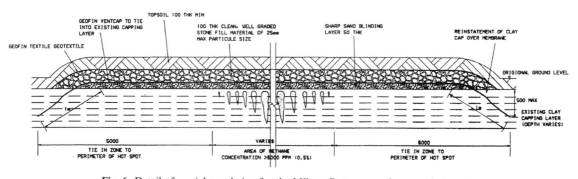

Fig. 6. Detail of special cap design for the Milton Common methane gas hot-spots.

Fig. 7. Dredging Baffins Pond and settling the solids in a lined lagoon on the Tangier Road fill site, with the laying of a geotextile filter fabric and covering with topsoil proceeding in the adjacent fields.

of clean sub and topsoil. Some of the subsoil was made available locally by dredging the adjacent Baffins Pond, settling out the pond silts and spreading them over the nearby field (Fig. 7). The silts were organic rich (3–12% C), nutritious (plenty of N P and K nutrients) and free of contamination and their use saved many thousands of pounds that otherwise would have been required for transporting-in more topsoil from the mainland. This combination of pond renovation and adjacent land reclamation, proved environmentally beneficial and financially economical for both environmental improvement projects.

The future

Looking to the future, Portsmouth City Council, in collaboration with the University of Portsmouth, are already using the substantial information on contamination gathered from investigating some 40 sites over the past six years to create a geographical information system (GIS) and associated database and are working towards the production of an integrated pollution ranking model for the city's land area. This will incorporate the geology, topography, hydrology, soil geotechnics and soil geochemistry results from all the many site investigations together with historical land use information, designated

land planning zones, aquifer protection criteria and coastal protection areas, etc., to provide a comprehensive ground quality dataset for any location within the city boundaries. Any site can then be ranked according to a specific set of objective criteria for each parameter in the data set.

The ultimate product of this work will then be a powerful, user-friendly tool which can be used to provide an objective prioritization model of the perceived contamination potential of any site or area. Such a tool will be of great benefit to planners, politicians, developers, environmentalists and the general public alike in providing instantly available, open and objective criteria upon which to make important decisions that will affect the lives of the local community. The model will also be used to ensure that the Council's limited resources are targeted at the highest priority areas.

Concluding discussion

The three case studies described above were chosen as being representative of more than a dozen similar sites across Portsea Island to show how Portsmouth City Council has been pro-actively investigating, prioritizing and remediating contaminated land sites within its boundaries, following the most up-to-date guidance on methodologies available at the time.

The decision to offer residents immediate re-housing from the infamous Lumsden Road (Glory Hole) site in 1991 was made on the basis of considerable site investigation data, but with little experience, at that time, of the interpretation of those data in terms of their impact on health risks to the residents from exposure to the identified contaminants. Therefore a conservative judgement was necessarily applied because of the many uncertainties at that time.

In contrast, the equally difficult political decision concerning the siting of a new school was made just four years later with the benefit of a full risk assessment methodology being applied to the substantial geochemical database collected during the Tangier Road site investigations. The risk assessment model used was the US-EPA approved 'Dermal Exposure' model (Tsuji & Seri 1996) and, whilst it contains some debatable and conservative assumptions, it produces a risk factor based upon all the known site data, and thereby allows a more openly understandable result to be made available to the press, public and councillors when debating the politically sensitive issue of the optimum location for a proposed new school.

This risk model is already becoming out of date and a number of new models, such as 'CLEA' (Ferguson & Denner 1998), are becoming available in the UK, with others currently being imported from Holland and the USA, such as 'C-SOIL', 'HESP' and 'Risk Assistant'.

Undoubtedly such methodologies and models will continue to improve, and, in combination with the Department of Environment's statutory guidance documents on contaminated land currently being issued (DoE 1997), should be able to provide clearer guidance in the future for decision makers to be able to make the best informed, transparent decisions in very often socially, politically and/or financially difficult development situations concerning contaminated land.

References

ANON. 1989. *Risk Assessment Guidance for Superfund: Human Health Evaluation Manual (Part A)*. US Environmental Protection Agency, Washington DC.

DoE 1997. *Environmental Protection Act 1990 Part IIA: Contaminated Land – Statutory Guidance on Contaminated Land*. Department of the Environment, HMSO, London.

FERGUSON, C. C. & DENNER, J. M. 1998. Human health risk assessment using UK Guideline Values for contaminants in soils. *This volume*.

PARKMAN, 1994. *Milton Lakes: ground investigation and risk assessment*. Consultant's Report for Portsmouth City Council.

PRIVETT, K. D. 1990. Port Solent Marina, Portsmouth – Photographic feature. *Quarterly Journal of Engineering Geology*, **23**, 191–192.

TSUIJI, J. S. & SERI, K. M. 1996. Current uses of the US-EPA lead model to assess health risk and action levels for soil. *Environmental Geochemistry and Health*, **18**, 25–33.

Human health risk assessment using UK Guideline Values for contaminants in soils

C. C. Ferguson[1] & J. M. Denner[2]

[1] Centre for Research into the Built Environment, The Nottingham Trent University, Burton Street, Nottingham NG1 4BU, UK
[2] The Environment Agency, Steel House, 11 Tothill Street, London SW1H 9NF, UK

Abstract. In recent years the UK Department of the Environment has, with others, developed a framework for contaminated land risk assessment, including the derivation of new Guideline Values. These are an important component in an integrated procedure for site-specific risk assessment which combines consistency of approach with flexibility to ensure that local circumstances are taken into account.

Guideline Values are derived using the Contaminated Land Exposure Assessment model (CLEA) which calculates human exposure via ten different exposure pathways. The relative contributions of the pathways vary according to site use, and hence the Guideline Values may also vary. This is consistent with the UK Government's 'suitable for use' policy. Guideline Values may also vary as a function of soil pH, soil organic matter, etc., reflecting the influence of such parameters on contaminant partitioning between soil solids and soil solution. The research described here is underpinned by complementary work to choose the most appropriate toxicological criteria for each contaminant.

Where Guideline Values are exceeded, the intention is that either a further phase of risk assessment or remedial action is triggered. If the former is chosen the emphasis will be on establishing whether exposure conditions differ significantly from the generic conditions assumed in CLEA. This is expected to be more cost-effective in general than site-specific risk assessment procedures. It does, however, require that the exposure assumptions and data values used in deriving the Guideline Values are understood by the risk assessor so that the necessary comparisons with site-specific conditions can be made.

Introduction

The development of UK government policy on contaminated land has been guided by a number of central objectives (Department of the Environment/Welsh Office 1994), including the following:

- prevention of future pollution
- sustainable development (Department of the Environment 1994a) which, in the context of contaminated land, includes removing unwanted environmental hazards, and making brownfield sites available for re-use and hence reducing pressure on greenfield sites
- a 'suitable for use' approach to remediation

The Environment Act 1995 sets out the principles that will govern the new legislative regime. The role of the supporting statutory guidance (Department of the Environment 1996) is to ensure that flexibility is maintained in the primary legislation necessary to deliver the policy objectives, while at the same time setting out a detailed framework within which professional judgement can be applied in a consistent and predictable manner.

Contaminated land is defined in the Environment Act 1995 as follows:

'any land which appears to the local authority in whose area it is situated to be in such a condition, by reason of substances in, on, or under the land, that

(a) significant harm is being caused or there is a significant possibility of such harm being caused; or
(b) pollution of controlled waters is being, or is likely to be, caused.'

In determining whether significant harm is being caused or there is a significant possibility of such harm being caused, either site-specific risk assessment or *appropriate* use of Guideline Values will be permitted. Of course, any risk assessment based on Guideline Values must demonstrate that the values are appropriate and relevant for the use and characteristics of the land in question.

The Guideline Values developed under the Department of the Environment's contaminated land research programme are based on generic assessment of *direct risks to human health* from exposure to contaminated

FERGUSON, C. C. & DENNER, J. M. 1998. Human health risk assessment using UK Guideline Values for contaminants in soils. *In:* LERNER, D. N. & WALTON, N. R. G. (eds) 1998. *Contaminated Land and Groundwater: Future Directions.* Geological Society, London, Engineering Geology Special Publications, **14**, 37–43.

soil. It is more difficult to develop generic soil guidelines for groundwater protection. This is because most of the key variables (thickness and attenuating capacity of soil and bedrock, depth to water table, source protection zone status, etc.) are highly site-specific. Generic guidance serves a somewhat different role; for example, to provide a set of worst case assumptions to screen out sites. But groundwater risks should always be assessed on a site-specific basis. The Environment Agency is developing guidance on methodologies for estimating the degree of soils clean-up required to protect groundwater.

Similarly, transfer of contaminants from soil to surface waters is highly site-specific and depends on run-off volume, peak flow rate, soil erodability, slope length and steepness, sorption capacity of the soil, vegetation cover type, and distance to receiving body. For many sites the major threat to surface water quality is likely to occur during site redevelopment, and will need to be assessed on a site-specific basis. Site assessors need to be aware that Guideline Values, or other guidance, often serve a narrower purpose and cannot be expected to indicate, even roughly, whether soil contaminants might impact adversely on surface waters. Guidance on assessing the impact of contaminated land on the water environment has been published by the Department of the Environment (1994b) and CIRIA (1995).

Developers and local authorities will also need to consider harm to or interference with ecosystems and habitats protected under the Wildlife and Countryside Act 1981, EC Directive 79/409/EEC on the Conservation of Wild Birds, and the Habitat Directive 92/43/EEC. Such considerations are, of course, highly site-specific. Some soil contaminants may adversely affect building materials. Guidance is provided in Building Research Establishment (1994).

Human health risk assessment

Site-specific assessment

Procedures for the systematic estimation of human health risks from exposure to contaminated soil have developed rapidly over the past 10–15 years. Reduced to its simplest form, the overall procedure can be represented as in Fig. 1. It is assumed that a single contaminant, x, occurs at a constant concentration $C(x)$ over the site; and that the concentration determined by laboratory analysis is appropriate for risk assessment.

These simplified source characteristics will serve to illustrate the principles of site-specific risk assessment while avoiding complications arising from multiple contaminants, spatial variability and relative bioavailability. The *exposure characteristics and assumptions* refer partly to site conditions (e.g. soil type, soil chemistry, exposed soil fraction) and partly to the site use and users (e.g. construction style of buildings, user activity patterns and time spent on site). Many of these are *assumptions* because chronic health risk assessments are concerned with predicting contaminant intakes up to 70 years into the future. Some of the soil characteristics may also change with time.

Exposure assessment involves modelling contaminant intakes via ingestion, inhalation and skin contact. Some of the algorithms are complex, and some may be difficult to validate. Allowance may also need to be made for

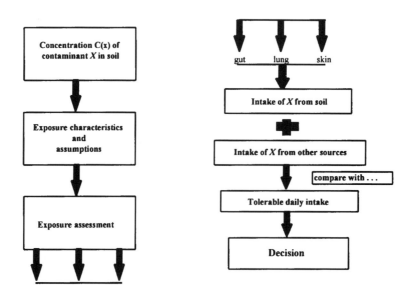

Fig. 1. Key elements in site-specific human risk assessment.

intake of the same contaminants from background, especially dietary, sources. At its simplest, risk assessment therefore consists of comparing total uptake (i.e. from both soil and background sources) with a tolerable daily uptake as advised by authoritative toxicologists. The latter may have embedded in them policy decisions on acceptable levels of risk which in turn may have been made taking costs and benefits into account. In practice, because data on uptake (absorbed dose) are not always available, the comparison is often between estimated intake and tolerable daily intake (TDI). This is precautionary because soil contaminants are not usually as bioavailable as the pure and soluble compounds typically used in the animal studies used to derive tolerable daily intakes.

Derivation of Guideline Values

The procedure for deriving generic Guideline Values, reduced to its basic elements, is shown in Fig. 2. The similarity with Fig. 1 is obvious. The main difference is that a *trial concentration* of the contaminant acts as input data along with a set of exposure assumptions. The subset of exposure assumptions relating to site use and users (types of activity, time spent on site, etc.) are in essence the same as those that would need to be assumed in a site-specific risk assessment. Of course, generic assumptions replace measurable site characteristics (e.g. soil pH, organic matter content) although separate Guideline Values can easily be derived, for example, to cover a range of soil pH values. The exposure assessment algorithms are exactly the same as one would use in a site-specific risk assessment and result in a hypothetical intake of the contaminant from soil, I_s, which reflects the initial trial concentration.

The estimated intake from background (non-soil) sources, I_{ns}, is exactly that which would be used in site-specific assessment. The sum of I_s and I_{ns} is compared with a tolerable daily intake which, again, is exactly that which would be used in a site-specific risk assessment. Then, if $I_s + I_{ns} > TDI$, the procedure is repeated with a smaller trial concentration (or if $I_s + I_{ns} < TDI$ with a greater trial value) until a total intake is found that exactly matches the TDI. This soil concentration is chosen as the Guideline Value for protection of human health. It follows therefore that, so long as the exposure characteristics and assumptions appropriate for the site are not significantly different from the exposure assumptions built into the generic model, the Guideline Values can be used as a cost-effective approach to risk assessment.

For some contaminants it needs to be recognized that sites with residual contaminants in the soil do not always occur in isolation. It may therefore be prudent to allow for the possibility, for example, that people exposed to residual contaminants in domestic gardens might also be exposed from other localities in the neighbourhood, e.g. playing fields, allotments and open spaces. In order to make allowances for such multiple exposure effects, it may be desirable to allocate only a proportion of the TDI (or the difference TDI $- I_{ns}$) to allowable intake from soil. CLEA is programmed to calculate Guideline Values for soil allocation factors less than or equal to unity.

The above approach to ensuring that total intake does not exceed some toxicity-based threshold is not necessarily appropriate for genotoxic carcinogens. This is

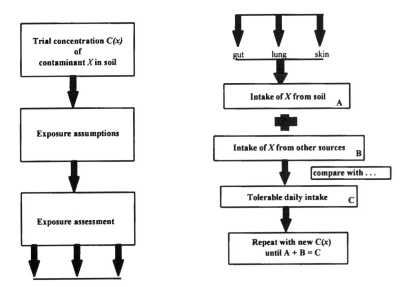

Fig. 2. Key elements in guideline values for contaminants in soil for protection of human health.

because such substances are usually assumed not to have a toxicity threshold. A modified approach may therefore be called for which is concerned with limiting the excess risk from the source (soil on a contaminated site) rather than with keeping total intake below some threshold value. CLEA is programmed to allow this option.

The CLEA model

The Contaminated Land Exposure Assessment (CLEA) model was developed by the Centre for Research into the Built Environment under contract to the Department of the Environment. Although it can be used for site-specific risk assessment, it was developed specifically for deriving human health Guideline Values to help determine whether 'significant harm is being caused or there is a significant possibility of such harm being caused' from exposure to contaminated soil. Ten exposure pathways are included, as summarized in Table 1. The relative importance of the different pathways will depend on the contaminants, and on site use which is assumed to fall into one of the following categories: residential with gardens; residential without gardens; allotments; parks, playing fields and open space; commercial/industrial.

In CLEA, contaminant intakes are calculated incrementally for 18 age intervals. The first 16 intervals correspond to the first 16 years of life, the 17th interval is the working life (taken as 16–59), and the 18th is 60–70 years. The user then has the choice of calculating an average daily intake with an averaging period of 70 years (the conventional lifetime) or any shorter period.

Table 1. *The exposure pathways included in the CLEA model*

Outdoor ingestion of soil
Indoor ingestion of dust
Consumption of home-grown vegetables
Ingestion of soil attached to vegetables
Skin contact with outdoor soil
Skin contact with indoor dust
Outdoor inhalation of fugitive dust
Indoor inhalation of fugitive dust
Outdoor inhalation of soil vapour
Indoor inhalation of soil vapour
Ingestion of drinking water from mains supply*
Skin contact with mains water during showering and
    bathing, etc.*
Inhalation of vapour during showering and bathing, and from
    ambient vapours otherwise derived from mains water*

*Not computed when an estimate of average daily intake from background (non-soil) sources is available.

For derivation of the UK soil Guideline Values, the tolerable daily intakes are taken from authoritative sources as summarized in Department of the Environment (in press).

Time-dependent effects

Because natural degradation and dispersion processes will gradually reduce the concentration of most contaminants in surface and near-surface soils, all exposure equations are written with concentration as a time-varying parameter. Removal processes include photolysis, chemical reaction, volatilization, biodegradation, run-off, erosion, leaching and crop offtake. Biodegradation is particularly important in determining risks from organic contaminants, but the rate of degradation is highly site-specific and depends on the types and growth rates of microbial populations, which in turn are influenced by moisture content, temperature, pH, Eh, nutrient availability and toxicity.

Most risk assessment models provide no explicit means for modelling natural attenuation of contaminants. In contrast, environmental models developed specifically for organics (e.g. Jury *et al.* 1983) usually represent chemical and biological degradation of organic contaminants as a single first-order process with rate constant specified by the user. This is the approach adopted for the CLEA model.

Thus if the initial concentration is C_o and first-order decay is assumed, then the concentration at time t is

$$C_t = C_o e^{(-kt)}$$

and the average concentration $\bar{C}_i$ over the time interval $(\Delta T)_i = t_i - t_{i-1}$ is given by

$$\bar{C}_i = \frac{C_o}{(\Delta T)_i} \int_{t_{i-1}}^{t_i} e^{(-kt)} dt$$

This formulation also provides a natural way of incorporating the lag interval between site assessment and first end-user access, which could be several years.

CLEA as a probabilistic (Monte Carlo) model

In recent years there has been a reaction against the worst-case exposure assessments typical of the 1980s. In particular, assessments based on a hypothetical maximally exposed individual (MEI) should properly be used only to determine whether exposure is insignificant. Often, however, they have been used to characterize actual or plausible human health risks. Keenan *et al.* (1993) drew attention to a US Environmental Protection Agency example – the theoretical cancer risk from dioxin exposure for a child living close to a

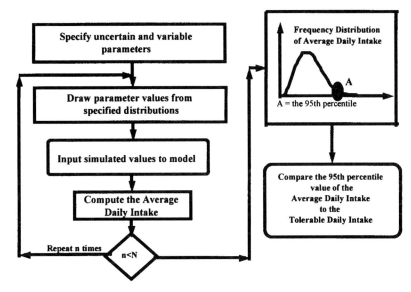

Fig. 3. Monte Carlo approach for deriving guideline values for soil contaminants.

hypothetical municipal incinerator (USEPA 1988). They comment that,

'at first review, the analysis seemed reasonable until one noted that the child ate about a teaspoon of dirt each day, that his house was downwind of the stack, that he ate fish from a pond near the incinerator, his fish consumption was at the 95th percentile level, he drank contaminated water from the pond, he ate food grown primarily from the family garden, and he drank milk from a cow that had grazed on forage at the farm.'

Analyses of this sort are of little value for guiding public decision-making unless they are accompanied by some indication of the number of individuals likely to be exposed at this level, and the range of exposure levels expected in a typical exposed community. MEI assessment is a particular case of a more general problem – that of repeated use of conservative assumptions. For example, if human health risk depended only on the product of three independent factors each of which was chosen at the 90th percentile level, the product would represent a 99.9th percentile risk.

The USEPA has long been the focus of criticism for overly conservative exposure assessments. But the Agency's decision-making now requires more detailed information on individual and population risks (Habicht 1992). Exposure assessment guidelines (USEPA 1992) endorse the use of simulation distributions, such as those produced by Monte Carlo models, in order to produce more realistic estimates of exposure.

The essence of Monte Carlo exposure modelling is that single-point values of certain key variables are replaced by probability density functions (PDFs) reflecting the variability or uncertainties associated with exposure parameters. Each pass through a Monte Carlo model involves random sampling from the relevant PDFs to produce a single estimate of intake or risk.

Multiple passes thus allow a distribution of intake or risk to be built up as shown in Fig. 3 for the Monte Carlo submodel in CLEA.

Often the most difficult aspect of Monte Carlo modelling is choosing appropriate PDFs for the key variables. In the CLEA model the user can choose from a range of PDFs as summarised in Table 2. The beta and gamma density functions are particularly flexible. For example, many densities that occur naturally are positively skewed corresponding to $\alpha_2 > \alpha_1$ in the beta family of distributions (Fig. 4).

The mean and mode of these densities, scaled to the interval (a, b) are given by

$$\text{mean:} \quad \mu = a + \frac{\alpha_1(b - a)}{\alpha_1 + \alpha_2} \tag{1}$$

$$\text{mode:} \quad m = a + \frac{(\alpha_1 - 1)(b - a)}{\alpha_1 + \alpha_2 - 2} \tag{2}$$

Table 2. *Probability density functions available in the CLEA model*

Uniform (a, b)
Triangular
Normal (Gaussian)
Lognormal
Beta
Gamma

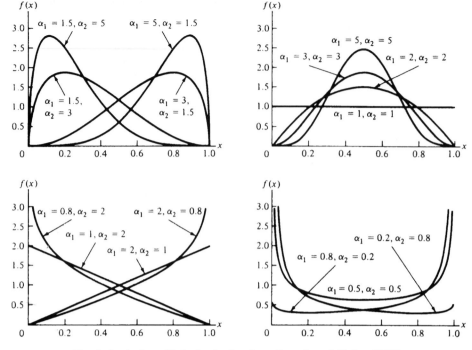

Fig. 4. A selection of beta density functions. From Law & Kelton (1982).

Thus if estimates of μ and m can be made, Equations (1) and (2) can be solved to give estimates of α_1 and α_2:

$$\alpha_1 = \frac{(\mu - 1)(2m - a - b)}{(m - \mu)(b - a)} \qquad (3)$$

$$\alpha_2 = \frac{(b - \mu)\alpha_1}{(\mu - a)} \qquad (4)$$

This technique is used in CLEA to provide a default PDF for the proportion of vegetable consumption that is homegrown. An average homegrown fraction may be estimated from the National Food Survey (MAFF 1990) for various vegetable types, and an upper bound homegrown fraction may be postulated from considerations of growing season and preservation potential. For example, for onions and leeks the average home-grown fraction, ϕ_{av}, is estimated at 10% and the upper bound fraction, ϕ_{ub}, at 100%. The homegrown fraction distribution can be normalized to $(0, 1)$ by dividing by ϕ_{ub}. This variate is denoted by H and has mean value $H_{av} = \phi_{av}/\phi_{ub}$ and upper bound $H_{ub} = 1$.

A default distribution has been derived subjectively based on the assumption that, on new housing developments, a large proportion of householders will grow none of their own vegetables or only a tiny fraction of their total intake. Conversely, only a very small proportion of householders will grow nearly all their onion and leek

intake. This suggests a reverse-J shaped distribution with a peak at zero consumption and in which consumption decreases monotonically to a small positive constant or to zero. This can be modelled using a beta density with shape parameters $\alpha_1 < 1$ and $\alpha_2 \geq 1$. The α_2 parameter is chosen subjectively to give a reasonable looking density. Then α_1 is calculated from Equation (4) by inserting $a = 0$, $b = 1$, $\mu = H_{av}$ and rearranging:

$$\alpha_1 = \alpha_2 H_{av}/(1 - H_{av}) \qquad (5)$$

A distribution derived from 2000 random simulations from this PDF is shown in Fig. 5.

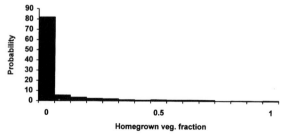

Fig. 5. Distribution of homegrown vegetable consumption based on 2000 values drawn randomly from the beta density function with shape parameters $\alpha_1 = 0.11$, $\alpha_2 = 1.0$.

Conclusions

UK Guideline Values for contaminants in soils are being derived using the CLEA model which calculates human exposure via ten different exposure pathways. CLEA is a Monte Carlo exposure assessment model which can be used to estimate a range of human intakes and their probability of occurrence. Whenever possible, critical input parameters are validated by careful comparison with experimental and field measurements. Risk assessors can therefore use the resulting Guideline Values with knowledge of the sources of uncertainty and variability, and their likely impact.

The research to develop the new Guideline Values forms part of a wider Department of the Environment research programme on risk assessment of contaminated land, including work on sampling, and risks to other targets such as the water environment, ecosystems and building materials. Some of the underlying risk analysis and risk management principles have been discussed by Ferguson & Denner (1994).

Acknowledgement. This work was funded by the Department of the Environment but the views expressed are those of the authors and do not necessarily represent those of the Department.

References

BUILDING RESEARCH ESTABLISHMENT 1994. *Performance of building materials in contaminated land*. BRE Report BR 255.

CIRIA 1995. *Remedial Treatment for Contaminated Land, Volume III: Site Investigation and Assessment*. Special Publication 103. CIRIA, London.

Department of the Environment 1994a. *Sustainable Development: the UK Strategy*. Cm 2426, HMSO, London.

——1994b. *A framework for assessing the impact of contaminated land on groundwater and surface water*. CLR Report No 1. Department of the Environment, London.

——1996. *Environment Act 1995: Statutory Guidance and Regulations on Contaminated Land* (draft).

—— (in press) *Contaminants in soil: collation of toxicological data and intake values for humans*. CLR Report, Department of the Environment, London.

Department of the Environment/Welsh Office 1994. *Framework for Contaminated Land: Outcome of the Government's Policy Review and Conclusions from the Consultation Paper Paying for our Past*. Department of the Environment, London.

FERGUSON, C. & DENNER, J. 1994. Developing guideline (trigger) values for contaminants in soil: underlying risk analysis and risk management concepts. *Land Contamination & Reclam*, **2**, 117–123

HABICHT, H. 1992. Guidance on risk characterisation for risk managers and risk assessors. Memorandum dated February 26 1992 to Assistant and Regional Administrators, United States Environmental Protection Agency.

JURY, W. A., SPENCER, W. F. & FARMER, W. J. 1983. Behaviour assessment model for trace organics in soil: I Model description. *Journal of Environmental Quality*, **12**, 558–564.

KEENAN, R. E., ALGEO, E. R., EBERT, E. S. & PAUSTENBACH, D. J. 1993. Taking a risk assessment approach to RCRA corrective action. *Proceedings of the Conference 'Developing Cleanup Standards for Contaminated Soil, Sediment, and Groundwater: How Clean is Clean?'* Water Environment Federation, Alexandria, VA, 225–275.

LAW, A. M. & KELTON, W. D. 1982. *Simulation Modeling and Analysis*. McGraw-Hill, New York.

MAFF 1990 *Household food consumption and expenditure*. Annual Report of the National Food Survey Committee. HMSO, London.

USEPA 1988. *Estimating exposures to 2,3,7,8 – TCDD*. Report EPA/600-6-8800 SA, Office of Health and Environmental Assessment, Washington DC.

——1992. Guidelines for exposure assessment. *Federal Register*, **57**, 22888–22938.

Biological treatment of crude oil contaminated soil in Russia

N. Christofi,[1] I. B. Ivshina,[2] M. S. Kuyukina[2] & J. C. Philp[1]

[1] Department of Biological Sciences, Napier University, 10 Colinton Road, Edinburgh
EH10 5DT, UK
[2] Institute of Ecology and Genetics of Microorganisms, The Russian Academy of Sciences, Urals
Branch, Perm, Russia

Abstract. Oil spillage on land accounts for the majority of hydrocarbon contamination of our planet and bioremediation of these habitats is possible because of the existence of hydrocarbon-oxidizing microorganisms *in situ* and in culture collections. A number of physical, chemical and environmental factors affect the degradation of oil in soils including soil pore structure, aeration, toxic oil constituents and nutrient availability. In addition, strongly sorbed hydrophobic constituents, such as polycyclic aromatic hydrocarbons, are difficult to solubilize and make available for degradation. Various remediation techniques were used in field experiments on bioremediation of oil contaminated agricultural soils after an accidental oil-spill which occurred on the territory of the Mezhevskoe oilfield ('Polaznaoil' company). Composting systems were utilized to increase oxygen transfer with degradation further enhanced by combination of nutrient additions, bulking with straw and inoculations of *Rhodococcus*-biosurfactant complexes. After a three-month bioremediation the content of chloroform extracts decreased to 2.85–1.60% (from an initial amount of 3.75%). The percentage oil degraded varied from 24.0 to 57.1 depending on the remediation methods used. CO_2 evolution rates ($36.1–54.6 \,\mu g \, g^{-1} \, day^{-1}$) indicated the intensity of aerobic oil degradation. It is not clear whether fertilization with NPK, and bulking, increased oil degradation rates in the systems used. Our initial results show that soil remediation progresses more effectively if composting systems are used with increased ventilation, nutrient additions and, particularly, inoculation of *Rhodococcus*-biosurfactant complexes.

Introduction

Biological remediation, employing *in* or *ex situ* techniques, is one of four methods used to deal with oil contamination of soils. These include encapsulation, and physical, chemical and biological treatments. In soil, bioremediation of oil is achieved by microorganisms which are able to degrade hydrocarbons, gaining energy from the process and increased microbial biomass. Co-metabolism where microbial enzymes are directed to the degradation of compounds without energy or biomass gains is also a possibility. Generally, hydrocarbons are converted to non-toxic substances such as carbon dioxide and water under aerobic conditions. The ultimate aims of bioremediation techniques are to enhance degradation of pollutants and to achieve this they involve functions such as increasing the aeration status of soil (e.g. composting, bulking), addition of nutrients (e.g. containing N and P), bioaugmentation (e.g. addition of hydrocarbon-degrading microorganisms) and addition of surfactants.

Many hydrocarbon species in crude oil are easily degraded but others appear to be persistent (Wilson & Jones 1993), such as polycyclic aromatic hydrocarbons (PAH) and include the high molecular weight ones with low solubilities. In order to complete degradation, they must be made available to microorganisms, and enzymes must be available for their degradation. Surfactants have been used to increase bioavailability of insoluble organics through, for example, desorption from solid matrices (Deschenes *et al.* 1995; Thibault *et al.* 1996). Synthetic and natural (bio-) surfactants have been tested with varying degrees of success (Deschenes *et al.* 1995; Roch & Alexander 1995; Tsomides *et al.* 1995). Recalcitrant substances can be oxidised chemically but this tends to be costly. A combination of chemical oxidation and bioremediation has been proposed as a cost-effective alternative (Kemenade *et al.* 1995) where the initial chemical process converts the pollutants to less toxic and biodegradable compounds.

Composting systems with or without bulking agents are utilized to increase oxygen input and enhance aerobic biodegradation. Together with exogenous inputs of microbial nutrients, this can be effective in hydrocarbon degradation. Hydrocarbon degradation also demands the presence of microorganisms capable of producing the necessary enzyme systems to facilitate this. Most soils contain hydrocarbon-degrading microorganisms including bacteria and fungi (Heitkamp *et al.* 1988; Bezalel *et al.* 1996) but their numbers and metabolic quality

Christofi, N., Ivshina, I. B., Kuyukina, M. S & Philp, J. C. 1998. Biological treatment of crude oil contaminated soil in Russia. *In:* Lerner, D. N. & Walton, N. R. G. (eds) 1998. *Contaminated Land and Groundwater: Future Directions.* Geological Society, London, Engineering Geology Special Publications, **14**, 45–51.

may not be significant. Bioaugmentation allows for the addition of populations of microorganisms with the appropriate metabolic capabilities, and increased populations can speed up the remediation process.

In this study composting systems with nutrient and microorganism additions were examined for the bioremediation of agricultural soil contaminated with crude oil discharged from a leaking subterranean oil pipeline in the Perm Region of Russia (West Urals).

Materials and methods

Crude oil contaminated site bioremediation

Site preparation. Soil from the contaminated area was excavated to a depth of 1 m and crudely mixed with a grab and manually with spades and shovels. The different pile systems (windrows) constructed are shown in Fig. 1. All stacks were built to a height of 1.5 m length 3 m and breadth 1.5 m. Some piles received NPK fertilizer to overcome inorganic nutrient limitations. The strain of *Rhodococcus* added was *R. ruber* IEGM AC 235 which was previously isolated from the same site. This is a biosurfactant-producing strain and addition of this organism to the piles included addition of biosurfactant complexes. The inclusion of straw in some systems was as both oil absorbent and bulking agent to enhance oxygen transfer. The emplacement of ceramic drainage pipes was to help enhance oxygen transfer by creating air flow on the basis of differences in temperature between the centre of the pile and the exterior atmosphere.

Microbiological analyses. Three samples were taken from the site before pile construction to determine the oil contamination level and to establish baseline data on the bacterial content of these soils. Two of these samples (A and B) were contaminated with oil. Sample A was loose oil-contaminated soil and B was from clumps

highly contaminated with oil. Sample C was from uncontaminated agricultural soil in the wheat field adjoining. Five random aliquots (0.5–1.0 kg) of the three different soils were removed from the contaminated site and transported to the laboratory. Each of the aliquots was thoroughly mixed and subsamples from each (150 g) were pooled and remixed. A sample from this (1 g) was taken for tenfold serial dilution in sterile saline. To help release the bacteria from clumps the first tenfold dilution was treated by ultrasonication for 90 s. Temporal variation in bacterial populations was determined for all composting systems. Samples were removed from a central position within the piles and from the outside and treated as above.

Total aerobic heterotrophic bacteria were enumerated on nutrient agar plates and hydrocarbon-oxidizing bacteria by the method of Rosenberg & Gutnick (1986). In this case the hydrocarbon source was a mixture of n-alkanes from C_{10} to C_{16}.

Oil content of soils (chloroform extractable material). Soil (100 g) was added to 250 ml chloroform and shaken to extract crude oil overnight. The liquid phase was separated by filtration and transferred to pre-weighed, round-bottomed flasks. The chloroform was removed by distillation and the crude oil quantity determined by reweighing. This procedure was repeated three times for each soil sample to extract the maximum amount of crude oil.

Activity measurements. Potential microbial activity in the soils was estimated by measurement of the CO_2 evolution rate in the head space of gas-tight vessels. Water was added to the soils to between 50 and 60% of water-holding capacity (WHC). Evolution of head space CO_2 was measured by gas chromatography. The difference in CO_2 evolution between uncontaminated soil and soil containing crude oil was used to determine oil degradation.

Laboratory fertilization experiments. Nitrogen was applied to soil samples as urea ($0.67 \, \text{mg g}^{-1}$) and phosphorus as superphosphate ($0.29 \, \text{mg g}^{-1}$). In addition, Inipol EAP-22 (Elf Aquitaine), an oleophilic fertilizer that is a microemulsion of urea, lauryl phosphate and oleic acid, was tested. The critical micelle dilution (CMD) of Inipol was determined and the critical micelle concentration (CMC) calculated. A range of concentrations below the CMC were used to assess the effect of Inipol on biodegradation.

Oil Washing using Rhodococcus-*biosurfactant complexes.* The role of biosurfactants produced by *R. ruber* on the removal of oil sorbed onto soil surfaces was tested. Cultures of *R. ruber* IEGM AC 219 were grown in the presence of *n*-hexadecane. Biosurfactants produced in

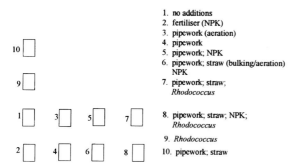

1. no additions
2. fertiliser (NPK)
3. pipework (aeration)
4. pipework
5. pipework; NPK
6. pipework; straw (bulking/aeration) NPK
7. pipework; straw; *Rhodococcus*
8. pipework; straw; NPK; *Rhodococcus*
9. *Rhodococcus*
10. pipework; straw

Fig. 1. Diagrammatic representation of the layout of the completed site.

Table 1. *Initial microbiological analyses (CFU g^{-1} dry weight)*

	Sample*		
	A	B	C
Aerobic heterotrophic bacteria	3×10^6	4×10^8	1×10^8
Hydrocarbon-oxidizing bacteria	6×10^5	3×10^6	4×10^3

* A = loose oiled soil, B = conglomerate, C = uncontaminated agricultural soil.

culture were quantified after extraction with petroleum ether by the method of Bligh & Dyer (1959).

Washed sand (10 g) was mixed with 1 g of crude oil in 250-ml flasks to which 100 ml water was added. Crude biosurfactant extract was obtained after sonication of centrifuged cultures of *R. ruber* and the hydrophobic oil hexadecane layer. Different concentrations of this extract were added to oil contaminated sand in the flasks and shaken for 48 h (70 rpm) at room temperature. Controls without surfactant extracts were run.

Results

Crude oil contaminated site bioremediation

Microbiological analyses. The physiological groups of bacteria most important to this study in the three samples taken prior to site preparation, yielded the counts shown in Table 1. The selective nature of such counting techniques tends to underestimate but such counts do show relative temporal variability. The pH of these soils were all in the range 5.0–5.5.

Counts for hydrocarbon-oxidizing bacteria should be regarded as overestimates as the method can be unreliable (with the production of false positives). There is a need for a more reliable counting method

for this group of organisms. Variations in total aerobic heterotrophic bacteria and hydrocarbon degraders for two of the pile systems are presented in Figs 2 and 3. Sample 1 represents pile 1 (composting system without any additions) and sample 8 represents pile 8 containing bulking, *R. ruber* additions, NPK fertilizer and pipework system to optimize aeration. I and II denote the surface and middle sampling positions respectively. The data for aerobic heterotrophic bacteria show no obvious trends in the different piles. Addition of nutrients and aeration does not necessarily increase the populations as determined by plate counting techniques.

Oil content of soil and degradation rates. Measurement of the oil content of soil samples taken before site preparation was done to obtain figures for the average and highest levels of contamination on the site. Subsequently, when the site had been completed, samples from each pile were taken to obtain zero time estimates of the concentration of oil in the soil from each pile.

Figure 3 shows that adding hydrocarbon-degrading microorganisms increases their numbers but that the populations decrease to those of the unamended soils after a period of time.

Samples were taken from the middle and surface of each pile to take account of volatilization of hydrocarbons from the surface, and also to monitor the progress of bioremediation at both regions. It is evident that there are obvious variations in the oil content in the remediation

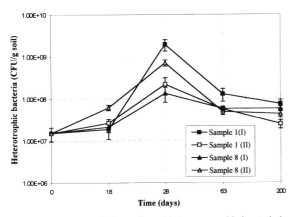

Fig. 2. Temporal variations of aerobic heterotrophic bacteria in stack piles (time 0 = 14 July 1995).

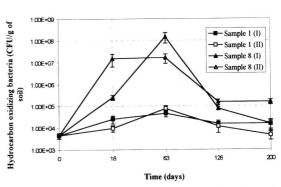

Fig. 3. Temporal variations of hydrocarbon-oxidizing bacteria in stack piles (time 0 = 14 July 1995).

piles which is due to their heterogeneous nature. However, it is evident that there is a decrease in oil content in the soil with time (Fig. 4). Data for the two piles 1 and 8 show a decrease in oil content, with initial oil removal rates being similar (possibly due to removal of volatile species within the soil). After three months, oil removal was greater in the bioaugmented pile 8. There appears to be no significant difference in the removal of oil from the surface of pile systems 1 and 8 chosen to highlight the importance of bioaugmentation. Lower microbial activity, measured by CO_2 evolution in laboratory systems, was evident for surface soil samples. Figure 5 shows differences in CO_2 evolution in soil samples removed from the middle of all stack piles. The data represent three replicate analyses from pooled subsamples (5) from each pile. Pile 8, containing *R. ruber* and surfactant complexes, showed the highest degradation ability.

Activity measurements. Table 2 shows the average changes in oil content over a three-month bioremediation period for all pile systems. The percentage oil changes in the soil have been converted to daily rates of oil and carbon degradation. The latter was calculated based on an oil carbon content of 80–88% (Eschrich 1980). It is unlikely that the CO_2 production rates based on carbon degradation are real. They are much higher than values derived from laboratory incubation experiments (Fig. 5). The higher theoretical rates are likely due to loss of oil in natural pile systems by volatilization. Laboratory results examining the rates of CO_2 evolution in oil contaminated and uncontaminated soils incubated with fertilizer N and P indicated average rates of between 36.1 and 54.6 $\mu g\,CO_2\ g^{-1}\,day^{-1}$. The temperature of laboratory incubation was 22°C whereas field systems experienced temperatures between 10 and 27°C. Soil samples from the middle and the surface of each pile were examined for CO_2 evolution rates at time zero. The lowest activity was obtained with the uncontaminated agricultural soil. The data show active degradation of oil constituents.

Inipol addition to oil contaminated soils at a concentration below the CMC enhanced degradation of oil, but the addition of urea and phosphate alone to systems led to higher degradation. Inipol contains the surfactants including lauryl phosphate. The use of biosurfactants to effect the release of hydrocarbons sorbed onto solid soil surfaces would provide a less toxic alternative to synthetic surfactants. Our studies on the release of sorbed oil from sands shows that crude *R. ruber* surfactant complexes have a high desorption capacity (Fig. 6). Rather than use synthetic surfactants it

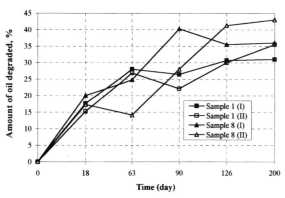

Fig. 4. Percentage of oil degradation in stack piles (time 0 = 14 July 1995).

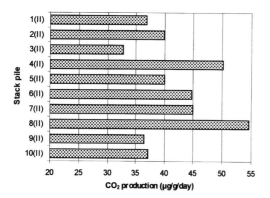

Fig. 5. Microbial activity (CO_2 production) in soil samples removed from the middle of stack piles receiving different treatment.

Table 2. *Changes in the mean chloroform extractable materials (CEM) of the surface pile systems (2–10) and theoretical rates of degradation*

Time (days)	Chloroform extractable material (%)	Oil degradation ($\mu g\,g^{-1}\,day^{-1}$)	Carbon degradation ($\mu g\,g^{-1}\,day^{-1}$)	CO_2 production ($\mu g\,g^{-1}\,day^{-1}$)
0	3.75	–	–	–
30	3.28	157	125.6	460.5
60	2.57	237	189.6	695.2
90	2.47	40	32.0	117.3

Note: CEM is used as the oil content for the calculation of CO_2 production.

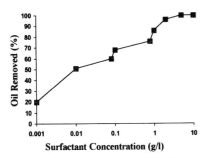

Fig. 6. Influence of *R. ruber* surfactant complexes on oil removal from crude oil contaminated sand samples. Water washed sands gave a maximum 21% removal.

would make sense to enhance the production of biosurfactants in hydrocarbon-degrading microorganisms added to or naturally present in soils.

Discussion

Large crude oil spillage incidents, especially those at sea, gain high profile in the media. It is clear that quantitatively smaller, but much more frequent, spills are of greater significance in ecological damage. Not only is crude oil directly toxic, but it also exerts a smothering effect.

The business of bioremediation as is reported in the literature can be confusing. When performed purely commercially, there is often no attempt to distinguish which factors contribute most to the success (or failure) of the venture. Each site is, of course, unique. Extraneous environmental factors (e.g. climate, soil fertility, pH, soil type) all have an effect. In Russia, a major consideration is climate, which can be considered to be extreme continental over most of the land mass. Summer, when bioremediation activity is at its peak, is short and can be very hot, leading to water limitation particularly within the piles. Winters are long and very cold. The site considered here represents a major spill resulting in the production of perhaps 4000 m³ of grossly contaminated land. The worst effects were on trees, which were killed by the concentration of crude oil within their root zone. Agricultural soil used to grow wheat was contaminated to a depth of approximately 1 m. The initial solution to the problem was to cover the site with uncontaminated topsoil.

In this bioremediation study, compost (windrow) systems were utilized. Such systems, manipulated to enhance the rates of oil removal through biological (primarily aerobic biodegradation) and physical (venting) means, exhibited significant contaminant removal over a three-month period (up to 57% oil removal

depending on the composting system). This high removal would not have occurred in the buried contaminated soil. Based on laboratory experiments, showing lower rates of CO_2 production (Fig. 5) than the theoretical rates calculated (Table 2), it is evident that a large proportion of oil was removed through ventilation. Laboratory rates (obtained using static incubation systems) of CO_2 production indicate a requirement of more than 8 years to degrade the oil. This is if the oil (3.75% of soil) represented biodegradable constituents. Of course, a large volatile fraction is present which would reduce the bioremediation time, but bioremediation of soil would still be lengthy without manipulation.

In a manipulated system, initial degradation would be rapid for labile hydrocarbons. GC–MS analyses of Polazna soils with time showed good removal of the lighter oil fractions. Refractive species such as PAHs would require longer periods if appropriate degrading microorganisms exist and their degradation is likely to require desorption from solid surfaces. The use of surfactants to desorb hydrocarbon pollutants and affect their biodegradation is widely studied. Non-ionic surfactants can enhance the concentration and degradation of phenanthrene, *n*-decane and tetradecane in the aqueous phase (Aronstein *et al.* 1991; Bury & Miller 1993). Laha & Luthy (1992) showed, however, that non-ionic surfactants at concentrations above their critical micelle concentration inhibited phenanthrene degradation. In a survey of eight synthetic surfactants (Tiehm 1994), the ability to solubilize PAH was variable. The more hydrophobic surfactants exhibited better solubilizing properties. Contradictory results have been obtained from tests on biodegradability of PAH solubilized by synthetic surfactants (Liu *et al.* 1995). In the study by Tiehm (1994), the more hydrophobic surfactants were less tolerated by bacteria. The experiments of Liu *et al.* (1995) showed that Brij 30 was degraded along with naphthalene, but that Triton X-100 was not. However, in both cases the addition of surfactant did not significantly affect either the rate of naphthalene degradation or the eventual amount degraded, despite improved bioavailability.

Inipol has been used in the bioremediation of the *Exxon Valdez* oil spill in Alaska (Pritchard & Costa 1991). Our studies with soils (data not presented) show that the presence of Inipol does enhance crude oil bioremediation but rates of degradation are lower than when using urea and phosphate additions alone. Inipol is a microemulsion containing synthetic surfactants which are the likely inhibitory compounds at the concentrations used. Using Microtox, the EC_{50} value for Inipol EAP 22 is $0.4 \, \text{mg} \, \text{l}^{-1}$, which is >1600 times more toxic than the *R. ruber* biosurfactant complexes ($EC_{50} = 650 \, \text{mg} \, \text{l}^{-1}$). However, although Inipol exhibits inhibitory activity, it has the advantage that the fertilizer in this oleophilic substrate is not easily washed out of soils.

There is no doubt that biosurfactants are generally less toxic and more biodegradable than synthetic ones and would be preferred in bioremediation. Production and use of biosurfactants either as crude microbial culture extracts or purified compounds is expensive. Biosurfactant production from monosaccharides or sugar alcohols and fatty acids has been achieved via enzyme-catalysed esterification in organic solvents (Ducret *et al.* 1995). It would make sense to encourage the growth of biosurfactant-producing microorganisms *in situ* to enhance desorption of hydrocarbon contaminants. Our study shows that biosurfactant complexes remove a high percentage of oil from contaminated sands, and oil shale material (data not presented). Addition of *R. ruber*, a surfactant-producing species, enhanced oil removal in Polazna soils. This was evident in pile 8 samples removed from the middle of the pile showing highest CO_2 evolution rates (Fig. 5). Methods need to be developed to enhance biosurfactant production in natural or introduced hydrocarbon degraders in soils.

Microbiologically, there are various limiting factors to be considered in a bioremediation programme. As previously stated, mass transfer of the organic pollutants from the soil particles to the liquid phase is likely to be limiting, hence the interest in synthetic and biosurfactants. As many of the enzymes involved have an absolute requirement for molecular oxygen (mono- and dioxygenases), oxygen mass transfer in soils is likely in many instances to be limiting. In the experimental programme initiated, we have used locally available materials to try to aid oxygen transfer.

An aspect of bioremediation which receives little attention is the possibility that microbiological limitation is due to catabolite repression. When presented with a variety of carbon substrates, it is logical for a bacterium to choose the substrates it can most easily utilize. If such substrates are abundant then, despite the presence of the necessary bacteria, biological degradation of the pollutants may not progress. There is some evidence that the rhodococci lack the catabolite repressions of other bacteria. In fact, it may be that the presence of glucose enhances the biodegradation of aromatic pollutants (Warhurst & Fewson 1994). If this is so, then rhodococci would be at a considerable advantage over others, and would therefore be organisms of choice for bioaugmentation.

The programme has been designed to try to discriminate between the influences of some commonly applied techniques in order that a full-scale treatment can be optimized and applied more generally to crude oil contaminated sites in Russia.

Acknowledgements. This work has been sponsored by three institutions: the Russian Academy of Sciences, Napier University and the Royal Society of London. We thank Elf Aquitaine for the samples of Inipol. We are grateful to all who have contributed at both technical and administrative levels.

References

ARONSTEIN, B. N., CALVILLO. Y. M. & ALEXANDER, M. 1991. Effects of surfactants at low concentrations on the desorption and biodegradation of sorbed aromatic compounds in soils. *Environmental Science and Technology*, **25**, 1728–1731.

BEZALEL, L., HADAR, Y. & CERNIGLIA, C. E. 1996. Mineralisation of polycyclic aromatic hydrocarbons by the white rot fungus *Pleurotus ostreatus*. *Applied and Environmental Microbiology*, **62**, 292–295.

BLIGH, E. G. & DYER, W. J. 1959. A rapid method of total lipid extraction and purification. *Canadian Journal of Biochemistry and Physiology*, **37**, 911–917.

BURY, S. J. & MILLER, C. A. 1993. Effect of micellar solubilisation on biodegradation rates of hydrocarbons. *Environmental Science and Technology*, **27**, 104–110.

DESCHENES, L., LAFRANCE, P. & VILLENEUVE, J. P. 1995. The effect of an anionic surfactant on the mobilisation and biodegradation of PAHs in a creosote-contaminated soil. *Hydrological Sciences*, **40**, 471–484.

DUCRET, A., GIROUX, A., TRANI, M. & LORTIE, R. 1995. Enzymatic preparation of biosurfactants from sugars or sugar alcohols and fatty acids in organic media under reduced pressure. *Biotechnology and Bioengineering*, **48**, 214–221.

ESCHRICH, H. 1980. *Properties and long term behaviour of bitumen and radioactive waste bitumen mixtures*. Swedish Nuclear Fuel and Waste Management Company (SKB) Technical Report TR 80–14.

HEITKAMP, M. A., FRANKLIN, W. & CERNIGLIA, C. E. 1988. Microbial metabolism of polycyclic aromatic hydrocarbons: isolation and characterization of a pyrene degrading bacterium. *Applied and Environmental Microbiology*, **54**, 2549–2555.

KEMENADE, I. V., ANDERSON, W. A., SCHARER, J. M. & MOO-YOUNG, M. 1995. Bioremediation enhancement of phenanthrene contaminated soils by chemical pre-oxidation. *Hazardous Wastes and Hazardous Materials*, **12**, 345–355.

LAHA, S. & LUTHY, R. G. 1992. Effects of nonionic surfactants on the solubilization and mineralization of phenanthrene in soil-water systems. *Biotechnology and Bioengineering*, **40**, 1367–1380.

LIU, Z., JACOBSON, A. M. & LUTHY, R. G. 1995. Biodegradation of naphthalene in aqueous nonionic surfactant systems. *Applied and Environmental Microbiology*, **61**, 145–151.

PRITCHARD, P. H. & COSTA, C. F. 1991. EPA's Alaska oil spill bioremediation project. *Environmental Science and Technology*, **25**, 372–379.

ROCH, F. & ALEXANDER, M. 1995. Biodegradation of hydrophobic compounds in the presence of surfactants. *Environmental Toxicology and Chemistry*, **14**, 1151–1158.

ROSENBERG, E. & GUTNICK, D. L. 1986. The hydrocarbon-oxidising bacteria. *In:* STARR, M. P., STOLP, TRUPER, H. G. BALOWS, A. & SCHLEGEL, H. G. (eds) *The Prokaryotes. A Handbook on Habitats, Isolation, and Identification of Bacteria*. Springer, Heidelberg, 903–912.

THIBAULT, S. L., ANDERSON, M. & FRANKENBERGER, W. T. 1996. Influence of surfactants on pyrene desorption and degradation in soils. *Applied and Environmental Microbiology*, **62**, 283–287.

TIEHM, A. 1994. Degradation of polycyclic aromatic hydrocarbons in the presence of synthetic surfactants. *Applied and Environmental Microbiology*, **60**, 258–263.

TSOMIDES, H. J., HUGHES, J. B., THOMAS, J. M. & WARD, C. H. 1995. Effect of surfactant addition on phenanthrene biodegradation in sediments. *Environmental Toxicology and Chemistry*, **14**, 953–959.

WARHURST, A. M. & FEWSON, C. A. 1994. Biotransformations catalysed by the genus *Rhodococcus*. *Critical Reviews in Biochemistry*, **14**, 29–73.

WILSON, S. C. & JONES, K. C. 1993. Bioremediation of soil contaminated with polynuclear aromatic hydrocarbons (PAHs): A review. *Environmental Pollution*, **81**, 229–249.

SECTION 2
POLICY, PROTECTION AND VULNERABILITY

A comparison of European state policies on 'orphan' sites

Stella Christie & Richard Teeuw

Department of Environmental Sciences, University of Hertfordshire, College Lane, Hatfield, Hertfordshire AL10 9AB, UK

Abstract. Contaminated land is a serious problem in most countries with any industrial history. Contaminated land policy is still being formed, and there is little commonality in approach. Some states have laws, either on statute, or in draft, which deal specifically with contaminated land. Some use other legislation to control this area. Those states with vulnerable water supplies tend to be most concerned, particularly with 'orphan' sites. However, responsibility for identification and remediation varies within countries, as well as between states, as does the funding regime. There are few specific remediation standards. The number of sites in need of remediation is also largely unknown. Costs are high, leading to prioritization due to inadequacies in funding. The European Environment Agency could act as a focus for co-ordination and dissemination of knowledge. 'Orphan' sites need to be part of national and international policy.

Introduction

Much of Europe was subject to early industrialization, and therefore probably has more old contaminated sites than anywhere else in the world. Sites are usually known about when land is being contaminated at the present, or has been in the recent past, and the owners or polluters can be traced. Where there is old contamination, it is more difficult to find a 'responsible' party.

Not all European states have a policy on contaminated land, and the European Union is only now addressing this problem. Land appears to be the 'poor relation' in comparison with air and water, both of which have been subject to policy and legislation at national, and international level, for some time.

Contaminated land policy is still being formed, and there is little commonality in approach. The way it is dealt with across the European Union is subject to huge variation. The administrative and legal frameworks differ from region to region within the same country, and once national borders are crossed, complications multiply. How states deal with 'orphan' sites is even more varied. Since there is no standard definition of 'contaminated', there is equally no standard definition of 'orphan'. However, the consensus is that 'orphan' sites are those which are likely to be contaminated, and have no 'responsible' person to pay for any necessary remediation.

Legislation

Austria, Denmark, Germany and the Netherlands have laws, either on statute, or in draft, which deal specifically with contaminated land. The Flemish region of Belgium, the Basque Autonomous Region of Spain, and various of the German Länder, also have such legislation. Other states do not have specific legislation, but use parts of other statutes. These include Finland, France, Belgium, Spain, Sweden and the UK. Greece, Ireland, Italy and Portugal have policy and legislation on waste, and link contaminated land to that (Table 1). Much of the legislation is new, or is being used in a new way, and so far there has been very little indication of its effectiveness.

Concerns with water

Many states have an awareness of the effect of contaminated land upon water supplies. However, some have more specific water protection concerns. For instance, the Basque Autonomous Region of Spain has much of their usable land on the flood plain of two rivers, which are also the drinking water supply. The contamination of unconfined alluvial aquifers is therefore of considerable concern (IHOBE 1995).

Austria's concern with contaminated land began because hazardous waste had been put into municipal landfill sites. One of these threatened the drinking water supply of about 500 000 people. This led to public discussion, and the introduction of a national clean-up programme, in which protection of ground and surface waters are seen as major concerns (Kasamas 1995). In Denmark the main aims are to protect surface and ground water, to set priorities on soil quality criteria, the re-use of soil (NRA 1994); and to maintain high standards for land with sensitive end uses, such as housing and schools (Skovgaard 1991). The Netherlands generally have a high water table, and are highly dependent on groundwater for potable supplies – about 80% of national demands. Their approach to contaminated land reflects their concern, with early legislation providing a legal and financial framework for dealing

CHRISTIE, S. & TEEUW, R. M. 1998. A comparison of European State Policies on 'orphan' sites. *In:* LERNER, D. N. & WALTON, N. R. G. (eds) 1998. *Contaminated Land and Groundwater: Future Directions.* Geological Society, London, Engineering Geology Special Publications, **14**, 55–61.

Table 1. *Countries with laws dealing with contaminated land*

Area	Legislation
Austria	Altlastensanierungsgesetz – July 1989
Denmark	Waste Deposits Act 1990 (applies before 1972/4/6), Environmental Protection Act 1991 (applies after 1972/4/6), Loss of Value Act 1993
Germany	Soil Protection Law (draft) 1992
Netherlands	Soil Protection Act 1994
Belgium: Flanders Region	Flemish Soil Remediation Decree 1995
Spain: Basque Autonomous Region	Basque Autonomous Region Environment Bill (draft) 1994
Germany: Baden-Württemberg Länder Saxony Länder NordRein-Westphalia Länder	Baden-Württemberg Soil Protection Act 1991 Saxony Law on Waste Management & Soil Protection 1991 NordRein-Westphalia Waste Management Act 1988, Waste Disposal & Contaminated Sites Rehabilitation Association (Establishment) Act 1988

Compiled from Azkona Landeta (1994), Bieber *et al.* (1994), Kasamas (1994), König (1995), OVAM (1995), Seppänen (1994), Skovgaard (undated) and Visser (1994).

with soil and groundwater pollution, culminating in an all encompassing Soil Protection Act (1994), which is aimed at achieving soil 'multifunctionality'. 'Soil protection' is defined as 'preventing, restricting or remedying changes of properties of the soil, which entail a reduction of or a threat to the functional properties the soil has for man, flora and fauna' (VROM 1994). In 1988 the Finns carried out a literature study for the National Board of Waters and the Environment (NBWE) looking at the development and use of remediation techniques in other countries, reflecting their concern with contamination of water supplies (Puolanne 1991). The Flemish Government, when assessing the serious nature of the threat presented by soil contamination, takes into account the risk that water collection operations may be exposed (The Flemish Government 1995). The Irish Environmental Protection Agency can require licensees to make proposals for remediation of soil or groundwater, if contamination has occurred (Leech 1994). The UK Environment Agency may undertake remediation if water supplies are, or are likely to be, polluted (Lane & Peto 1995).

Ministry of the Environment. In Germany, this Ministry shares the responsibility with the Länder, which are autonomous regions. In Spain and Belgium, the Regional Authorities have the responsibility, although not all Regions have policy on contaminated land. Responsibility lies with the municipalities in Finland and Sweden (Table 2).

Identification and remediation of sites is more usually done under the auspices of the regional or local authorities. In both Austria and Denmark, the regional authorities undertake the remediation under national pro-grammes. In Austria, UK, and the Flanders and Wallonne Regions of Belgium, local authorities may remediate urgent cases, and apply for retrospective funding.

Remediation standards are mostly set nationally, but in Belgium and Spain, the Regions are to set their own standards. In fact, most remediation measures are site-specific, with the end use of the site setting the standard of clean-up, even in those places where the aim is to return the soil to a pristine condition.

Responsibilities

Some European countries address 'orphan' sites specifically, but who takes the responsibility for them varies, as does the financial liability. Those who give groundwater protection a high priority tend also to have specific policy on 'orphan' sites.

The responsibility for 'orphan' sites varies. In Austria, Denmark and France, they are the responsibility of the

Funding

Contaminated land remediation is very expensive, and funding regimes vary hugely. In Austria the Minister of the Environment has the responsibility for abandoned or 'orphan' sites. A charge (*Altlastenbeitrag*) is levied on waste for landfilling, export, or temporary storage exceeding a year. The Federal Ministry of Finance collects the money – originally expected to total about £640

Table 2. *Responsibilities for 'orphan' sites*

Country	Responsibility	Funding	Identification	Remediation	Remediation standards
Austria	Ministry of Environment	National goverment	Regional authorities	National, but local authorities for urgent cases	National
Belgium	Regional government	Regional government	Regional government	Regional government, but local authorities for urgent cases in Flanders & Wallonne	Regional government
Denmark	National government	National government	Regional authorities	Regional authorities	National
Finland	Municipalities	Municipalities, national government; share in some cases	Municipalities	Municipalities	National
France	Ministry of Environment	National government and industry	Local authorities	Local authorities	None as yet
Germany	Ministry of Environment + Länder	50% National; 50% municipalities	Municipalities	Municipalities	National
Greece	No policy				
Ireland	No policy				
Italy	No policy				
Netherlands	Ministry of Housing, Spatial Planning & Environment	90% National government; 10% regions	Regional	National, over £3.7 million; municipalities under this	National
Portugal	No policy				
Spain	Regional government	Regional government and apply to national government ≤ 50%	Regional government	Regional government	Regional – but only Basque Autonomous Region has as yet
Sweden	Municipalities	Municipalities	County councils and municipalities	Local authorities	None as yet
UK	Local authorities Environment Agency	Local authorities + national government	Local authorities	Local authorities; Environment Agency for 'special sites'	Site-specific

Compiled from Azkona Landeta (1994), Anon (1993), Department of the Environment (1996), Hasselsten (1994), Kasamas (1994), König (1995), Ministere de la Region Wallonne (1996), Seppänen (1994), Skovgaard (undated), Strebell (1994), van Dyck (1994), van Sandick (1994).

million. This is being revised upwards in the light of experience, as costs are higher than envisaged, and only about one-third of the expected finance has been collected. Control of collection is also to be strengthened (Kasamas 1995).

In Belgium, only the Flemish Region is currently implementing policy on contaminated land. The Wallonne Region is still in the process of setting policy, and how it will fund remediation has not yet been decided.

However, it has been suggested that waste producers should be taxed, with the revenue used to remediate 'orphan sites', or those where the owner is unable to pay. It has also been suggested that such sites should be taken into public ownership, rehabilitated and then sold, with the money being returned to fund further remediation work (Ministere de la Region Wallonne 1991). In Flanders, the Flemish Council makes a grant from the Prevention and Decontamination Fund for Nature and the Environment, to the Public Waste Company of Flanders (OVAM), to finance the rehabilitation of some orphan sites. A list of such sites is drawn up each year, together with their costs, for government funding (The Flemish Government 1995).

The Danish regional authorities carry out and pay for remediation and then recover the costs from the Ministry of the Environment (Hasselsten 1994). The Dutch have a similar system, but the State pays 90% of the bill, while the local area finds the other 10% (van Sandick 1994).

In Finland the polluter must pay the cost of remediation. If the polluter is no longer there, the present owner of the property is liable. If the owner is unable to pay, the municipality is liable for the cost. If the costs are higher than those of waste management in the area, the state pays up to 50% of the cost. Up to December 1994, this had happened in 22 cases. For orphan sites, money is set aside in the state budget each year. However, this has proved inadequate, and a separate fund is to be established, using fees from chemical producers and importers. A State Waste Management Fee is also proposed, to deal with old sites in particular (Seppanen 1994).

The French industry association EPE (Enterprises pour l'Environnement) was established in January 1992, partly in response to the possibility of a tax on special industrial waste. Part of their mandate is to provide funds for the clean-up of orphan contaminated sites (FRF15 million (£1.8 million) per annum), which is administered by the Agence de l'Environnement et de la Maitrise de l'Energie (ADEME) (Anon 1993). The French Government is to introduce a tax on industrial solid wastes, and this is to be used to create a fund to clean up orphan industrial sites (Strebell 1994). About FRF300 million (£35.9 million) will need to be raised for this clean-up. Twenty sites have been identified so far. A further 38 sites are being investigated for ownership. Rehabilitation of all sites is expected to take around 15 years to complete at a cost of FRF1 billion (£120 million) (Anon 1995).

In the UK, responsibility for contaminated land lies with 'appropriate' persons, who are (a) the polluter, and (b) the owner. However, if no 'appropriate' person is found to be liable, the 'enforcing' authorities have to meet the cost of carrying out any remediation action (DoE 1996). The 'enforcing' authority will usually be the local authority or, with special sites, will be the national Environment Agency. Both public and private sectors may apply for funding using the Derelict Land Grant, and a high priority is given to projects involving treatment of contamination (ENDS 1996). Local authorities and the Environment Agency may use monies borrowed from central government under the system of Supplementary Credit Approvals.

The German situation is unique. For the original Länder of the Federal Republic, the municipality carries out the remediation and then applies to the Ministry of the Environment for 50% of the costs of any one site (König 1995). The new Länder essentially are all classified as 'orphan sites'. When, after the 3rd October 1990, the States of the former GDR united with the States of the Federal Republic of Germany, most of the former GDR-owned enterprises were handed over to the 'Treuhandanstalt', an institution belonging to the Federal Ministry of Finance, responsible for transferring these enterprises into private ownership. Since most of the industrial sites were contaminated, investors were not willing to pay for the pollution of the former GDR industries. Therefore an Exemption Clause was created: this exempts owners or investors for liability for damages caused prior to 1st July 1990, if the responsible state government agrees. Liability arising from claims based on civil law remains unaffected (Franzius & Grimski 1995). About 69 000 applications for the exemption clause had been made by the end of 1994. Thus financing remediation of exempted sites had to be set up by the Federal Government and the new Länder. This has been done by two sets of regulations. The first shares the cost of remediation of exempted sites between the Federal Government (60%) and the new Länder (40%). A total of DEM1 billion (£412 million) a year for a period of 10 years are committed for these projects. The second set of regulations concerns 'large remediation projects'. The costs of these are shared by the Federal Government (75%) and the new Länder (25%), where remediation costs are expected to be over DEM100 million (£41 million). There are currently 21 large remediation projects with an estimated cost of DEM6 billion (£2.5 billion). As well as these, DEM15 billion (£6 billion) a year have been made available over the period 1993–1997, for the remediation of lignite surface mining in the new Länder (Bieber et al. 1994). The federal government has also made available DEM13 billion (£5.4 billion) for clean-up of the Wismut uranium mining sites (Franzius & Grimski 1995).

The Spanish Regions are responsible for contaminated land. The State Secretariat for the Environment and Housing will provide 50% of the funding, from its budget or by channelling resources from the European Cohesion Fund (UECF), for both initial studies and remediation of all sites. The Autonomous Regions must provide the other 50%. Sites may be sold after remediation and any gain in value must return to the Treasury and, as far as possible, act as additional resources to continue action upon contaminated soils (Lázaro-Carrasco 1994).

Countries with no specific policy for 'orphan' sites include Greece, Ireland, Italy and Portugal. Italy, Greece and Portugal are all only concerned with waste sites, and have government-funded remediation for specific sites. These may or may not be 'orphan'. In Ireland remediation of sites is development driven, and responsibility for all sites is with the owner, thus, technically, 'orphan' sites do not exist. There are no separate funding mechanisms for remediating such sites.

Discussion

Although there are huge differences in the perception of the problem of contaminated land, and how to deal with it, the actuality of the scientific and technical ways of management are similar across all states, because the problems to be solved are similar on the ground. Remediation techniques are used internationally, and although the setting of numerical standards and risk assessment methods are not, the problems associated with their development are common to all.

There are some similarities in policy. It is noticeable that those states which have concerns about potable water supplies, all have legislation in place. Several of the German Länder have pre-empted the Federal Government by putting soil protection measures in place. Austria, Denmark and the Netherlands have all enacted legislation in this area. The Basque Autonomous Region of Spain is leading the way in that country, because of its concern with water quality, and because it has a scarcity of usable land. The Flemish Region of Belgium has similar concerns.

States have independently arrived at similar ranking systems for the 'sensitivity' of the use of soils, with industrial uses, or sealed areas such as car parks, being considered less 'sensitive' than residential usage. Sensitivity indicators are particularly important where sites are remediated to a 'suitable for use' standard, which, due to technical difficulties, and shear cost, is becoming more prevalent. The cost of remediation also leads most regions to prioritize sites. For instance, OVAM is responsible for prioritizing orphan sites for remediation, which the Flemish Government fund. In Austria, Federal Agencies concentrate on the most dangerous contaminated sites, leaving the more minor ones to the provincial governments.

Soil standards are hard to lay down, as there is such natural variation within soil. A number of countries have set standards for certain contaminants, with a maximum permissible level set for different land uses. These have usually been in the form of threshold values, below which there is no need for remedial action, and an action value, above which some remediation must take place. Between the two, consideration of the proposed use of the site has formed the basis for any remediation. The UK, Germany, the Netherlands, Finland, as well as the USA and Canada, have all set some standards, which have been used extensively. However, these standards vary between countries, and they are derived from doubtful scientific bases.

Site-specific risk assessment is the only way to take into account all the contributing factors of any site, and such methods are being developed by a number of countries. The European Union, as part of the Environment & Climate Programme 1994–1998, has set up a programme of Concerted Action of Risk Assessment for Contaminated Land (CARACAS), to co-ordinate research and develop recommendations and guidelines (DG XII 1996).

There has been a lack of information exchange at international level, particularly at the policy level. At the scientific and technical level there has been more international communication, and the European Commission is setting up a network for co-operation on industrially contaminated land (DG XII 1996). This is greatly to be welcomed, as duplication of effort in both policy and scientific fields has been the norm.

The number of orphan sites in Europe is unknown. Most countries only have estimates for the total number of contaminated sites, and only a few countries have some idea of how many orphan sites they may have. Those countries with no registration system do not even know that. The costs of such remediations are likely to be high, but few countries have put money aside for them. The French are remediating 20 orphan sites at an estimated cost of £35.9 million (Strebell 1994). The Federal German Republic Ministry for the Environment has an annual fund of £16.5 million for local authorities to use for investigation and remediation of abandoned sites. This will pay for up to 50% of the costs of any one site, the rest of the money to come from the municipality (König 1995). The Danish Government funded the remediation of 80 orphan sites between 1990 and 1994 (Hasselsten 1994). In Finland, 22 sites were funded, also up to 1994 (Seppänen 1994). The costs of these remediations are unknown. The UK are using Supplementary Credit Approvals totalling £14.1 million in the year 1996/7 for remediation on 85 new projects, and continued support for a further 94 projects (ENDS 1996). Funding for orphan sites can also be a problem where a strict liability legal regime is in place. This often means that landowners become responsible for contamination that they have not caused, and of which they have no knowledge. The ensuing legal battles can cost more than the remediation, as the USA has found.

Conclusions

The European Union does not as yet, have a stated position on contaminated land, much less on orphan sites. Ground and surface water protection has featured in a number of Directives, and the Union has advocated the 'polluter pays' ideal in all environmental matters. However, contaminated land remediation is very expensive. A number of member states, including Austria, Finland, Sweden, Germany and the Netherlands, have come to the conclusion that to finance remediation, extra money is going to have to be raised. The European Union could assist by using the European Environment Agency to give advice on registration, water quality threats, standards of remediation, and monitoring.

'Orphan' sites need to be part of national and international policy. The number of sites needs to be known, even if these are only estimated, so that the size of the problem can be assessed. This will give an indication of the finances needed to deal with them, and appropriate fiscal policies can be constructed. This may come in the form of direct government grants, or from environmental or industrial taxes. A clear legal framework needs to be in place, so that all monies available can be used for remediation, and are not dissipated in long drawn out legal battles over liability. The European Union could also consider part-funding remediation of 'orphan' sites, which would help governments to clean them up before large-scale environmental damage is done.

References

ANON 1993. Government industry link on environmental protection. *Chemical Week*, October, 18.
——1995. FFr 1bn to clean up pollution. *Chemistry and Industry*, 2 January, (1), 4.
AZKONA LANDETA, A. 1994. Soil protection master plan of the Basque Autonomous Community. *In: Policies and Strategies. Proceedings of the International Workshop on Contaminated Sites in the European Union*, 8–9 December 1994 Bonn, Germany. Bundesumweltministerium für Umwelt, 14.1–19.
BIEBER, A., FRANZIUS, V. & STIETZEL, H.-J. 1994. Contaminated sites in Germany. *In: Policies and Strategies. Proceedings of the International Workshop on Contaminated Sites in the European Union*, 8–9 December 1994, Bonn, Germany. Bundesumweltministerium für Umwelt, 6.1–12.
DEPARTMENT OF THE ENVIRONMENT 1996. *Part IIA of the Environmental Protection Act 1990 – Contaminated Land – Draft Statutory Guidance.* London: Marine, Land and Liability Division, Department of the Environment, 24 June 1996.
DG XII 1996. *Environmental Technologies – Environment and Climate Programme 1994–1998.* European Commission. Directorate-General for Science, Research and Development, DG XII/D-1
ENDS 1996. Funds for contaminated land clean-up. *ENDS Report* , **258** (July) 29–30.
THE FLEMISH GOVERNMENT (BELGIUM) 1995. *Decree on Soil Decontamination.* The Belgian Statute Book, 29 April 1995.
FRANZIUS, V. & GRIMSKI, D. 1995. Recent developments in contaminated land remediation in the federal republic of Germany: current programmes and future research. *Land Contamination & Reclamation*, **3**(1), 47–54.
HASSELSTEN, I. 1994. Contaminated sites – the situation in Sweden. *In: Policies and Strategies. Proceedings of the International Workshop on Contaminated Sites in the European Union*, 8–9 December 1994, Bonn, Germany. Bundesumweltministerium für Umwelt, 15.1–21.

IHOBE Sociedad Pública Gestión Ambiental 1995. *Soil Protection Master Plan.* Departmento de Urbanismo, Vivienda y Medio Ambiente del Gobierno Vasco.
KASAMAS, H. 1994. Contaminated sites programme in Austria. *In: Policies and Strategies. Proceedings of the International Workshop on Contaminated Sites in the European Union*, 8–9 December 1994, Bonn, Germany. Bundesumweltministerium für Umwelt, 1.1–10.
——1995. The Contaminated Land Programme in Austria. *Chemistry & Industry*, **13**, 512–513.
KÖNIG, W. 1995. *Report on contaminated sites in North Rhine – Westphalia.* Ministerium für Umwelt, Raumordnung und Landwirtschaft des Landes Nordrhein-Westfalen.
LANE, P. & PETO, M. 1995. *Blackstone's Guide to the Environment Act 1995.* Blackstone, London.
LÁZARO-CARRASCO, J. 1994. Contaminated sites in Spain. *In: Policies and Strategies. Proceedings of the International Workshop on Contaminated Sites in the European Union*, 8–9 December 1994, Bonn, Germany. Bundesumweltministerium für Umwelt, 13.1–19.
LEECH, B. 1994. Contaminated land – the situation in Ireland. *In: Policies and Strategies. Proceedings of the International Workshop on Contaminated Sites in the European Union.* 8–9 December 1994, Bonn, Germany. Bundesumweltministerium für Umwelt, 8.1–5.
MINISTERE DE LA REGION WALLONNE 1991. *Decree Relatif à la Taxation des Déchets in Région Wallonne.* Ministere de l'Environnement, des Ressources naturelles et de l'Agriculture.
——1996. Direction générale des Ressources naturelles et de l'Environnement. 1996. *Les sols pollués, quel passif?* Journée d'étude à la SRB11 le 18 janvier 1996 à Bruxelles. Office régional wallon des déchets. Bruxelles.
NRA 1994 *Contaminated land and the water environment.* Report of the National Rivers Authority, March 1994. Water Quality Series No.15. HMSO, London.
OVAM 1995. *Decree on Soil Decontamination.* OVAM, Mechelen, 22 February 1995.
PUOLANNE, J. 1991. Strategies and means of solving the problem of soil contamination in Finland. Paper presented at the conference *Deteccion y recuperacion de suelos contaminados.* May 1991, Madrid, Spain.
SEPPÄNEN, A. 1994. Contaminated soil sites in Finland. *In: Policies and Strategies. Proceedings of the International Workshop on Contaminated Sites in the European Union*, 8–9 December 1994, Bonn, Germany. Bundesumweltministerium für Umwelt, 4.1–14.
SKOVGAARD, I.-M. 1991. The Danish list of priorities concerning clean up actions. *In: Advanced Training Course in Soil and Groundwater Quality, Pollution and Cleaning Technology*, 9–17 November 1991.
—— undated. *Contaminated Land Policy in Denmark.* Waste Deposits and Ground Water Division, Danish Environmental Protection Agency, Occasional Paper.
STREBELL, A. 1994. Contribution of France. *In: Policies and Strategies. Proceedings of the International Workshop on Contaminated Sites in the European Union*, 8–9 December 1994, Bonn, Germany. Bundesumweltministerium für Umwelt, 5.1–6.
VAN DYCK, E. 1994. The contaminated sites policy in Flanders (Belgium). *In: Policies and Strategies. Proceedings of the International Workshop on Contaminated Sites in the European Union*, 8–9 December 1994, Bonn, Germany. Bundesumweltministerium für Umwelt, 2.1–16.

VAN SANDICK, O. 1994. Policy and legal framework regarding contaminated sites in the Netherlands. *In: Policies and Strategies. Proceedings of the International Workshop on Contaminated Sites in the European Union*, 8–9 December 1994, Bonn, Germany. Bundesumweltministerium für Umwelt, 10.1–8.

VISSER, W. 1994. *Contaminated Land Policies in Some Industrialised Countries*, 2nd edn. Technical Soil Protection Committee, The Hague.

VROM 1994. *Soil Protection Act*. Directorate-General for Environmental Protection, Department of Soil Protection, Ministry of Housing, Spatial Planning, and the Environment, The Hague.

The economics of contaminated site remediation: decision making and technology selection

Paul E. Hardisty, Robert A. Bracken & Mark Knight

Komex Clarke Bond Ltd., 129 Cumberland Road, Bristol BS1 6UY, UK

Abstract. Most activities associated with production of goods and services in modern society are linked directly or indirectly to the production of wastes and pollution. In general, environmental impacts increase with the level of production (as measured by the Gross National Product, or GNP). The decision to remediate a contaminated site can be seen from the macroeconomic and microeconomic viewpoints. Macroeconomics can be used to plan and account for the overall cost of pollution as part of a firm's production, and thus make overall decisions on the real cost of pollution and the level of clean-up that may be called for. Valuation of damaged resources, option values and intrinsic worth is an important part of this process. Once the decision to remediate has been taken, the question becomes how best to remediate. It is safe to say that cost is one of the single most important factors in site clean-up decision making. A basic rule of remediation is often taken to be the maximization of contaminant mass removed for the money spent. However, remediation may also be governed by other objectives and constraints. In some situations, minimization of time, rather than cost, could be the constraint. Evaluation of the economics of a clean-up project is directly linked to the objectives of the site owner, and the constraints within which the remediation is to be performed. Once objectives and constraints have been clearly identified, a range of possible remedial approaches and technologies can be developed, and each option evaluated on a comparative basis. One of the most powerful tools for comparative options analysis is technical–economic analysis. This approach combines evaluation of technical feasibility and effect, with consideration of capital, operation and maintenance costs over a selected time horizon. By constraining remedial alternatives within cost and time boundaries, possible solutions can be evaluated with respect to specific criteria. Two examples illustrate these concepts. Economic analysis of remedial options for containment of a 350 000 l hydrocarbon spill migrating through fractured rock into a river in Alberta, Canada, provided clear direction to the site owner. Economic analysis of remedial alternatives for contaminated sites in the UK sheds interesting light on the common practice of landfilling, when compared to other alternatives.

Introduction

Most activities associated with production of goods and services in modern society are linked directly or indirectly to the production of wastes and pollution (World Bank 1992). Benefits to society are accrued through this production, measured as GNP (Gross National Product). However, with the benefits also come costs associated with environmental damage. These typically include degraded air quality, polluted rivers and coastlines, damaged aquifers and soil, and habitat destruction. Until recently, however, these costs have not been explicitly accounted for in the balance of accounts. If environmental costs are included in calculation of GNP, a more realistic picture of a nation's actual progress and well-being is provided. Some activities which appear on first analysis to benefit society, may in fact be net detriments when environmental impacts are taken into consideration. This approach can be extended to a private firm's accounts. The full value of environmental damage caused by a private corporation's operations is considered to be an external cost (society suffers a loss), and is typically not accounted for in the corporation's financial statements. However, under the polluter-pays principle, which has been adopted by many industrialized nations, private firms are now economically responsible for at least a portion of the damage. Thus, a more accurate view of a firm's balance of accounts would involve discounting corporate profits based on the costs of environmental damage that occurred during the production of those profits.

Typically, one of the major impediments to site remediation is the perception that money spent provides no return to the corporation. In some cases this may indeed be true. However, there clearly exist situations where a certain level of expenditure for site clean-up is both warranted and beneficial to the corporation, and thus to society.

HARDISTY, P. E., BRACKEN, R. A. & KNIGHT, M. 1998. The economics of contaminated site remediation: decision making and technology selection. *In:* LERNER, D. N. & WALTON, N. R. G. (eds) 1998. *Contaminated Land and Groundwater: Future Directions.* Geological Society, London, Engineering Geology Special Publications, **14**, 63–71.

Remedial decision making

Many different factors go into the decision to remediate a site. These include the level and type of contamination, the nature of off-site impacts, the regulatory and political climate, corporate policy, the availability of suitable technology, and the financial resources available. In reality, one of the most important factors is cost.

Economic framework

No matter what the technical or regulatory situation, remediation cannot take place unless funds are available, and often the level of funding dictates the level to which the site will be remediated. Regulations may exist which can drive remediation, but if private firms are forced out of business by the costs of remediation, society is twice the loser. The site remains contaminated, and the firm no longer contributes employment and taxes to the national economy.

The decision to remediate a contaminated site can be seen from the macroeconomic and microeconomic viewpoints. Macroeconomics can be used to plan and account for the overall cost of pollution as part of a firm's production, and thus make overall decisions on the real cost of pollution and the level of clean-up that may be called for. This process can be used to assist firms in setting economically realistic and justifiable remedial goals for individual sites, groups of sites, or as corporate policy. In addition, cost constraints on remediation can be set. Valuation of damaged resources, option values and intrinsic worth is also an important part of this process, but is beyond the scope of this paper.

Once the decision to remediate has been taken, the question becomes how best to remediate; which of the myriad of available remedial approaches and technologies is best able to reach the intended goals. Microeconomic analysis deals with providing efficient allocative decisions for reaching those overall goals.

The decision making process

The economic analysis of remediation is only one part of the decision making process. The first steps must involve understanding the nature and extent of the problem through site characterization, and identification of the associated risks by some form of risk analysis. The following steps should be considered:

1. *Understand the problems at the site.* Through proper site characterization, a picture of the types, distribution and concentrations of contaminants and wastes is provided. This information serves as the basis for all other activities.
2. *Assess the risks posed by the problem.* Using the tools of risk assessment, either in a qualitative or quantitative fashion, the implications of the problem are

determined. Many different types of risk exist (human health, ecological, economic, public relations, personal and corporate liability), and one or more may be important at the site. These risks can be economically valued.

3. *Set remedial goals and constraints for the site.* Once the problem, and the risks posed by it, are understood, a remedial goal can be set. This may be based on corporate and regulatory requirements by considering the principles of Risk Based Corrective Action (RBCA). Constraints which apply to the situation must also be identified. Two of the most important are cost (what maximum expenditure is warranted to solve the problem), and time (how long is the firm willing to wait for a satisfactory resolution). Additional information may be required from the site to complete this analysis.
4. *Identify an optimal remedial approach.* Using technical and economic analysis, various possible remedial approaches can be evaluated and compared. The approach best able to reach the set goal within the applied constraints of cost and time (or others as required) is selected. Pilot testing of one or more selected technologies should occurr before finalizing the full-scale remedial design.
5. *Implement the optimal remediation programme at the site.* By fully integrating technical and project management functions, the project can be implemented efficiently and successfully with project goals and constraints fully in mind.
6. *Monitor results.* Assess remedial progress through careful monitoring, and modify as necessary for efficient improvements.

Setting remedial goals and constraint

Remedial goals and constraints are in many ways inseparable and interdependent. There is no use in setting an aggressive remedial goal (such as clean-up to background conditions), if the resources to achieve this are not available. An optimal approach would involve first determining the cost constraint, and then selecting a remedial goal that could be accomplished at or below that cost.

Remedial goal definition

Remedial goals for contaminated sites can range from complete clean-up to no action supported by risk assessment. Between these extremes lie a range of more realistic and achievable goals, including removal of the bulk of contaminants of concern to levels below applicable guidelines, or to levels deemed suitable based on risk assessment, protection of key receptor such as rivers, or even *in situ* stabilization or isolation. Each of

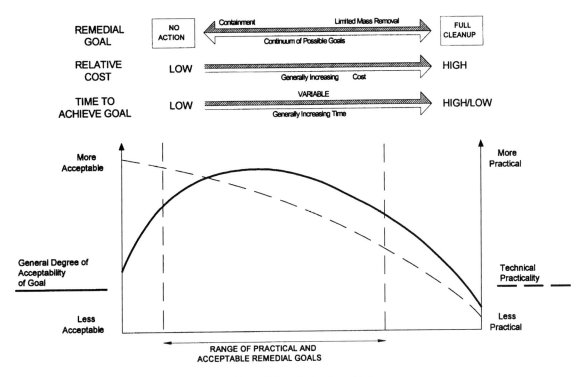

Fig. 1. Remedial goal selection criteria.

these goals involves different remedial technologies, different costs and different long-term implications. The goal will in many ways determine which remedial technologies and designs are eventually selected. Figure 1 presents a schematic representation of typical remedial goals and associated relative costs and timeframes.

Identification of constraints

Many constraints can be applied to the remedial decision making process. The foremost, and subject of this paper, is cost. Other constraints include time, the physical characteristics of the site, specific regulatory requirements and limitations, the needs of the public, and the imperatives of corporate policy. For instance, a firm may require that remediation be completed within three years in order to realize the economic benefits of selling the property. Remediation of soil and groundwater at the site could be hampered by the depth of the impacted aquifer and the presence of permanent surface structures at and near to the site. Each of these requirements will constrain the types of solutions that are selected.

Cost–benefit analysis

Determination of the cost constraint is best accomplished using cost–benefit analysis. For a given project, the decision to proceed is taken when the net benefits of the programme exceed the costs, as

$$\sum_{t=1}^{t=n} (B_t - C_t) \frac{1}{(1+i)^t} > 0 \qquad (1)$$

where B_t are the benefits accrued by the project over time, C_t are the costs of the programme at time t, i is the discount rate, and n is the total period of time the programme is expected to run. Unfortunately, for environmental remediation projects, it is usually the costs that are easiest to quantify, and receive most of the attention from corporate decision makers. Financial risk derives from several sources, including uncertainty in the future discount rate, programme completion time, and the inherent difficulties associated with determining remedial costs for subsurface contamination. The environmental benefits of remediation are harder to quantify in economic terms, but no less important.

Remedial benefit. If we consider the example of a contaminated site that has been used to generate corporate profits through production of goods for sale, benefits of remediation could be expressed as

$$\sum_{t=1}^{t=n} B_t = \pi_{nh} + \sum_{t=1}^{t=n} \{B_{ne} + B_{np}\} \qquad (2)$$

where π_{nh} is that portion of the historical profits generated by the operation which can be attributed to the fact that spending did not occur on mitigative measures which would have prevented the present contamination. This distinction explicitly accounts for the fact that money spent in the past on measures such as liners for ponds, double-walled USTs, proper land-filling practices and spill control could have prevented the need for present-day remediation. In addition, the fact that these funds were not spent would have shown up as profit in previous years. For this reason, this type of benefit is often referred to as a shifted benefit (Pearce & Warford 1993). Note that if no profits were generated by the operation, this term goes to zero. It is important to stress that the method for accounting for historical profits presented in no way suggests that operators should have employed present-day mitigative techniques in the past. Clearly many of these techniques were not available 20 or even 10 years ago. Certainly in the case of gasworks sites in the UK, for example, many of which were operational from the late 1890s to the middle of this century, it is difficult to assign a shifted benefit to a present-day analysis. However, this does provide a methodology for assigning a reasonable historical benefit to the firm. Clearly, the inclusion of this term would depend on the perspective taken: optimization of societal benefit might call for some accounting for historic profits realized as a direct result of contaminant generation; a private commercial interest would likely resist its inclusion in many cases. However, it is useful to consider this concept in a balanced and dispassionate discussion.

The term B_{ne} refers to the net environmental benefit accrued to society as a result of the remediation going ahead, and is an external benefit (from the firm's viewpoint). This could include the value to the public of access to a reclaimed coastline or wetland area, the ecological value of the restored habitat, the value of elimination of human health risks and ecological risks posed by the contamination, or the value of the groundwater resource being protected or remediated. This term does not, however, explicitly account for 'shifted irreversibilities', defined as costs shifted to future generations by non-reversible environmental impacts. Shifted irreversibilities would include species extinction, permanent loss of sensitive habitat, and the like. These societal benefits are more difficult to quantify for use in a cost–benefit analysis. However, a relatively extensive literature on this subject has been developed in recent years (Edwards 1988; Green *et al.* 1988, 1989, 1990; Willis & Benson 1988; Button & Pearce 1989).

The net private benefits (B_{np}) to the firm must also be accounted for. These would include the value of fines, control orders or lost production not incurred because the remediation went ahead, and the public relations value of the clean-up, especially as related to goodwill generated within the marketplace and the resulting increase in sales of the firm's product. Conversely, the avoidance of a boycott of the firm's products could also be very valuable. Increased land value, and the ability to sell or lease property, would also benefit the firm directly.

Remedial costs. The costs of a remediation project are much easier to determine, and are governed in part by the remedial goal set for the site. The cost–benefit analysis can be used to estimate a maximum cost which could be reasonably considered by the firm for clean-up of a given site. Using Equation (2), the maximum remediation cost that would be contemplated would be equal to B_t. Note that the lower the profits generated by the operation (or the greater the effort devoted to impact mitigation measures), the lower the risks (human health and ecological) posed by the problem; and the more flexible the regulatory environment, the lower the sum that would be devoted to the clean-up. Conversely, if a firm has generated considerable historical profit from an operation that produced substantial contamination, and the risks posed by that contamination were significant, a greater remedial cost would be justified, even in the absence of regulatory incentives. Thus, this type of analysis provides a powerful tool with which corporate decision makers can identify a realistic and economically justifiable cost constraint for remediation.

Optimization of the level of clean-up. Another way of considering the questions of remedial goals and determining the cost constraint is to consider the level of clean-up (or more generally the level of remediation) to be achieved, and the marginal cost and benefits of clean-up. In this case, marginal cost refers to the additional cost required to achieve an increment of clean-up. As shown in Fig. 2 the marginal cost of clean-up typically drops as clean-up begins, due to economies of scale and apportionment of fixed costs; it reaches a minimum, and then rises steeply after remediation of the most concentrated and easy-to-access contamination has occurred. Often, remediation of the last 10% of the contamination can cost as much as clean-up of the first 90% (National Research Council, 1994). Conversely, marginal benefit is high initially, and decreases as more and more of the contamination is removed. The optimal level of clean-up would occur when marginal costs are equal to marginal benefits (Fig. 2). The effects of government incentives (tax breaks or subsidies for remediation) can also be seen in Fig. 2. Incentives will tend to shift the marginal

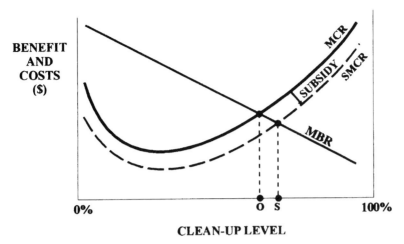

MCR - Marginal cost of remediation
SMCR - Subsidized cost of remediation
MBR - Marginal benefit of remediation
O - Optimum clean up level
S - Subsidized clean-up level

Fig. 2. Determination of optimal clean-up level.

cost curve down, allowing a greater level of clean-up to occur for the same cost to the firm.

Remedial technology selection

Once the goals and constraints for the remediation have been determined, and the decision to remediate made, attention turns to the most effective technical means of achieving the objectives. A wide variety of remedial technologies have been developed over the past 15 years for both soil and groundwater. Different methods are suitable for different situations, and involve different levels of cost.

Technology life-cycle cost curves

It is useful when discussing remedial technologies to consider the life-cycle cost curve of each method. A typical cost curve is shown in Fig. 3. The initial capital cost reflects what is required to purchase and commission the remedial system, or effect the remedial works (such as excavation of contaminated soil and subsequent treatment). Capital costs may also be required in subsequent years, depending on the nature and scale of the project. Operation and maintenance (O&M) and monitoring costs may also be required for systems which operate over time. Costs of monitoring remedial progress will almost certainly be required.

To provide a consistent basis for comparison of costs in time, and recognizing the time value of money, costs are expressed as net present value (NPV) costs. The net present value (P) of a sum of money (F) obtained n years in the future, given an interest rate of i, is expressed as follows (Barish & Kaplan 1978):

$$P = F \frac{1}{(1+i)^n} \qquad (4)$$

Capital-intensive methods (such as excavation and thermal treatment of contaminated soil, for instance) are

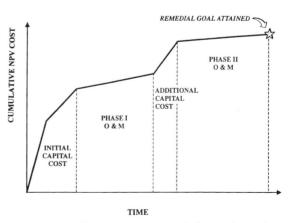

Fig. 3. Typical life-cycle cost curve: capital, operation and maintenance phases.

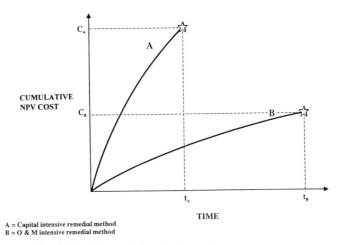

A = Capital intensive remedial method
B = O & M intensive remedial method

Fig. 4. Typical remedial technology life-cycle cost curves.

characterized by cost curves which are initially very steep, but which reach the remedial objectives quickly and are thus short in duration (Fig. 4). In contrast, *in situ* methods (such as a system designed to achieve containment of groundwater contamination and gradual mass removal) may have smaller initial capital costs, but significant annual O&M requirements, and may require considerable periods of time to reach specified goals (Fig. 4).

Economic evaluation of alternatives

By applying the procedures discussed above, goals and cost–time constraints for remediation which optimize net societal benefit (including the well-being of firms operating within society) can be determined. Life-cycle cost curves can be generated for a number of remedial technologies (or technology combinations) which will achieve the specified goals. By applying the constraints of

maximum cost and maximum time to the alternatives, an envelope of acceptable solutions is described, as shown in Fig. 5. Remedial approaches whose end-points fall within the envelope are acceptable. The final choice between two or more acceptable solutions would be based on a comparison of total overall cost, and the firm's requirements for cost allocation over time. In Fig. 5 alternatives A and C fall outside the constraint envelope, and are not acceptable (even though they are capable of achieving the technical goals of the project). Alternatives B and D are acceptable solutions. Note that despite a higher initial capital cost, alternative B has lower O&M costs, and ends up as the lowest cost solution. Alternative D would be chosen only if the firm wished to spend less initially, and were willing to provide for higher subsequent outlays.

Remediation of hydrocarbon in a fractured bedrock aquifer

Background

Operation of a natural gas processing plant in Alberta, Canada, has generated considerable profits for the site owner since its construction in 1971. The facility processes raw natural gas from nearby well fields, producing sales gas, hydrocarbon liquids (natural gas condensate) and elemental sulphur. In 1987, hydrocarbon was found seeping from a fractured bedrock aquifer into a nearby river. Subsequent investigations revealed a plume of more than $350 \, m^3$ of gas condensate within a fractured sandstone unit underlying the plant (Hardisty *et al.* 1995). Contamination had resulted from improper disposal practices and inadequately lined containment ponds. The regulatory agencies required that some form of remedial action be taken as soon as possible.

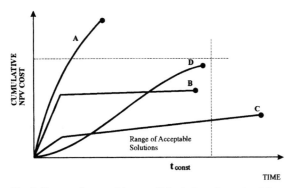

Fig. 5. Range of acceptable remedial solutions determined from life-cycle cost curves. A, capital intensive remedial method; B, O & M intensive remedial method.

Constraints to remediation

Since 1971, profits had been generated in part due to savings from not implementing proper disposal practices, or installing systems required to prevent contamination of the subsurface. It was estimated that these savings were worth a total of about $30 000 1993 Canadian dollars per year, which was recorded as profit. Discharge of contaminants to the river was significant, and had the potential to affect aquatic receptors (including trout), and amenity value. The existence value of pristine Rocky Mountain streams such as this one is high in Alberta. Fishermen, hikers and hunters all frequent the area. In part due to this existence value, manifested as public pressure to protect watercourses from industrial pollution, the regulatory agency threatened the facility with a control order if remediation were not undertaken. Such an order would effectively shut-down the plant, resulting in about $35 000 per day in lost revenue to the company. Despite the fact that the environmental benefit of remediation was never quantified (although it was clearly positive), the above information was used to estimate the benefits in time of remedial action.

The total historical profit assigned as a remedial benefit was $660 000, based on the annual 1993 dollar value discussed above. It was assumed that a plant shut-down of about three months would cost the company about $3.5 million in lost revenue, roughly equivalent to the annual profit for the operation. This was deemed unacceptable by the plant's operators. Thus, it was determined that a reasonable cost constraint for remedial action at the plant would be approximately $4 million and that a working time horizon of 20 years would be used for evaluation of alternatives. Note that inclusion of more societal-oriented factors (such as historical profit and net environmental benefit) was not necessary to justify a suitable technical response. The net private benefit (in the form of revenue loss prevention) alone was sufficient to justify the remediation. The plant is expected to be closed in 2013.

Remedial goals

A detailed characterization and remedial testing programme was implemented to assess the nature, extent and behaviour of the contaminants. The data obtained indicated clearly that complete clean-up of the hydrocarbon from the fractured sandstone was beyond current technological capabilities, and prohibitively expensive. In addition, the main environmental concern was protection of the river. The aquifer itself is of limited extent, in a remote location, and is not used. For these reasons, the remedial goal was determined to be the prevention of flow of separate phase hydrocarbon liquids to the river. This objective was presented to the regulatory officials, along with the anticipated costs and problems of full clean-up, and eventually accepted.

Technology selection

Five alternatives were considered for achieving the goal of preventing flow of liquid hydrocarbons to the river:

1. construction of a cofferdam in the river valley at the discharge point from the outcropping aquifer;
2. driving an interception tunnel from the river valley into the aquifer and collecting the contaminated water and hydrocarbon;
3. constructing a hanging grout curtain within the aquifer, to be supplemented by low rate pumping and LNAPL extraction;
4. constructing a physical in-place barrier similar to 3 by ground freezing (frost curtain); and
5. hydraulic containment by pumping from wells.

Life-cycle cost curves for each alternative are shown in Fig. 6 along with the cost and time constraints developed above. Only alternatives 3 and 4 were found to fit within the envelope of acceptable solutions. Although initially more expensive, alternative 3 (a grout curtain) had lower annual O&M costs by virtue of substantially lower groundwater pumping and treatment requirements, and was found to be the lowest-cost solution. The grout curtain and associated recovery systems were installed in 1993 and have been operating successfully since.

Remediation of contaminated land in the UK

The techniques and concepts discussed above can be used to evaluate general trends in contaminated land remediation in the UK. As environmental regulations and the powers of the Environment Agency strengthen, remediation of contaminated land will become more common. At present, for example, a major effort to remediate old gasworks sites is being undertaken by British Gas (Munro *et al.* 1995). Currently in the UK, excavation and landfilling remains the most widely used remedial technique. While development of alternative remedial methods has been intensively pursued in North America, their application in the UK lags behind. In part, this has been due to the strong legislation which has been in place in the US and Canada for over a decade.

The benefits of properly assessing and, if necessary, remediating contaminated land are now being increasingly recognized by the private sector in the UK. To a large extent, this is being driven by large property firms, banks, and insurance companies, wary of exposing themselves to long-term environmental liability. Property transactions, for example, can harness the unwary purchaser with a significant environmental problem, for which he may be financially liable. Clearly, any property

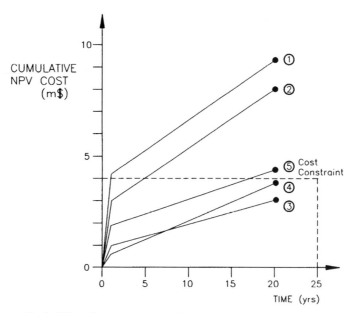

Fig. 6. Life-cycle cost curve analysis remedial alternatives – example site.

transaction should be subject to a full and complete environmental assessment. In cases where contamination is detected, a reduction in the purchase price can be negotiated to reflect the cost of remediation to a level appropriate with the site's intended use. Assessment of a reasonable cost for remediation, then, can become an important part of the economics of the transaction. A sound economic analysis of the remedial goals and constraints is therefore a prerequisite.

Unfortunately, excavation and tipping of contaminated material, or in some cases importation of clean cover, are the methods most often used to value remediation. Workers in the field should be aware of the wide range of alternative remedial solutions that are presently available, and are currently under development. Many of these have been designed expressly to reduce remedial costs. For instance, most volatile organic contaminants can be dealt with on-site, through methods such as soil vapour extraction, bioventing, and *ex situ* soil treatment. On site remedial methods include *in situ* and *ex situ* thermal treatment, soil washing and bioremediation, passive and assisted barriers for groundwater contamination, and a wide variety of treatment systems for contaminated groundwater.

As landfill space in the UK declines, and as taxes and tipping charges rise, excavation and tipping will become more and more costly. On-site alternatives will become increasingly cost competitive. On the environmental benefit side of the cost–benefit equation, there is an intrinsic societal advantage to on-site solutions, particu-

larly those which result in actual destruction of the contaminants (rather than their immobilization or isolation). Excavation and tipping simply move the problem from one place to another. The site owner transfers some of his liability to another party (the landfill owner), but the contaminants remain as a potential threat to the environment. Presumably, the landfill represents a decrease in the overall risk posed to the public and the environment, but the incidence of contaminant releases from landfills cannot be ignored. Landfills which impact groundwater supplies, for instance, have resulted in considerable expenditure in the USA (Mackay & Cherry 1989). Both the public and corporations which contributed waste to the tip could conceivably be held financially responsible for major future landfill remediations.

By explicitly considering and valuing the net change in societal and private benefit accrued by excavation and tip remediation, and accounting for the increasing cost of landfilling, it can be seen that the overall CBA ratio increases considerably compared to on-site techniques. Thus, if an on-site remedial method and the excavate and tip solution were found to cost the same amount, and if both achieved the remedial goals within the set constraints, it is highly likely that a full cost–benefit analysis would reveal the on-site solution to be considerably superior.

Completion of this type of economic analysis can have a major impact on remedial decision making, and may reveal that a solution which was considered to be 'cost-effective' may in fact not be economic.

Conclusions

The tools of economic analysis can assist in rational decision making regarding site remediation. The fundamental questions of whether to remediate or not, and if so to what level, can be examined in economic terms. Establishing a maximum acceptable cost for remediation puts an important constraint on remedial goal selection. The cost of remediation ideally should be balanced against the benefits accrued by site clean-up. Accounting for some portion of the historical profits generated by the site, and adding expected external and corporate benefits of clean-up provides an estimate of maximum clean-up cost which optimizes benefits to society as a whole. While it is clear that individual corporate interests are not always linked directly to soceital maxima, there are clearly strong overlaps between what is good for a corporation, and what is good for the society within which it exists and operates.

Once a remedial goal has been set, and the cost and time constraints determined, remedial technology options can be compared using life-cycle cost analysis. Only techniques which meet the goals within the constraints are deemed acceptable. This approach provides corporate and regulatory decision makers with a framework for determining how best to use the limited resources available for environmental protection and enhancement.

References

BARISH, N. N. & KAPLAN, S. 1978. *Economic Analysis: For Engineering and Managerial Decision Making*. McGraw Hill, New York.

BUTTON, K. & PEARCE, D. W. 1989. Infrastructure restoration as a tool for stimulating urban renewal: The Glasgow Canal. *Urban Studies*, **26**, 559–573.

EDWARDS, S. F. 1988. Option prices for groundwater protection. *Journal of Environmental Economics and Management*, **15**, 475–487.

GREEN, C. H., TUNSTALL, S. M., N'JAI, A. & ROGERS, A. 1988. *Evaluating the Benefits of River Water Quality Improvements*. Middlesex Polytechnic Flood Hazard Research Centre, Middlesex.

——, ——, —— & ——1989. Water quality: the public dimension. *In: Watershed '89: The Future of Water Quality in Europe*. Pergamon, Oxford.

——, ——, —— & ——1990. The economic evaluation of environmental goods. *Project Appraisal*, **5**(2), 70–82.

HARDISTY, P. E., ROSS, S. D., DABROWSKI, T. L. & BROWN, A. 1995. Remediation of LNAPL in fractured rocks: theory and application. *Proceedings, IAH Solutions '95*, Edmonton, Canada. International Association of Hydrogeologists.

MACKAY, D. M. & CHERRY, J. A. 1989. Ground water contamination – pump-and-treat remediation. *Environmental Science and Technology*, **23**(6).

MUNRO, S., WALLACE, S. & KIRBY, P. 1995. Meeting the environmental challenge: managing our former gasworks sites. *Land Contamination and Reclamation*, **3**(4), 1.4–1.5.

NATIONAL RESEARCH COUNCIL 1994. *Alternatives for Groundwater Clean-Up*. National Academy, Washington, DC.

PEARCE, D. W. & WARFORD, J. J. 1993. *World Without End*. Published for the World Bank, OUP, Oxford.

WILLIS, K. G. & BENSON, J. 1988. Valuation of wildlife: a case study on the Upper Teesdale site of special scientific interest and comparison of methods in environmental Economics. *In: Sustainable Environmental Management: Principles and Practice*. Belhaven, London.

WORLD BANK 1992. *World Development Report 1992: Development and the Environment*. OUP, Oxford.

Professional training for geologists in contaminated land management

C. P. Nathanail[1] & J. F. Nathanail[2]

[1] CRBE, The Nottingham Trent University, Nottingham NG1 4BU, UK
[2] Delta-Simons Environmental Consultants Ltd, Waterside South, Lincoln, UK

Abstract. Contaminated land management comprises the identification, investigation, assessment and remediation of contaminated land. It is a multi-disciplinary, rapidly developing subject which involves input from, and communication between, a wide range of science, engineering and other professionals. Geologists have a key role to play at the investigation and assessment stages and have much to offer at the identification and remediation stages.

The undergraduate and post-graduate education of geologists provides many of the skills required, but many other skills can only be developed 'on the job'. To ensure that early industrial experience covers a broad range of subjects, there is a need for training to be formalized.

The training needs for geologists working in contaminated land management have been evaluated and a training guide for geologists in contaminated land management has been written. Use of the guide will ensure that on the job training is comprehensive, relevant and assists trainee graduate geologists gain chartered geologist status within a reasonable timeframe.

The role of geologists in contaminated land management

There are an estimated 100 000–200 000 hectares of potentially contaminated land in the UK (House of Commons Environment Committee 1996). The cost of remediating this land is estimated to be £2 billion.

The identification, investigation, assessment and remediation of contaminated land involves input from, and communication between, a wide range of science, engineering and other professionals. The geologist is at the core of the investigation and assessment stages and has much to offer at the identification and remediation stages.

Geologists have unique skills in being able to think in three dimensions, deal with long time spans and handle uncertainty in their data and predictions (Woodcock 1995). Indeed, Woodcock (1995) argued that geology is *the* holistic environmental science. Nathanail (1995) and McCall (1993) highlighted the contribution that geologists can make to protecting the environment and to sustainable development. Within geology, various sub-disciplines have emerged and many of these make a contribution to contaminated land management.

The major contribution of a geologist to a contaminated land assessment project is an ability to understand the nature of the materials at the surface and subsurface and their impact on migration/containment of contamination, and to plan an investigation that will give the best information on the distribution of contamination within each stratum. A geologist should also be able to contribute to the selection and design of remediation systems.

Contaminated land management involves the investigation of pollution hazards, the assessment of the risks they pose, the mitigation of unacceptable risks and demonstration of the effectiveness of the mitigation. Many of the sub-disciplines represented by the specialist groups of the Geological Society are pertinent to contaminated land management, particularly

- environment
- engineering
- hydrogeology
- geochemistry
- environmental and industrial geophysics
- geoscience information
- geomorphological research

Other geoscience specialists provide fundamental information about geological environments, processes and products that are essential in specific situations.

A multi-disciplinary approach

Contaminated land management is a very competitive area. While multi-disciplinary teams are essential, this inevitably leads to a number of grey areas in which several professions can claim, rightly or wrongly, to have particular expertise.

The Engineering Council awards the C.Eng. qualification to members of several institutions whose members are active in contaminated land: civil engineers, structural engineers, water and environmental management, chemical engineering, mining and metallurgy to name but a few. Surveyors play an important role in property transactions, largely centring on providing an estimate

NATHANAIL, C. P. & NATHANAIL, J. F. 1998. Professional training for geologists in contaminated land management. *In:* LERNER, D. N. & WALTON, N. R. G. (eds) 1998. *Contaminated Land and Groundwater: Future Directions.* Geological Society, London, Engineering Geology Special Publications, **14**, 73–77.

of the value of the land that reflects its environmental condition. Chemists produce the analytical results on which risk assessment depends. The Royal Society of Chemistry has a register of analytical chemists with particular expertise in contaminated land.

The geologist wishing to compete and collaborate successfully with other professionals, such as chartered engineers, chemists or surveyors, will enhance his or her chances by becoming a chartered geologist. Professional indemnity insurance is both easier to obtain and cheaper for chartered geologists. Certain employers reward gaining chartered status with a pay rise while others make it a precondition for promotion above a certain level. For those embarking on their careers, the earlier the process of working towards chartered status is started, the smoother the path is likely to be.

Training needs analysis

In order to identify the specific training needs for geologists working in contaminated land management, the tasks performed by geologists have been analysed (task analysis). The requirements for each task have then been considered and those areas not routinely addressed by university or professional experience have been identified (training requirement analysis). Finally the range of ways of meeting the training requirements is discussed (options analysis).

Task analysis

In the period between March 1996 and March 1997 the Environment Agency was set up, a new Special Waste regime was introduced, new insurance products dealing with contaminated land have come on to the market, novel methods of investigation have appeared, and several versions of the draft statutory guidance on the contaminated land provisions of the Environment Act 1995 were published for consultation. Contaminated land management is clearly a broad and rapidly evolving subject. Changes in the legal, commercial and technological milieux require contaminated land management specialists to regularly update their skills and knowledge.

Although the subject area is relatively new, it is one in which geologists have worked, to a greater or lesser extent, for over two decades. There is now sufficient experience of the activities involved to define the training needs for such geologists. Geologists have a contribution to make at the Phase 1 (preliminary risk assessment) stage, an essential role in Phase 2 (intrusive investigation and full risk assessment), and a further contribution to make at Phase 3 (remediation) and Phase 4 (post remediation monitoring). The tasks required for each phase are summarized below and the nature of the geologist's contribution discussed.

Phase 1 risk assessment. This comprises the collection and collation of existing information on site history, regulatory history and site setting followed by a walk-over survey to examine the current use and look for evidence of potential contamination. The main purpose is to identify whether plausible contamination source–pathway–receptor linkages are present with a view to deciding whether a physical investigation is required. Collection and evaluation of information on site history and current use does not need to be done by a geologist. However, a geologist is required to interpret the available geological and hydrogeological data which are key to assessing whether a groundwater receptor is present and the nature of the pathways between identified sources and receptors. This includes considering the presence of pathways between off-site sources of contamination and the site.

Training in this area should ensure that data collection is systematic, thorough and relevant and that the data enable a preliminary risk assessment and the design and planning of the next stage of investigation to be carried out. The information must be stored in such a way that it can be re-evaluated and updated as the investigation proceeds.

Phase 2 risk assessment. Phase 2 comprises an intrusive site investigation, geochemical analysis of soil, water or gas samples, and risk assessment. The purpose is both to determine whether the potential sources of contamination have resulted in contamination of soil or groundwater and to gain better information on the underlying ground conditions, with a view to evaluating the sub-surface pathways and groundwater conditions.

Geologists have an essential role to play in characterizing the ground conditions and providing good geomechanical and geochemical descriptions of the soil, rock material and rock mass. Where sub-surface pathways for migration of gas, leachate or water are a concern, then the geologist's role is to define the nature of the pathways and contribute to the risk estimation step of risk assessment. Further details of the major components of Phase 2 projects are given below.

Training will be required to provide knowledge of the type of parameters used in risk assessment, how the parameters relate to the predicted ground conditions and how they can be obtained by various methods of investigation and testing. For this reason some experience of site supervision and risk analysis is needed before taking sole charge of planning an investigation.

Design of site investigation
The design of site investigations should be driven by the needs of the proposed risk assessment. For example, if human health is of concern, sampling needs to be carried out in the shallow soils. Alternatively, where the issue is the risk of contamination of an aquifer, deeper soil sampling and groundwater sampling will be required.

The design of the investigation is also affected by the phase of investigation (preliminary, detailed, supplementary, compliance), the medium of concern (soil, water, soil gas), the characteristics of the contaminant (concentration, volatility, solubility) and ground conditions (particle size distribution, permeability) (CIRIA 1995). The geologist's ability to think in three dimensions coupled with an understanding of the likely ground conditions directs many of the choices made in the investigation design.

Schedule of geochemical laboratory testing
The testing regime should be based on the aims of the investigation, the results of the desk study and any previous investigations and visual inspection of the samples investigated (CIRIA 1995).

This requires an understanding of how the sampling process disturbs the sample, how representative the sample is likely to be, the probable rate of deterioration of the sample and the amount of data needed. Again, being able to think in three dimensions and having an understanding of geological heterogeneity greatly assists the selection of samples for testing. The geologist needs to liaise with the analytical chemist to ensure that the correct samples are taken, stored in appropriate containers and under the correct conditions for the intended analyses. The chemist should be briefed on the purpose of the risk assessment and, hence, ensure analytical methods and reporting procedures are appropriate.

Risk assessment
The recently published CIRIA guidance on site investigation and assessment of contaminated land (CIRIA 1995) and the forthcoming model risk assessment procedure (Harris 1997) break down the risk assessment process into the following four steps:

- hazard identification (the possible hazards present)
- hazard assessment (the degree of hazard)
- risk estimation (the likelihood that an adverse effect will result)
- risk evaluation (the significance of the estimated risks)

The outcome of the process is an assessment of the risk to humans, the natural and built environment on and off site, or the risk of polluting controlled waters or contaminating (or being contaminated by) adjacent sites. It covers both current risks and the effects of foreseeable events such as rises in the water table, flooding or tidal effects (CIRIA 1995). The geologist has a key role to play in assessing the presence and nature of plausible pollutant linkages. In many cases a qualitative or semi-quantitative understanding of ground conditions will be sufficient for risk assessment purposes. In selected cases, however, recourse to fully quantitative approaches to risk assessment involving human exposure or contaminant flow modelling will be needed. Geologists will require specialist training in these

modelling approaches, their implicit and explicit assumptions and their data requirements.

Phase 3. There are over 25 remediation strategies (Martin & Bardos 1995). Whether *in situ* or *ex situ*, the geologist has a role to play in determining the applicability of a given strategy and in implementing the selected strategy. *In situ* strategies require a thorough characterization of the ground, in particular the likely presence and extent of pockets of ground which may not be reached by the remediation technology. These pockets may be clay lenses in sand which are not treated by air sparging or pyrite rich zones where enhanced oxygen flow may accelerate the formation of sulphuric acid. *Ex situ* strategies require assessments of soil excavatability, slope stability and groundwater control.

Phase 4. The monitoring and validation of remediation is a form of site investigation and the geologist's contribution is similar to that in Phase 2.

Training requirements analysis

The 'new' tasks that geologists have to face in contaminated land management include the following:

- liaison with other science and engineering professionals
- liaison with non-technical professionals (e.g. surveyors, lawyers, bankers)
- contaminated land geochemistry
- contaminated groundwater hydrogeology
- site investigation of potentially hazardous ground
- producing risk assessment reports

Options analysis

The training needs can be met in several ways:

- education at undergraduate level
- education and training at post-graduate level
- on-the-job training
- continuous professional development

For those beginning their career in contaminated land management, their undergraduate education will act as the first of many stepping stones. First degree programmes have included modules in contaminated land for a few years. Education at this level could be directed towards providing knowledge about contaminated land with a view to creating an intellectual framework which enables that knowledge to be used and further knowledge to be gained (de Freitas 1994).

Post-graduate courses have been developed at several British universities. These range from full-time conversion courses based on existing undergraduate material (e.g. at Portsmouth University), through full-time advanced courses drawing on research strengths (e.g. at

Bradford University), to part-time industrially focused and research supported courses (e.g. at Nottingham Trent University). Masters courses should provide specialist knowledge and develop the intellectual framework into a logical problem-solving approach, using real examples where possible.

Early industrial experience is essential since much essential knowledge can be acquired 'on the job'. The methodology followed, terminology employed, project management, technology performance, and client needs and constraints can all be best studied in the 'real world'. However it is important to ensure that experience covers a broad range of subjects. Too often recent graduates find themselves carrying out the same routine tasks and not being given the opportunity to do other tasks, both routine and otherwise. Hence professional experience should be structured and tailored to provide both variety and depth in the skills the professional geologist will need throughout her career.

Continuous professional development (CPD) has a particularly important role in this rapidly evolving subject. Short courses abound and vary in both price and quality. Prices of commercial courses start at around £100 per day and go up to over £350 per day (1997 prices). Several Geological Society Special and Regional Groups are including CPD events in their annual programmes and a number of these have been and will be pertinent to contaminated land. These events and the Society's normal programme of meetings tend to be much cheaper than commercial alternatives.

Gaining training

Training during employment may be gained in several ways in addition to on-the-job experience:

- in-house training programmes
- short courses
- reading technical literature
- browsing the World Wide Web
- following and contributing to Internet discussion lists

Training guide for geologists in contaminated land management

In response to the need for continuing training in contaminated land management and in recognition of the rapid changes in contaminated land assessment practices and policy, the Environment and Engineering groups of the Geological Society have prepared a draft training guide for geologists working in the contaminated land management industry (Nathanail & Nathanail 1996). A separate guide is being produced for hydrogeologists.

The guide follows a similar format to that prepared for engineering geologists working within the civil engineering and construction industry (Bowden et al. 1994). It describes the process of becoming a chartered geologist and explains the training objectives included. For each phase of contaminated land management, the concepts involved are described and the training objectives listed. There are four standards of attainment: appreciation, knowledge, experience and ability. The standard expected for a chartered geologist is identified. The training objectives are tabulated and there is space for the date at which each of these objectives was obtained to be recorded. The appendices comprise a guide to employers, whose support for the training scheme is crucial, and a list of qualifying degrees. Training objectives are worded in generic terms so that a wide range of different experience will meet these objectives. A company may wish (and is encouraged) to write its own more specific training guide.

The guide is set out in stages reflecting the various stages of a site investigation, risk assessment and remediation project. It is intended that every trainee will fulfil the core objectives and a number of others listed in each section. Completion of every objective is neither required nor realistic. The sections are as follows:

- collection and collation of data
- planning of ground investigation
- field experience
- laboratory experience
- risk assessment
- design of remediation systems
- management, administration and communication
- professional matters (further education, codes of conduct, health and safety, etc.)

Conclusions

Geologists work in contaminated land management in multi-disciplinary teams. The subject is developing fast and there is a need for training to be formalized. Geologists already have many of the skills required, by virtue of their undergraduate and post-graduate education, but many other skills can only be developed 'on the job'.

Following a training needs analysis, a training guide for geologists in contaminated land management has been written. Use of the guide will ensure that on-the-job training is comprehensive, relevant and assists trainees to gain chartered geologist within a reasonable timeframe.

The need for training does not stop on achieving chartered status. The training guide can also assist in the planning of CPD and in developing CPD events for geologists.

References

BOWDEN, A. 1994. *Training Guide for Engineering Geologists in the Construction Industry*. Geological Society, London.

CIRIA 1995. *Remedial Treatment for Contaminated Land, Volume III: Site Investigation and Assessment*. Construction Industry Research and Information Association, London.

DE FREITAS, M. H. 1994. Teaching and training in engineering geology: professional practice and registration. *In*: OLIVEIRA, R., RODRIGUES, L. F., COELHO, A. G. & CUNHA, A. P. (eds) *Proc. 7th Int. Cong IAEG*, **V1**, LVII–LXXV, Balkema, Rotterdam.

HARRIS, M. 1997. Risk assessment and risk management. *Proceedings, The Environment Act 1995: The Practical Implications of Contaminated Land*. Central Law Training, Sutton Coldfield.

HOUSE OF COMMONS ENVIRONMENT COMMITTEE 1996. *Contaminated Land*, 2nd Report. The Stationery Office, London.

McCALL, J. 1993. Geoscience education and training: a unique meeting at Southampton. *Geoscientist*, **3**(5), 11–13.

MARTIN, I. & BARDOS, P. 1995. *A review of full scale treatment technologies for the remediation of contaminated soil*. Report for The Royal Commission on Environmental Protection, EPP Publications, Richmond.

NATHANAIL, C. P. 1995. What is environmental geology? *Geoscientist*, **5**(6), 14–15.

—— & NATHANAIL, J. 1996. A (draft) training guide for geologists in the contaminated land assessment and remediation industry. *In:* LERNER, D. & WALTON, N. (eds) *Pre-prints Engineering Group Annual Conference: Contaminated Land and Groundwater – Future Directions*, Portsmouth University, 359–378.

WOODCOCK, N. H. 1995. Environmental geology: educational threat or opportunity? *Geoscientist*, **5**(6), 11–13.

Policy maturity and the development of novel remedial techniques

J. G. C. Wills[1] & C. J. F. P. Jones[2]

[1] Stats Geotechnical Ltd, St Albans AL3 6PQ, UK
[2] Geotechnical Group, Department of Civil Engineering, University of Newcastle, Newcastle upon Tyne NE1 4DA, UK

Abstract. The need for a legislative framework to deal with contaminated land and its relationship to the market for novel remedial techniques is described. Problems of bureaucracy, inflexibility and liability are cited as reasons for a move towards more mature policy approaches, including brownfield development, the use of economic incentives, and remedial action based on suitability of land use. The contaminated land policy of the UK is outlined and the question as to whether this policy will prevent the kind of protracted legal battles experienced in the USA under Superfund is posed. Regulatory capture is suggested as a reason for the UK's predominantly deregulatory stance and it is proposed that this has the potential to stifle the development of advanced techniques. Barriers and opportunities to development are outlined: licensing, pilot studies and perception. It is concluded that 'Suitable for Use' will protect public health and the environment cost effectively – albeit at the expense of a strong market for advanced remedial techniques in the UK. Poor policy decisions by government are highlighted as a reason for uncertainty in the UK's remedial market. Niche markets and turnkey operations are identified as areas where UK firms have the potential to succeed.

Introduction

A fundamental problem with contaminated land is that as its potential for adverse effects on health and the environment have been realized, an extensive stock of contamination has come to light. Estimates of the scale of the problem vary between 50 000 and 100 000 sites in the UK covering an area of between 50 000 and 100 000 ha (ENDS 1991). The actual figure may well be higher if the UK's experience mirrors that found on the European mainland (ENDS 1991).

This stock of contamination has been caused not only by widespread ignorance of the effects of industrial activity but also by a failure of industry to internalize the external costs associated with contaminated land. As industry inevitably seeks to minimize costs, the only realistic solution is legislation. Although consumers may pay lip service to the need for a cleaner environment they are less willing to demand and pay for it directly. In addition, many of the external environmental, costs involved may well have been caused many years ago by polluters that have long since gone out of business or who cannot be traced.

Considering the potential scale of contamination, a structured approach is required to alleviate the greatest risks to health first and then progressively deal with the less serious sites. This is where CERCLA and more recently SARA, the American remediation programme commonly referred to as Superfund, experienced problems. By requiring stringent clean-up standards and by using a strict, retroactive, joint and several liability regime, the process failed. However, despite this apparent failure a strong market for advanced remedial treatment has developed. This market serves both the Superfund sites and more importantly the less contaminated – though far more widespread – brownfield or derelict sites.

The system proposed in the UK attempts to avoid the mistakes made in the USA by taking the wealth-creating sectors of the economy into account. It is intended that the redevelopment of contaminated land should occur as a part of the natural economic cycle. Furthermore, remediation should be to a level that makes the land concerned suitable for a proposed, rather than a multi-functional use. Consequently, although 'Suitable for Use' has the potential to promote the voluntary redevelopment of derelict land, it could also prevent the development of a strong market for advanced remedial techniques.

Policy maturity

There is international recognition of the need to move towards more mature forms of contaminated land regulation. Contaminated land regimes have and continue to be hindered by problems of bureaucracy, inflexibility and liability. They can require unrealistic, prescriptive or rigid clean-up standards backed by complex liability regimes that inevitably spawn litigation because of their tendency to be strict, retroactive and joint and several.

The UK, having been late to develop a contaminated land specific policy, is attempting to develop a mature

WILLS, J. G. C. & JONES, C. J. F. P. 1998. Policy maturity and the development of novel remedial techniques. *In:* LERNER, D. N. & WALTON, N. R. G. (eds) 1998. *Contaminated Land and Groundwater: Future Directions.* Geological Society, London, Engineering Geology Special Publications, **14**, 79–83.

policy approach based on what the DoE describes as pragmatism with room for voluntary improvement by industry. Increasingly, this approach is being recognized as the most effective way of dealing with contaminated land. Both the Dutch and American regimes are relaxing the requirement that multi-functionality be achieved in favour of site-specific clean-ups that are flexible and less prescriptive.

By encouraging the development of brownfield over greenfield sites, governments are attempting to encourage sustainable development or, more accurately, redevelopment. There is also the aim of reducing the financial burden on government by encouraging a market for the redevelopment of these sites. In addition, economic incentives are vaunted as a solution to some of the problems of command and control regulations. In this respect the UK Government has received criticism for not imposing the Landfill Tax on contaminated soil: such a tax would have been a good example of an economic incentive. Critics argue that this decision has taken the UK's policy approach too far in the drive towards deregulation at the expense of sustainable development.

The legislative framework

In Framework for Contaminated Land (DoE 1994), or 'Framework' as it is also known, the DoE proposes that the UK's existing legislative framework can be applied to the problem of contaminated land. 'Suitable for Use' relies on the planning system to bring contaminated land, or brownfield sites, back into use when they come up for redevelopment; remedial activity is only required to the extent that sites are fit for their intended purpose. Local planning authorities are required to draw up strategic development plans that are to be used to aid plan-led, as opposed to development-led, planning.

Just as the ICRCL guidelines were only voluntary, 'Suitable for Use', as discussed in the draft guidance issued to local authorities on the definition of contaminated land, requires that the levels of any remedial action be based on 'the fundamental principles of risk assessment' (DoE 1995).

Framework states:

'This approach requires remedial action only where:

- the contamination poses unacceptable actual or potential risks to human health or the environment; and
- there are appropriate and cost-effective means available to do so, taking into account the actual or intended use of the site'.

Defining contaminated land

In relation to the remediation of land that poses a threat to human health or the environment, Section 57 of the Environment Act 1995 introduces the following definition after Section 78 of the Environmental Protection Act 1990:

'"Contaminated land" is any land which appears to the local authority in whose area it is situated to be in such a condition, by reason of substances in, on or under the land, that:

(a) significant harm is being caused or there is a significant possibility of such harm being caused; or

(b) pollution of controlled waters is being, or is likely to be caused.'

Uncertainty still exists as to precisely what this definition means as the guidance that instructs local authorities how to decide is still undergoing consultation. This guidance is important as section 57 of the Act is only a framework. Until the guidance is issued, local authorities will not be in a position to assess whether there is contamination in their areas. If all goes to plan the final version of the guidance should be published by the summer of 1997.

However, when the guidance is published this still does not mean that local authorities will actually carry out any surveys of contamination or issue any remediation notices. Undoubtedly the level of activity will vary depending on the diligence of the authority in question. Some will know where contamination exists as a result of the aborted Section 143 registers; others will have to start from scratch.

Learning by experience

In the production of the new policy framework the Government considered it important that the major pitfalls encountered by other regulatory regimes be avoided. As stated, Superfund has experienced a great many problems both in terms of the massive amount of litigation it has spawned but also to the extent that it has largely failed in the most important task of actually remediating contaminated land. Of the original 1320 Superfund sites designated for clean-up, fewer than 300 have seen remedial action (Anon 1995). In the Netherlands the multi-functionality approach, which requires sites to be cleaned to a level that they be suitable for agricultural use, is also being backed away from for reasons of cost and the technical limitations of many remedial techniques. The DoE intends that 'Suitable for Use' will fall into neither of these traps. By encouraging voluntary remediation the aim is to limit litigation and prevent issues of liability from reaching the courts. The important question is will 'Suitable for Use' encourage those people who are potentially responsible for contaminated land to take action voluntarily or will local authorities and the Environment Agency become embroiled in protracted litigation when they attempt to force remedial action? Furthermore, if remediation is encouraged will it involve advanced or novel techniques or will the emphasis be towards encapsulation in the majority of cases.

The potential for development

Framework states that the objectives of the government's policy are to 'encourage an efficient market in land which may have been contaminated; to encourage the development of such land; and to remove unnecessary financial and regulatory burdens.' This attitude is evident in the draft guidance issued to local authorities. The guidance illustrates the risk-based approach to remediation in an example where the encapsulation of cadmium contamination under a concrete hard standing is considered a valid remedial technique based on the fact that it successfully prevents an immediate threat to human health. However, despite a commitment by the DoE to restrict the amount of contaminated soil being sent to landfill the non-prescriptive nature of the legislation means that landfilling and encapsulation is the remedial technique most commonly used.

The 19th report by the Royal Commission on Environmental Pollution (RCEP) argues that contaminated land legislation places too little emphasis on environmental protection and sustainable development. It calls for the use of the Best Practicable Environmental Option to be taken into account when dealing with contaminated land. It states, 'We recommend as a general principle that sites be remediated to the highest standard that can be reached without excessive cost and not merely the standard required for the use immediately intended' (RCEP 1996). It is implied that encapsulation methods should be used only for limited amounts of soil, provided long-term safety can be assured, and that eventually more sustainable techniques should be used.

Regulatory capture

The RCEP also contends that the 'Suitable for Use' system does little to encourage the development of advanced techniques that will be required if encapsulation is to be replaced. As Wilkes (1995) remarks, the UK is a relative newcomer to the contaminated land policy arena. It is contended that there has been little impetus for the development of the type of techniques called for by the RCEP. In addition, this is a situation that seems unlikely to improve due to the decision to exempt contaminated soil from the new Landfill Tax. This latter decision has been a blow to the developers of remedial techniques as it makes it difficult for them to compete on price. It is also a further indication of the uncertainty that the developers of such techniques have had to deal with. Just as the Section 143 registers were prevented by lobbying, so has the levying of Landfill Tax on contaminated soil.

It appears that regulatory capture is occurring. This is a process whereby entry to a market is prevented by powerful lobbying by, for example, landowners and developers with vested interests and a desire to maintain the status quo.

Technical barriers and opportunities

There are further reasons why advanced remedial techniques are prevented from operating. These include the following:

- *Licensing.* New and/or novel technologies present problems that can include the definition of waste or contaminated soil in relation to the process; having to obtain a new licence for individual sites; inconsistent treatment by different regulatory authorities; and attempting to operate new techniques that do not readily lend themselves to existing regulations.
- *Pilot Study.* The developers of new techniques find it difficult to move laboratory-scale projects to the field. Funding tends to be concentrated on basic and laboratory-scale work in universities and on validation by regulators. There is a lack of full size work.
- *Perception.* Remedial techniques can be perceived as being unreliable in their ability to meet clean-up targets; prohibitively expensive; and inflexible in their ability to treat a wide variety of soil types and contaminants.

Bardos & Martin (1995) highlight particular areas in which work into improving the effectiveness of remedial techniques can be considered most promising:

- process integration, i.e. the integration of a number of processes to achieve an enhancement of treatment effectiveness;
- extensive technologies, i.e. the use of technologies with low resource needs but longer treatment times;
- *in situ* treatment zones, which involve the *in situ* movement of contaminants to address the problems of accessibility; and
- active containment, which attempts to address the concerns over long-term barrier integrity.

The global market for remediation

By taking a pragmatic, deregulatory stance, the UK Government risks inhibiting the development of a market for advanced remedial techniques and access to the international contaminated land market. Table 1 from a study conducted by the OECD (1994), illustrates the size of the Western European market for remedial techniques. It is a market worth US$2.3 billion per annum and is growing at a rapid rate. In addition, the report describes the UK's opportunities for growth in relation to contaminated land remediation technology as

Table 1. *Western Euroopean land remediation growth (US$ billion) (OECD 1994)*

1990	1991	1995	Annual growth (%)
1.0	1.1	2.3	16.1

Table 2. *Global sector growth opportunities in contaminated land (OECD 1994)*

Region	High growth	Moderate growth	Low growth
Germany		✓	
France			✓
UK			✓
Italy			✓
USA	✓		
Australia	✓		

'poor' (see Table 2). This is a view backed by research carried out for the Joint Environmental Markets Unit – a body established by the DTI and DoE to help British firms exploit opportunities in the environmental industry (see Table 3).

Summary and conclusion

'Suitable for Use' is an example of a mature environmental policy. The system should achieve the desired effect of providing a realistic solution to the immediate health and environmental risks posed by contaminated land.

However, policy decisions have and continue to be effected by lobby groups. Landowners and developers have prevented the introduction of legislation that would have introduced economic incentives on two recent occasions: the Section 143 registers and the levying of Landfill Tax on contaminated soil. Both of these measures would have stimulated the use and development of advanced remedial techniques. Furthermore, the withdrawal of these policies at the eleventh hour caused uncertainty within the developing market for remedial techniques.

There is a fine line to be drawn between imposing draconian measures on industry and adopting a *laissez faire* attitude. The regulatory environment in the UK has encouraged cheap solutions to contaminated land problems. As a result, the incentive to develop innovative technologies has been minimal and the inability to offer sophisticated methods of land remediation has left UK firms with a handicap when competing in overseas markets.

In the absence of a mainsream remediation industry successful British firms will be those who can find a market niche or be adaptable to site-specific criteria by offering flexible integrated solutions. This could involve dealing with specific waste streams as a subcontractor or offering turnkey solutions.

Changes in policy and the uncertainty surrounding the publication of guidance to local authorities continues to cause problems for the developers of innovative remedial

Table 3. *UK strengths in relation to opportunities in the world environmental market (JEMU 1995)*

	Technology	Systems/ Applications	Contracting/ Engineering	Operation	Maintenance/ Support
Air Pollution Control	✱	✱ ✱ ✱	✱	✱	✱
Water & Wastewater Treatment	✱	✱ ✱	✱	✱ ✱ ✱	✱ ✱ ✱
Waste Management	✱	✱ ✱	✱	✱ ✱ ✱	✱ ✱ ✱
Contaminated Land	✱ ✱ ✱	✱ ✱	✱ ✱ ✱	N/A	✱
Energy & Renewables	✱ ✱	✱ ✱ ✱	✱	✱ ✱ ✱	✱ ✱ ✱
Environmental Monitoring & Instrumentation	✱ ✱ ✱	✱ ✱ ✱	✱	✱ ✱ ✱	✱ ✱ ✱
Environmental Services	N/A	✱ ✱	✱	N/A	N/A

Key:	✱ ✱ ✱	High Value Opportunity	United Kingdom Strengths	
	✱ ✱	Medium Value Opportunity		
	✱	Low value Opportunity		

techniques. However, advantages can be had by keeping track of developments in legislation provided not too much trust is placed in its speedy development or reliance placed on the introduction of measures that promote the use of specific techniques.

References

ANON 1995. *New Nightmare on Lime Street Evening Standard,* London, 8 February 1994.

BARDOS, P. & MARTIN, I. 1995. *International review of the state of the art in contaminated land treatment technology research and a framework for treatment process technology research in the United Kingdom.* Draft, Department of the Environment, London.

DoE 1994. *Framework for Contaminated Land.* Department of the Environment and the Welsh Office, London.

——1995. *Guidance on determination of whether land is contaminated land under the provisions of Part IIA of the Environmental Protection Act 1991.* Draft, Department of the Environment, London.

ENDS 1991a. *£10–30 billion and rising: United Kingdom's contaminated land clean-up bill.* Report, Environmental Data Services, London, Issue 201.

——1991b. *Contaminated land policy stutters forward.* Report, Environmental Data Services, London, Issue 193.

JEMU 1995. *The United Kingdom environmental industry: strategies for success.* Joint Environmental Markets Unit, London.

OECD 1994. *The environment industry: the Washington meeting.* Organisation for Economic Co-operation and Development, Paris.

RCEP 1996. *19th Report, Sustainable Use of Soil.* Royal Commission on Environmental Pollution, HMSO, London.

WILKES, A. 1995. *Government policies as the catalyst for the British environmental industry.* Environmental Industries Commission, London.

The delineation of capture zones around small sources

T. Keating,[1] M. J. Packman[1] & A. Peacock[2]

[1] Southern Water Technology Group, Crawley, West Sussex RH10 2PN, UK
[2] Environment Agency, North West Region, Warrington WA4 1HG, UK

Abstract. The delineation of capture zones and the subsequent designation of protection zones around groundwater sources is a key element of the Environment Agency 'Policy and Practice for the Protection of Groundwater'. The protection principles apply to all sources, but priority in defining protection zones has been afforded hitherto to the major public supply sources. The EA recognizes the need to have available a methodology for establishing protection zones around the smaller sources, of which there are upwards of 76 000 in England and Wales, compared with some 4000 larger sources used principally for public water supply. The delineation of capture zones around the smaller sources presents a number of technical and practical problems which tend not to arise when carrying out such procedures for the larger sources. This paper reviews the methods for delineating groundwater source capture zones which are readily available; it discusses the practical issues associated with the application of these methods to the smaller sources, and presents recommendations for their use in a range of hydrogeological settings.

Introduction

In 1992, the NRA published the national policy document entitled 'Policy and Practice for the Protection of Groundwater' (NRA 1992). The purpose of the policy was to take account of the duties imposed on the former NRA whilst consolidating and standardizing the groundwater protection practices inherited from the former water authorities which, although relatively successful, were based on differences in approach and technical foundations.

The delineation of protection zones around groundwater sources (GPZs) is a key element of the 'Policy and Practice for the Protection of Groundwater' (PPPG) (Keating & Packman 1995). The PPPG's source protection principles apply to all sources, but priority in defining protection zones has been afforded hitherto to the major public supply sources. To date, protection zones have been defined around approximately 800 sources, covering over half of the existing major potable groundwater supplies in England and Wales (Morris 1994). It is proposed that by 1997 zones will have been determined for all the public supply sources and certain private supplies which abstract more than $0.5 \, Ml \, day^{-1}$.

While priority has been afforded to protection zone designation around the major potable supply sources, the Environment Agency (EA) recognizes the need to have available a consistent, technically valid but pragmatic methodology that is suitable for defining such zones around the smaller potable sources, of which there are upwards of 76 000 throughout England and Wales. Many of these are located in minor aquifers in rural areas where complex fissure flow may occur or whose hydrogeology is not well understood, thereby restricting the opportunity to develop or use numerical models within the delineation process.

This paper presents the results of an investigation, carried out on behalf of the former NRA, into the suitability of the currently available methodologies for determining capture zones around small sources (SSL 1995). The investigation comprised the following:

- a review and assessment of existing GPZ practice within the former NRA;
- a literature review to determine current international GPZ practices;
- comparisons and suitability assessments of the alternative methodologies that are currently available;
- recommendations of techniques to produce best available methodology.

In the following sections, the methods currently available for delineating groundwater source capture zones are reviewed; the practical issues associated with applying such methods to the smaller sources are discussed, and recommendations for the use of such methods under differing hydrogeological conditions are presented.

Principles of protection zone delineation

The EA's approach to GPZ designation is based upon three protection zones, two of which (the inner and outer zones) are determined by the travel time of potential pollutants within the saturated zone, and one

KEATING, T., PACKMAN, M. J. & PEACOCK, A. 1998. The delineation of capture zones around small sources. *In:* LERNER, D. N. & WALTON, N. R. G. (eds) 1998. *Contaminated Land and Groundwater: Future Directions.* Geological Society, London, Engineering Geology Special Publications, **14**, 85–91.

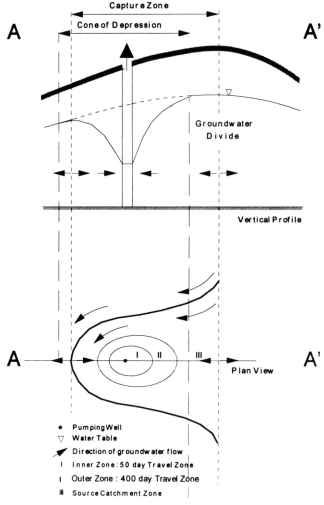

Fig. 1. Definition of capture zones

by the source catchment area itself (see Fig. 1). These three zones are each subject to a set of policies contained within the PPPG.

The *Inner Zone I* is defined by a 50-day travel time from any point below the water table to the source and, additionally, as a minimum 50 m radius from the source. It is located immediately adjacent to the source and the selection of the 50-day travel time is based principally on accepted bacteriological decay criteria.

The *Outer Zone II* is defined by the 400-day travel time or 25% of the source catchment area, based on the protected yield of the source, whichever is larger. The travel time is derived from consideration of the minimum time required to provide delay, dilution and attenuation of slowly degrading pollutants. The zone is generally not delineated for confined aquifers.

The *Source Catchment Zone III* is defined as the area needed to support the protected yield from long-term groundwater recharge (effective rainfall). In areas where the aquifer is confined beneath impermeable strata, the source catchment may be located some distance from the actual abstraction.

Methods of capture zone delineation

The choice of zone delineation technique depends upon the following:

- the degree of understanding of the groundwater setting;
- the quality and extent of the data available;

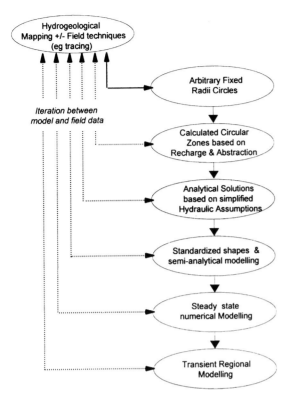

Fig. 2. Techniques for defining source capture zones

and the local aquifer recharge. For example, if q denotes the daily abstraction rate, and R_e represents the average daily rainfall recharge, then an area q/R_e is required to support the abstraction, and the radius of the equivalent circular zone follows from simple geometry.

Zones of this form are likely to be more defensible than those derived using an 'arbitrary' radius, for they provide a unique but universally reproducible circular area. However, they will generally exhibit little relationship in terms of shape, and hence area covered, to those delineated on the basis of (darcian) groundwater theory, particularly where the aquifer parameters would combine with the hydraulic gradient to give an elongated 'time' catchment (SSL 1995). Their general use is not recommended unless hydraulic gradients and/or geological relationships are unknown or cannot be estimated.

Numerical and analytical methods

Numerical models. While the use of fixed radius and standard-shaped protection zones have been used in the UK in the past (Selby & Skinner 1978; SWA 1985), alternative methodologies are now available which enable borehole capture zones in the major (darcian flow) aquifers to be delineated with some confidence subject to the availability of data.

The use of particle tracking techniques to generate flow paths and time of travel isochrons, (i.e. the loci of all points within the flow field from which the travel time to the source is identical) and consequently to delineate capture zones is relatively well established (Guiguer & Franz 1991). In general, particles are tracked explicitly through a computed flow field by calculating the directional components of velocity at the particle's current position and then moving it to a new position that is computed by multiplying the velocity components by a time increment to obtain the incremental changes.

Particle tracking routines are readily incorporated into numerical models (e.g. FLOWPATH, the 2D steady-state groundwater flow model from Waterloo Hydrogeologic Software, and MODFLOW from the US Geological Survey), but are also available with analytical and semi-analytical models. Numerical modelling is clearly the preferred method for determining capture zones based on travel times and FLOWPATH has been used extensively within the EA national GPZ programme for this purpose. To date, it has been used to delineate the capture zones around some 70% of all the public water supply sources for which zones have been delineated.

The application of numerical techniques to the determination of capture zones around the smaller, private sources, however, presents a number of practical difficulties. For example, the density of the computational grid necessary to accurately resolve variations across the flow field induced by the source is likely to be

- the operational importance of the source;
- the resources available for the particular zoning exercise.

Figure 2 shows the range of techniques currently available to delineate capture zones around groundwater sources in increasing order of technical sophistication and hence data requirement, while Table 1 lists the hydrogeological parameters that may be represented with each method together with the advantages and disadvantages.

Approximate methods

The simplest form of protection zone is a circle of arbitrary radius centred on the well or borehole. However, without regard to the local geological or hydrogeological conditions, such zones, unless they are very small (e.g. when protecting the immediate vicinity of the source), are unlikely to be technically defensible in public and therefore cannot be recommended.

If a fixed radius circular protection zone is proposed, then one, equivalent in size to the source catchment area, may be defined based on the rate of abstraction

Table 1. *Available methodologies for capture zone delineation*

Capture zone methodology	Parameters that can be represented	Advantages	Disadvantages
Hydrogeological mapping	• System boundaries and approximated divides	• Should be combined with all other methods • Good for karst and fractured aquifers with strong geological control	• Poor in areas with complex boundaries • Not quantitative
Fixed radii circular zones	• None	• Low cost • Easy and quick to implement • Highlights lack of data	• No technical basis • Does not have regard to local hydrogeological conditions
Calculated circular zone based on recharge and abstraction	• Recharge • Time of travel • Abstraction rate	• Low cost • Easy and quick to implement with minimal data requirements • Some technical basis	• Does not have regard to local hydrogeological conditions • Does not represent catchment or time of travel zones
Standard-shaped zones based on idealized representation of local conditions	• Hydraulic gradient • Hydraulic conductivity • Aquifer thickness • Effective porosity • Recharge But all as single value parameters	• Can represent a very simple system • Easy and quick to implement • Semi-quantitative	• Local conditions may differ significantly from those used in the initial delineation • Data may not be available
Analytical modelling: WHPA, Quickflow, ABARM	• Hydraulic gradient • Hydraulic conductivity • Aquifer thickness • Effective porosity • Recharge • Simple recharge/barrier boundaries • Some limited parameter variability possible	• Modest data requirements • Capture zones based on idealized representation of local aquifer conditions • Can represent a simple system • Quantitative • Simple and uniform boundaries and recharge allowed for	• Darcian flow assumed • Simple aquifer geometries only • Does not allow complex boundary and recharge effects to be considered
Numerical modelling: FLOWPATH, MODFLOW	• All hydrogeological parameters • Much flexibility in varying parameters	• Can represent most geological and hydrogeological boundaries	• Conceptual model of local hydrogeology required • Significant data requirements • Darcian flow assumed • Practical difficulties of obtaining adequate resolution of the flow field

locally very high, which tends to be impractical in terms of accuracy and efficiency. In addition, numerical models typically have a significant data requirement, the collection and validation of which may require a major resource input (Packman *et al.* 1996) because many of the smaller sources in England and Wales are located in rural areas on minor aquifers whose hydrogeology is not well understood or documented.

WHPA model. In many of these circumstances, analytical models, with less stringent data requirements than the numerical models, may be more appropriate tools for capture zone delineation, and WHPA, the Well-Head Protection Area model developed by the US Environmental Protection Agency, is currently the recommended tool. Capture zones around the majority of the 30% of sources within the national programme not delineated using FLOWPATH were obtained with WHPA.

The WHPA model is based on steady-state uniform groundwater flow in an aquifer of infinite areal extent, and source catchment areas derived on this basis are unbounded upgradient of the source. In reality, geological controls and hydrogeological boundaries must influence the shape of capture zones, and unless such factors are taken into account, the computed zones will be in error. It is recommended, therefore, that local knowledge be used as necessary to modify source catchment zones, and possibly time of travel zones, delineated by WHPA on a case by case basis.

Aquifer boundary and recharge Model (ABARM). An alternative approach (Lerner 1992), based on a series of analytical equations describing groundwater flow within finite rectangular aquifers, subject to variations in recharge and boundary conditions, overcomes many of the limitations of WHPA. In particular, the model allows the simulation of the flow field due to a (small) abstraction close to a catchment divide. Comparisons between the results from this model and those obtained using FLOWPATH were carried out as part of the *Small sources* study (SSL 1995) and were found to be in good agreement, with the added advantages of robustness and accuracy over the numerical solutions which were subject to computational difficulties arising from the resolution of the problem.

This model represents a compromise between the simplistic analytical models (e.g. WHPA), and the more complex (in terms of aquifer representation) numerical models. At present, however, it is not available as a commercial package and therefore cannot be recommended for general use.

Capture zone delineation in non-darcian or poorly documented aquifers

Many small sources are located in aquifers where the flow regime is non-darcian. In these aquifers classical groundwater flow theory does not apply and the analytical and numerical methods based on darcian flow principles should not be employed. The extent to which they may be used, however, depends upon the distribution of fissures and fractures at the catchment scale and the degree of homogeneity in their distribution. Such research that has been carried out on non-darcian flow (Bradbury & Muldoon 1994) has suggested that capture zones delineated by classical methods are likely to underestimate the extent of the zones calculated by more appropriate numerical methods, which have regard to the longer flow paths within the fractures. Unfortunately, the degree to which classical methods understate actual zones is likely to be aquifer dependent, and thus they should be used with caution, with local knowledge being used to modify the predicted zones.

In karstic aquifers the discrete nature and distribution of the fissures ensures that even dual porosity models are inappropriate and the delineation of capture zones around specific sources should be carried out on a case by case basis. This suggests that source protection in karst should be guided by pragmatic considerations rather than strict adherence to more rigorous numerical methods. A similar approach is necessary for mine-related sources. Zone delineation in these circumstances relies heavily on any historical tracing studies, caving records, mine plans, and hydrometric or hydrochemical studies available, in combination with the basic hydrogeology.

It should be normal practice to use hydrogeological mapping techniques (outcrop pattern, dip, thickness, structure and flow behaviour estimation, topographic divide, stream baseflow behaviour, hydrochemical anomalies, etc.) to complement computational zonal delineation techniques to ensure that the resultant zones make hydrogeological/geological sense. In those aquifers where groundwater flow behaviour is poorly understood or the flow regime distinctly non-darcian, the use of such field techniques may be the only applicable zone delineation method.

Capture zones around springs

In many areas groundwater abstraction takes place from springs or points of groundwater discharge at the surface. Springs present slightly different problems for protection zone delineation in that the discharge is governed by essentially natural groundwater flow driven by gravity. The size of the capture zone should be based on the total spring flow, rather than that proportion which may actually be abstracted. Further problems may arise if the discharge is intermittent, reduces or even dries up during the summer months as the water table falls.

Capture zones around springs may be delineated using numerical methods, subject to the limitations outlined above, but the nature of the aquifer and/or the

Table 2. *Applicability of zone delineation techniques to aquifer flow conditions*

Aquifer flow conditions	Ample data available	Poor data availability
Intergranular flow dominant	e.g. q, k, b, n, R_e ($q > 20\,\mathrm{m^3\,day^{-1}}$) Analytical/semi-analytical modelling (e.g. WHPA, ABARM) supplemented by local knowledge and mapping Minimum 50 m radius for zone 1	e.g. q, R_e ($q > 20\,\mathrm{m^3\,day^{-1}}$) Hydrogeological mapping and calculated circular zones based on abstraction and recharge
Fissure flow dominant but aquifer approximates to darcian conditions	No satisfactory methods yet available but use of methods for intergranular flow supplemented by local knowledge	
Non-darcian conditions or poorly documented aquifers	q and location plus field data, tracer studies or mapping available Hydrogeological mapping Professional judgement supplemented by local knowledge Minimum 50 m radius for zone I Combined zone II and III across all or part or the outcrop	Only q and location available Minimum 50 m radius for zone I Combined zone II and III across all or part of outcrop

Note: q = abstraction rate; k = permeability; b = saturated aquifer thickness; n = effective porosity; R_e = rainfall recharge.

availability of data could ensure that this is a non-viable option in the majority of circumstances. Again, hydrogeological mapping techniques may be the only way of determining the catchment area.

Minimum levels of protection

Computed capture zones around very small sources tend to be very narrow and impractical to implement. This problem may be overcome, to an extent, by specifying a minimum abstraction rate and using this instead of the actual rate to construct the zone. Since domestic abstractions of less than $20\,\mathrm{m^3\,d^{-1}}$ are excluded from EA water resource licensing control, it is recommended that this value be used to ensure minimum levels of protection for all sources abstracting below this limit. In the vicinity of the source, however, capture zone geometry is also dependent upon the local permeability and saturated thickness together with the hydraulic gradient, and the combination of these parameters may still result in impractical zones.

Therefore it is recommended that regardless of the method of zone delineation used, the minimum radius of an inner protection zone in the vicinity of the source should be 50 m in accordance with PPPG and also with the MAFF Code of Good Agricultural Practice (MAFF 1991). The degree of protection, in terms of travel time, afforded by such a zone clearly varies across the country. Nevertheless, the pedigree is sound and it is likely to be the more defensible for being consistent with existing practice in the rural environment. This is the only arbitrary fixed radius zone that is recommended

Recommendations

Table 2 summarizes the currently available methods for borehole capture zone delineation and gives recommendations for their use in particular aquifer flow conditions. It is recommended that the available methods be applied on a case by case basis for each source is located in a unique setting, and insights arising from the hydrogeological mapping of features around the source should not be ignored. Developed in this manner, the delineated zones are likely to be more realistic and therefore more useful, with the added bonus of better defensibility.

References

BRADBURY, K. R. & MULDOON, M. A. 1994. Effects of fracture density and anisotropy on delineation of wellhead protection areas in fractured rock aquifers. *Applied Hydrogeology*, **3**, 17–23.

GUIGUER, N. & FRANZ, T. 1991. Development and application of a wellhead protection area delineation computer program. *Water Science & Technology*, **24**(11), 51–62.

KEATING, T. & PACKMAN, M. J. (eds) 1995. *Guide to Groundwater Protection Zones in England and Wales*. HMSO, London.

LERNER, D. N. 1992. A semi-analytical model for borehole catchments and time of travel zones which incorporates recharge and aquifer boundaries. *Quarterly Journal of Engineering Geology*, **25**, 137–144.

MAFF 1991. *Code of Good Agricultural Practice for the Protection of Water*. MAFF, London.

MORRIS, B. L. 1994. *Providing the tools: The British experience in groundwater protection zoning*. 2nd Latin American Congress on Groundwater Hydrology, Santiago, Chile, 7–11 November.

NRA 1992. Policy and practice for the protection of groundwater. Report, NRA.

PACKMAN, M. J., KEATING, T. & FLETCHER, S. 1996. The importance of data acquisition and conceptualisation in groundwater protection zone delineation. *Contaminated Land and Groundwater – Future Directions*. Geological Society Conference, Portsmouth University.

SELBY, K. H. & SKINNER, A. C. 1978. *Aquifer protection in the Severn-Trent region: policy & practice*. The Institute of Water Pollution Control, Annual Conference Paper 11.

SSL 1995. *Small source protection zone delineation: Volume 1 Review of available methodologies and existing practice*. Southern Science Contract Report 94/7/984 for NRA.

SWA 1985. *Aquifer protection policy*. Policy Document, Southern Water Authority.

Application of the GLEAMS model to assess groundwater pollution risk caused by animal waste land disposal

M. Garnier,[1] A. Leone,[2] V. Uricchio[1] & R. Marini[1]

[1] National Research Council, Water Research Institute, via De Blasio 5, 70123 Bari, Italy
[2] Department of Agricultural Engineering, Tuscia University, via S. Camillo de Lellis, 00100 Viterbo, Italy

Abstract. In modern intensive animal farming the disposal of a large amount of waste represents a great concern. It is commonly accepted that the utilization of this waste as a fertilizer on agricultural soil has to be preferred to a treatment process that is extremely expensive and involves problems of final sludge disposal. Both solid and liquid animal wastes are an important resource for agriculture because they can substitute for synthetic fertilizers and contribute to the improvement of the soil structure. Land disposal of animal waste, particularly from swine husbandry, if not properly performed, can pollute surface and groundwater, mainly because of the high nitrate and phosphate content.

This paper presents the results of an application of the GLEAMS (Groundwater Loading Effects of Agricultural Management Systems) model, aimed at assessing the consequences on groundwater of animal waste application on different kinds of soils and agricultural arrangements, which are typical of the Chiana River Valley in central Italy. In this area this matter is of great concern because of the high concentration of swine breeding farms affecting directly a shallow unconfined aquifer.

GLEAMS model simulations were intended to assess the maximum rate of waste that can be applied on different types of soil, without exceeding in the aquifer the nitrate limit determined by law for drinking water. The results confirm that manure, although used according to regulations, in many cases does not allow such a limit to be respected, especially for the most sensitive soils. Some suggestions are given to identify a suitable quantity of animal waste for disposal that is compatible with minimizing the risk to groundwater in the area of concern.

Introduction

The treatment of animal waste from animal farming represents a relevant problem, from both an environmental and an economic point of view. On the other hand, the high nutrient content of this waste makes it particularly suitable for use as a fertilizer. In traditional agriculture, animal wastes represent the main source of crop nutrient and, for this reason, in the past, farms were always integrated with animal breeding. The development of modern arable agriculture and intensive breeding has broken this equilibrium and nowadays they are almost always separate activities. Nevertheless, mainly because of the growing importance of environmental problems, a trend to change this situation can be noticed, consisting of singling out well-defined agricultural lands that can be used as the most natural and cheapest destination for animal waste.

Apart from the separation between cropping and breeding activities, the most important problem in this regard, is the organization of an effective and environmentally compatible animal waste distribution on agricultural land. The planning of agricultural land use plays a key role in this concern; the importance of using simulation models, which allow us to assess the effectiveness of management practices in reducing environmental impact, is also clear (Khaleel *et al.* 1979). Edwards *et al.* (1991), for instance, employed the EPIC model to single out the best period for poultry litter disposal on Arkansas soils, one of the main environmental problems in that State, taking into account the spatial variability of the climate and soil pattern. A number of other papers demonstrating the growing interest in the subject have recently been presented. Fraisse *et al.* (1994), for example, developed the 'Generic Interactive Dairy Model' (GIDM), which integrates the GLEAMS model with ARC/INFO GIS software, to help planners and decision-makers to analyse the effects of alternative dairy waste management practices.

This paper presents a methodology to assess the susceptibility of agricultural land to receive the waste produced by the many breeding farms existing in Chiana River Valley (southern Tuscany). Different animal waste disposal and management criteria, consequent to the local regulation enforcement, have been compared in terms of groundwater nitrate pollution risk.

GARNIER, M., LEONE, A., URICCHIO, V. & MARINI, R. 1998. Application of the GLEAMS model to assess groundwater pollution risk caused by animal waste land disposal. *In:* LERNER, D. N. & WALTON, N. R. G. (eds) 1998. *Contaminated Land and Groundwater: Future Directions*. Geological Society, London, Engineering Geology Special Publications, **14**, 93–99.

Normative framework

Animal waste disposal in Italy is regulated by a number of rules, all stemming from the national law n.319 of May 1976, which delegates the local administrations (regions) for issuing detailed regulations, promoting also the regional plans for water reclamation. Law 319, however, establishes that, at most, the manure produced by a number of animals correspondent to a total weight of 4000 kg, that is to say 4000 kg of live weight (l.w.), can be disposed of every year on one hectare. Many Italian regions have lowered this limit. Moreover, the problem of establishing differentiated local limits for animal waste disposal has been transferred to the responsibility of local (provinces, municipalities, etc.) administrations (DPR n. 236, 1988). This is mainly because the regulations issued at the national or regional level are not able to enter the structural and management details of specific methods of breeding and plant growing.

With the aim to make a comparison with the results of GLEAMS simulation, the regulations concerning the study area, issued by Arezzo municipality and Local Health Centre (USL n.31), have been examined to single out limits for animal waste disposal relative to different crops.

The municipal law limits concerning the crops examined in the present paper are as follows:

- winter wheat   2000 kg l.w. ha^{-1}
- sunflower   2000 kg l.w. ha^{-1}
- maize   4000 kg l.w. ha^{-1}

The rules established by USL n.31 are more detailed, since they also take into consideration the types of soils, classified, on the basis of main physical characteristics, into three classes: A, B and C, in order of decreasing pollution potential. In short, the limits established for each kind of soil are as follows:

- soil A: only manure (solid waste) disposal is allowed;
- soil B: liquid waste disposal is allowed with limits of 1500 kg l.w. ha^{-1} for beef and dairy cattle, 1200 kg l.w. ha^{-1} for swine, and 900 kg l.w. ha^{-1} for poultry.
- soil C: liquid waste less restrictive limits are 2500 kg l.w. ha^{-1} for beef and dairy cattle, 1600 kg l.w. ha^{-1} for swine, and 1260 kg l.w. ha^{-1} for poultry.

The same regulations, moreover, fix in 250 kg ha^{-1} a^{-1} the maximum allowable amount of nitrogen, and 100 kg ha^{-1} a^{-1} per year that of phosphorous. These limits are relevant to the cumulative amount of manure and synthetic fertilizers on whichever class of soil.

Materials and methods

The study area is the alluvial plain of the Chiana River, a tributary of Arno (Tuscany, Italy), characterized by a shallow aquifer with a considerable capacity which is threatened by a growing nitrate pollution (USL 1995). As shown in Table 1 animal breeding is one of the most significant activities as regards the production of wastes with a high nitrate content (ISTAT 1991).

When manure is utilized on agricultural soil, nitrate can leach and cause groundwater pollution. To assess this risk the GLEAMS (Groundwater Loading Effects of Agricultural Management Systems, version 2.01) management model has been used (Leonard *et al.* 1987; Knisel 1993). The model, by means of a detailed description of agronomic practices, simulates the mobilization of nutrients and pesticides from soil. Even though the model only simulates nutrient mobilization within and through the plant root zone, without taking into account the complex interaction mechanisms occurring between nitrates and the deep rocky layers, it works very well in terms of output reliability, and in a shallow aquifer, such as the study area.

Model application has been aimed to assess the environmental compatibility of different schemes of animal waste disposal. With this purpose, the main crop rotations have been considered with reference to the different types of soils (Bigi *et al.* 1981), on the assumption that they are also the most suitable to manure disposal. The simulated crop rotations were a triennial rotation winter wheat–sunflower–winter wheat (WSW) and a triennial rotation winter wheat–maize–winter wheat (WMW).

It has to be pointed out that GLEAMS was not intended to be a predictive model, but only as a preliminary, semi-quantitative screening tool for decision makers in comparing the impact of different disposal

Table 1. *Breeding activities in the study area*

Communes	Area (ha)	Swine		Bovine		Poultry	
		Farms	Head	Farms	Head	Farms	Head
Castiglion Fiorentino	10 249.9	98	6 586	43	435	956	50 811
Cortona	28 103.3	399	41 375	122	1 407	1 886	112 928
Foiano della Chiana	3 377.7	85	3 159	33	977	503	9 590
Lucignano	3 668.3	80	11 387	19	285	323	8 406
Marciano della Chiana	2 127.4	45	1 774	7	126	259	16 677

schemes (Yoon *et al.* 1994). From this viewpoint, as explained in detail in a previous paper (Leone *et al.* 1995), it is the authors' opinion that the use of uncalibrated management models at large scale (e.g. regional, river basin) is allowable and turns out profitable on the condition that the temptation to consider absolute the model results is rejected.

Simulations have been oriented to the assessment of nitrate leaching in groundwater, assuming a waste application equal to the normal annual nutrient needs of the analysed crop. Furthermore, because of the uncertainty degree of the model estimations, with the aim to manage significantly different data series, only two types of soil, with different hydrologic and pedologic characteristics, were taken into consideration, namely:

- Soil 1: recent alluvial and fan, non-calcareous, with medium–coarse texture (fine sandy loam).
- Soil 2: riverine–lacustrine sediments, calcareous, with moderately fine texture (clay loam).

Table 2. *Fertilization and tillage scheme for the simulated cultural arrangements*

Cultural arrangment: winter wheat–sunflower–winter wheat

Crop	Date	Organic N application ($kg\,ha^{-1}$)	Mineral N application ($kg\,ha^{-1}$)		Tillage
			$NO_3^- N$	$NH_4^+ N$	
Winter wheat	Sept. 19	96			
Winter wheat	Sept. 20				Moldboard plow
Winter wheat	Nov. 6				Disc harrow, offset
Winter wheat	Nov. 7				Disc harrow, offset
Winter wheat	Feb. 18		24	12	
Sunflower	July 25				Moldboard plow
Sunflower	Feb. 25			60	
Sunflower	Feb. 28				Disc harrow, offset
Sunflower	Mar. 2				Disc harrow, offset
Sunflower	May 28		20	20	
Winter wheat	Sept. 19	96			
Winter wheat	Sept. 20				Moldboard plow
Winter wheat	Nov. 6				Disc harrow, offset
Winter wheat	Nov. 7				Disc harrow, plow
Winter wheat	Feb. 18		24	12	

Cultural arrangment: winter wheat–maize–winter wheat

Crop	Date	Organic N application ($kg\,ha^{-1}$)	Mineral N application ($kg\,ha^{-1}$)		Tillage
			$NO_3^- N$	$NH_4^+ N$	
Winter wheat	Oct. 28				Moldboard plow
Winter wheat	Oct. 28	96			
Winter wheat	Nov. 6				Dics harrow, offset
Winter wheat	Nov. 7				Disc harrow, offset
Winter wheat	Feb. 18		24	12	
Maize	Mar. 16	200			
Maize	Mar. 17				Moldboard plow
Maize	Apr. 8				Disc harrow, offset
Maize	Apr. 9				Disc harrow, offset
Maize	June 15			50	
Winter wheat	Oct. 28				Moldboard plow
Winter wheat	Oct. 28	96			
Winter wheat	Nov. 6				Disc harrow, offset
Winter wheat	Nov. 7				Disc harrow, offset
Winter wheat	Feb. 18		24	12	

Table 3. *Average nutrient concentration in the applied manure*

	Total N%	Organic N %	NO_3^- %	NH_4^+ %
Swine liquid	0.28	0.04	0.01	0.23
Beef solid	4.8	4.23	0.03	1.54
Poultry solid	6.2	4.12	0.03	2.05

Table 4. *Total nitrogen needs, alivde weight and head number corresponding to the applied manure*

		Swine		Bovine		Poultry	
	Total N $(kg\,ha^{-1}\,a^{-1})$	l.w. (kg)	Head number	l.w. (kg)	Head number	l.w. (kg)	Head number
Winter wheat	132	550	9.2	710	2.0	300	200.0
Maize	250	1140	19.0	1470	4.2	620	413.3

Note: In the table sunflower has been neglected because it needs only mineral fertilization.

Taking into account the law limits described in the previous section, nitrate leaching has been simulated, for a 40-year period, on the above-mentioned crop rotations. A scheme of the simulated tillages and fertilizations is shown in Table 2. The nutrient content of the animal waste employed in the simulations has been calculated by means of an average value of the data taken from the literature (Giardini 1991; Knisel 1993) and are displayed in Table 3. Total animal waste amounts supplied to each crop and the correspondent nitrogen content are reported in Table 4.

Because the model has been applied in non-calibrated form, rather pessimistic hypotheses have been considered in the assignment of values to those parameters, such as field capacity (FC), that proved to influence nitrate leaching more than others. This is also in accordance with the sensitivity analysis undertaken in a previous paper, referring to a similar environment (Leone *et al.* 1995).

As a reference point for discussion, the maximum nitrate limit of $11.3\,mg\,l^{-1}$ of nitrate nitrogen (NO_3-N) for drinking water (imposed by Republic President Decree n.236/1988) has been considered.

In this study the whole replenishment of the aquifer has not been taken into account. In any case, considering the dilution effect, it seems opportune to compare the consequences of different agricultural practices in terms of nitrate concentration (milligrams per litre), rather than simply considering the total amount of leached nitrates (kilograms per hectare). A rather permeable soil, which allows greater nutrient leaching, will cause greater groundwater pollution because of its lower water retention capacity, but the dilution effect mitigates this impact which at first glance could have seemed to be most relevant. This confirms the need to employ rather sophisticated models, such as GLEAMS, which allows a 'global' system's analysis to be performed.

Table 5. *Percolate (from the root zone), leached NO_3-N and NO_3-N concentration related to manure application on the examined soils*

	Percolate (mm)		Leached N-NO_3^- $(kg\,ha^{-1}\,a^{-1})$				N-NO_3^- concentration in the leachate $(mg\,l^{-1})$			
	WSW m*	WMW m	WSW m	σ†	WMW m	σ	WSW m	σ	WMW m	σ
Soil 1										
Swine liquid	253.9	249.7	80.5	48.0	92.2	53.1	35.9	24.0	41.2	28.6
Beef solid	255.9	249.7	69.2	42.8	75.4	44.3	30.0	20.3	32.3	20.3
Poultry solid	253.9	249.7	69.3	42.9	75.5	44.5	30.1	20.3	32.5	20.4
Soil 2										
Swine liquid	187.1	184.5	19.7	15.1	27.1	33.1	10.3	6.4	13.3	11.9
Beef solid	189.1	184.5	15.1	13.6	16.2	17.5	7.7	5.8	8.3	6.7
Poultry solid	187.1	184.5	15.2	13.7	16.8	17.6	7.8	5.8	8.4	6.8

*m = Mean annual value.
†σ = Standard deviation.

Results and discussion

Because GLEAMS has been used in non-calibrated form, it has to be pointed out that the results are reliable and coherent with theoretical expectations, especially as far as hydrological phenomena are concerned.

The most significant simulation results for each type of soil and manure examined are summarized in Table 5. They concern the annual average values of percolate, the annual average values of leached nitrate and the nitrate concentration in the leachate.

The results show that, in general, the 40-year average values of nitrate concentration, in the case of soil 1 are nearly always three times higher than the above-mentioned maximum limit for drinking water; for soil 2 they are very close to this limit, but this is not a reassuring result, since the standard deviation is of the same order of magnitude as the average concentration. Annual nitrate concentration in the leachate has been proved to be higher than $11.3\,mg\,l^{-1}$ in many cases. It should be noted that the historical data from the 40-year simulation period show some outliers (see Fig. 1), occurring either when particularly abundant rain falls just after fertilizer application, or when it rains just on the day of fertilizer application. The first case is realistic because farmers cannot know exactly when it will rain; the second is unrealistic because farmers do not apply fertilizers on rainy days. GLEAMS is unable to take into account the difference between these two cases, because it uses the same fertilization dates during the whole simulation period. This is the reason why the causes of such outliers should be checked and fertilization dates should be slightly changed if necessary.

Another drawback of this model is its inability to update soil parameters. For instance, animal waste fertilization, since it improves soil structure, also improves soil hydrologic performance (e.g. field capacity increases with organic matter). In this way leachate quantity decreases year by year. Such a drawback, which can be easily overcome, has been neglected in this work since the most pessimistic hypothesis is always considered. These are all reasons why the model results should be examined with caution. In any case, it is possible to assert that nitrate leaching from soil 2 satisfies the nitrate limit for drinking water, while a remarkable risk has to be considered in the case of soil 1.

Another interesting result is the emphasis on the rather chaotic behaviour of annual nitrate leaching. As proved also by the application of GLEAMS to other study areas (Leone et al. 1995), this is a confirmation of theoretical expectations. In fact, the correlation between annual nitrate leaching and percolate is very weak (Fig. 1); this means that the causes of pollution risk are not the heavy rains and percolation but the quantity of nutrient there is on the soil when percolation occurs and consequently the dates of fertilization that qualify, in each geographic area, several other factors (e.g. rates of nitrogen crop uptake and biodegradation, crop stage, soil temperature) which directly influence nitrate leaching.

As far as peculiar aspects are concerned, the following points can be noted:

- the significance of the type of soil: soils with the finest granulometry almost always entail a halved nitrate leaching;
- substantial differences among different agricultural arrangements have not been observed, apart from the case of swine manure, which, being liquid and because of the great amount of nitrate required by maize, increases the probability of leaching;
- the agricultural arrangement based on maize cultivation proves to be responsible for the most significant impact, although this crop is a strong nitrate consumer. This result can perhaps be ascribed to the already mentioned influence of fertilization dates. Because maize needs the higher nutrient quantity in a rainy month, the probability of occurrence of important nitrate leaching events increases.

Conclusions

The study aimed to assess the environment sustainability of animal waste disposal on agriculture soil in the alluvial plain of Chiana River, which is characterized by numerous breeding farms. Two agricultural arrangements have been compared in terms of nitrate leaching in order to analyse the influence of two types of soil. The examined environmental system is particularly sensitive, because of the high vulnerability of the shallow aquifer, intensive agricultural activity, and intensive animal breeding.

Nitrate mobilization from soil has been simulated by means of GLEAMS model, applied in uncalibrated form, which has provided results that agree with theoretical expectations. The high variability of GLEAMS outputs with field capacity variation has been verified, together with an evident output stability in terms of comparisons: differences between agricultural arrangements and the influence of different types of soils.

The analysis of results suggests the following considerations, the usefulness of which in land use planning and decision making is evident:

- The amount of animal waste that can be applied on agricultural soil without risks for groundwater resources is lower than that fixed by present local regulations, particularly in the case of liquid manure. Nevertheless, since GLEAMS considers rain and irrigation as the unique contributions of the aquifer recharge, NO_3-N concentration will be probably lower than that estimated, because of the dilution caused by other components of the recharge. This allows GLEAMS's estimations to be considered with a good enough margin of safety.

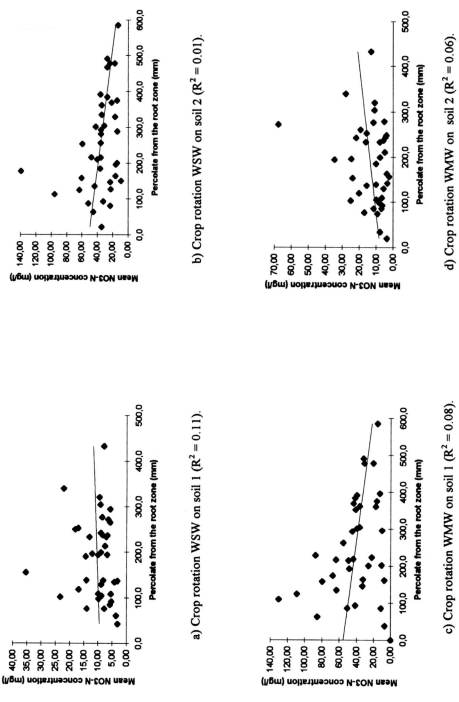

a) Crop rotation WSW on soil 1 ($R^2 = 0.11$).

b) Crop rotation WSW on soil 2 ($R^2 = 0.01$).

c) Crop rotation WMW on soil 1 ($R^2 = 0.08$).

d) Crop rotation WMW on soil 2 ($R^2 = 0.06$).

Fig. 1. Annual values of nitrate concentration in the percolate vs. percolate quantity for swine manure application.

• The cultural arrangement based on maize proves to be responsible for the most significant impact.

Further studies are then necessary to assess details for the best management practices to be undertaken in the study area (optimization of fertilizer application dates, changes in agricultural practices, etc.). Taking into account that total nitrogen application rates are those correspondent to typical intensive agricultural systems, and that nitrate quantities leaving the soil surface are in practice the same either in the case of organic or synthetic nutrients application (Leone *et al.* 1995), simulation results indicate a significant impact of agriculture on groundwater, whichever crop rotation, animal waste or soil type is considered.

This suggests that legislators have to be cautious when issuing regulations, and decision makers have to plan the use of agricultural soil taking into account the need to safeguard water resources. In this way suitable management models and other provisional tools can be effectively employed.

References

BIGI, L., BOCCIAI, P., FAVI, E., GALANTI, E., GONNELLI, I., HAIANI, S., ROSSI, R., RUSTICI, L. & VINCI, A. 1981. *Carta Generale dei Suoli 1:50.000*, Regione Toscana-Dipartimento Agricoltura e foreste.

DPR n.236, 1988. Attuazione della Dir. CEE n. 80/778 concernente la qualità delle acque destinate al consumo umano, ai sensi dell'art.15 della Legge n.183, 16 April 1987.

EDWARDS, D. R., MARBURN, W. R. & DANIEL, T. C. 1991. Use of the EPIC model to identify optimal timing of broiler litter disposal. *Proceedings of the International Seminar of CGR on Environmental Challenges and Solutions in Agricultural Engineering*, AS Norwal, 1–4 July, 139–145.

FRAISSE, C. W. 1994. Integration of GIS and GLEAMS for alternative dairy waste management analysis. *Proceeding ASAE International Winter Meeting*, Atlanta, Georgia, 13–16 December, paper 942508.

GIARDINI, L. 1991. Relazione generale di sintesi del capitolo su: Problemi dell'inquinamento dei corpi idrici da parte degli allevamenti zootecnici intensivi e in generale, della concimazione dei campi. Agricoltura e ambiente, Edagricole, Bologna, 239–275.

ISTAT 1991. *Caratterizzazione della struttura delle aziende agricole*. Fascicolo provinciale – Arezzo. 4° Censimento generale dell'agricoltura. Istuto Nazionale di Statistica.

KHALEEL, R., FOSTER, G. R., REDDY, K. R., OVERCASH, H. R. & WESTERMAN, P. W. 1979. A nonpoint source model for land areas receiving animal wastes: III. A conceptual model for sediment and manure transport. *Transactions of the ASAE*, 1353–1368.

KNISEL, W. G. (ed.) 1993. *GLEAMS – Groundwater Loading Effects of Agricultural Management Systems. Version 2.10*. University of Georgia, Coastal Plain Experimental Station, Tifton, GA.

LEONARD, R. A., KNISEL, W. G. & STILL, D. A. 1987. GLEAMS: ground water loading effects of agricultural management systems. *Transactions of the ASAE*, **30**, 1403–1418.

LEONE, A., GARNIER, M., CAMPIGLIA, E. & MARINI, R. 1995. Uncalibrated management models to assess agricultural diffuse pollution: their use in decision making. *Journal of Environmental Management*, in press.

ROSSI, N. 1990. Uso Razionale dei Liquami in Agricoltura. *Genio Rurale*, **6**, 25–34.

USL n.31, 1995. Adeguamento igienico ambientace degli allevamenti zootechnici.

YOON, K. S. *et al.* 1994. Application of GLEAMS to predict nutrient losses from land application of poultry litter. *Transactions of the ASAE*, **37**(2), 453–459.

Groundwater vulnerability and the Channel Tunnel Rail Link Bill

T. J. Bishop,[1] M. J. Packman[1] & P. J. Aldous[2]

[1] Southern Water Services Ltd., Victory House, Manor Royal, West Sussecx RH10 2PN, UK
[2] Thames Water Utilities, Ltd., Nugent House, Vastern Road, Reading, Berkshire RG1 8DB, UK

Abstract. The Channel Tunnel Rail Link (CTRL) Bill 1994 authorizes the construction, maintenance and operation of a high speed rail link between St Pancras in London and Folkstone in Kent. Furthermore, the Bill makes identical provision for widening works associated with the A2 at Cobham and the M2 in Kent between junctions 1 and 4. The publication of the Bill raised a number of very serious issues affecting the responsibilities of both the Statutory Water Undertakers and those of the Environment Agency (the Agency). Furthermore, the Bill failed to define suitable mitigation measures that would reduce the risk of public groundwater supply contamination, introduced by the construction and operation of the CTRL, to within tolerable limits.

This paper explores how both the Promoters of this major transportation link and the water companies sought protective provisions utilizing the Agency's Groundwater Protection Policy and risk assessment methodologies in order to define the potential for groundwater contamination. This process culminated in the Statutory Water Undertakers presenting evidence at the All Party Parliamentary Select Committee in order to demonstrate the necessity for suitable protective measures. Furthermore, this paper assesses the current status of the Agency's Groundwater Protection Policy in the light of this major test of resolve and the apparent paradox of Statutory Duties for both the Agency and Statutory Water Undertakers with regard to groundwater contamination.

Introduction

The high speed Channel Tunnel Rail Link (CTRL) between St Pancras in London and Folkstone in Kent is considered by government to be of national importance. Consequently, in 1994 a Hybrid Bill was presented to Parliament in order to facilitate the most rapid construction and operation of the route with the minimum of delay. A Hybrid Bill is specifically one which is jointly sponsored and affects local and private interests. The writing of the Bill presented enormous problems for planners, engineers and the legal profession with regard to the range of potential impacts and implications of building such a major undertaking, the first major railway to be constructed in the UK for over 100 years.

The construction and operation of the CTRL would not only impact upon the local populous, business and environment, but also many of the Statutory Undertakers along the route including Water, Electricity, Gas and Telecommunications. Statutory Water Undertakers have dealt successfully with the construction of major transportation links, on a range of issues, for many years and had reached satisfactory agreements with the Channel Tunnel Promoters and the Highways Agency on the protective measures required for the adjacent M2 widening associated with the CTRL Bill.

The proposed rail route passes across approximately 88 km of vulnerable major and minor aquifers as classified by the Agency, including the North Kent Chalk and the Lower Greensand. The Promoters' consultants completed an environmental evaluation and risk assessment addressing the potential for groundwater contamination. The Promoters concluded that the outcome of the exercise established that the CTRL as an operational railway will not represent an appreciable pollution risk and will therefore not infringe the fundamental basis of the Policy and Practice for the Protection of Groundwater (PPPG) established by the National Rivers Authority (NRA 1992) and subsequently adopted by the Environment Agency. Therefore, the promoters initially chose not to follow commonly perceived best practice advice as indicated by both the Statutory Water Undertakers and the NRA with regard to the protection of groundwater from contamination through suitable drainage design and other appropriate design/mitigation measures.

The Promoters' position that the CTRL will not represent an appreciable pollution risk necessitated the Statutory Water Undertakers (Southern Water Services Ltd, Thames Water Utilities Ltd and Mid Kent Water plc) to Petition the Bill and enter into negotiations with the Promoters.

The high speed rail route infringes upon Groundwater Protection Zones (GPZ), either I, II or III, for over twenty major Public Supply Groundwater Abstractions on some of the UK's most vulnerable aquifers, as classified by the Agency. Irrespective of the most stringent protective measure, or codes of practice, the Agency's Policy and Practice for the Protection of Groundwater document states a position for each Groundwater Protection Zone with regard to drainage to groundwater from the construction and operation of major transportation links.

BISHOP, T. J., PACKMAN, M. J. & ALDOUS, P. J. 1998. Groundwater vulnerability and the Channel Tunnel Rail Link Bill. *In*: LERNER, D. N. & WALTON, N. R. G. (eds) 1998. *Contaminated Land and Groundwater: Future Directions*. Geological Society, London, Engineering Geology Special Publications, **14**, 101–107.

A description of the three different protection zones and the Agency's stated position to groundwater discharge is given below.

- *Groundwater Protection Zone I* (50 day travel time to abstraction or less). Not acceptable; the Agency will normally object in principle to such activities which would involve a high risk of contamination to controlled waters or a resource.
- *Groundwater Protection Zone II* (400 day travel time to abstraction or less). Presumption against; the Agency will seek to prohibit this activity by seeking an absolute prohibition notice wherever possible. An objection will only be withdrawn in exceptional circumstances, or where detailed investigation can demonstrate that the activity does not represent a high risk of contamination to controlled waters and can be adequately controlled by conditions that form part of a statutory consent or agreement.
- *Groundwater Protection Zone III* (any inflow to the aquifer within this zone will travel to the abstraction). Prohibition notice or consent to discharge with conditions that may restrict the quality and quantity of the discharge.

Consequently, the decision by the promoters not to follow the Agency's stated position of using a well established methodology represented a major test for the policy, since successes on the part of the Promoters would set a precedent for future developers to bypass the policy, utilizing risk assessments to question its necessity or application.

Groundwater resources of the region, public supply vulnerability and the CTRL route

Chalk aquifers are the UK's principal groundwater resource, representing over 30% of the nation's entire water supply and 77% of that utilized by Southern Water Services Ltd. In addition many major centres of population, water treatment works and distribution networks have evolved to reflect the geographical availability of groundwater resources in the region. Consequently, many of the key groundwater abstractions are of vital strategic importance if the demand/resource balance is to be maintained. The strategic role of groundwater becomes even more acute during periods of drought when the reliance on water stored underground increases as surface storage and river flows become depleted.

The route of the CTRL is shown in Fig. 1 along with the major aquifer units and principle groundwater abstraction sources. Figure 1 demonstrates that the route may have been chosen for sound engineering, commercial, socio-economic and political reasons, but that it is somewhat unfortunate with regard to water resource locations and therefore to the potential risk of contamination.

The Channel Tunnel Rail Link will traverse the regions two principal aquifers, the Lower Cretaceous Lower Greensand and the Upper Cretaceous Chalk. In its central section the CTRL straddles the Gault Clay and Lower Greensand. Public supply groundwater abstractions generally draw water from the confined Lower Greensand aquifer, which is recharged, principally, from the outcrop area to the south, where the rail route is proposed. North and west of Maidstone as far as the River Thames, the CTRL will pass across the unconfined Chalk aquifer which is drawn upon by numerous public supply groundwater abstractions, one of which is only 20 m from the centre of the proposed track line. The very high vulnerability of the Chalk aquifer is demonstrated by the lack of surface water features, which are absent, since the highly permeable soils and unsaturated zone transmit water rapidly, vertically and horizontally, to the permanent water table.

Groundwater protection zones

The Environment Agency, in line with the Water Resources Act 1991, have developed a methodology for the definition of public supply borehole Groundwater Protection Zones. The aim of this process is to define borehole capture zones, and time-based zones within the capture zone, which are significant in terms of their time of travel to a groundwater abstraction. The prime objective is to define tangible zones within which any activity that may impact upon public supply groundwater sources may be assessed objectively.

In order to refine the process of evaluating potential impacts and suitable mitigation measures the policy also encourages protection zones to be used in conjunction with aquifer vulnerability. The policy document defines aquifer vulnerability as depending 'upon the natural characteristics of a site and is assessed on the physical, chemical and biological properties of the soil and rocks beneath the site, which control the ease with which an unprotected hazard can affect groundwater'.

Combining the Agency's defined vulnerability and groundwater protection zones reveals that certain sections of the CTRL impact upon a number of the UK's most vulnerable public supply groundwater sources, which form a fundamental component of the strategic water resource plan for southeast England. Figure 2 illustrates these factors schematically for just one public supply Chalk groundwater source (Nashenden near Chatham).

The promoters' position with regard to groundwater contamination risks

In line with common practice, the highly complex nature of the CTRL Hybrid Bill required a range of supporting documentation in order to validate the scheme and

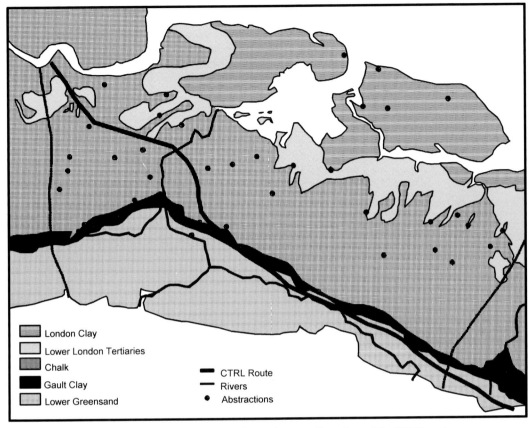

Fig. 1. Public supply groundwater abstractions, aquifer units and the CTRL route.

to clarify the procedures to be adopted. With regard to groundwater contamination risks the nominated undertaker would be required to follow Codes of Practice for both the construction and operation/maintenance of the CTRL, further supported by an Environmental Memorandum.

Groundwater contamination mitigation measures, and specifically drainage design features, were evaluated through a series of 'Assessment of Aquatic Effect' reports and detailed risk assessments presented in the 'CTRL Outline Railway Safety Case'. The aquatic effects reports essentially complete the initial stages of an Environmental Impact Assessment for the full range of potential aquatic effects, including contamination from acute source spillage, or longer term chronic source contamination of the groundwater regime.

The Assessment of Aquatic Effects, Final Report made a series of statements/recommendations which are entirely consistent with the Agency's Policy and Practice for the Protection of Groundwater document and the concerns of the Statutory Water Undertakers:

'...isolated contaminant spillages during construction pose a potentially strategic risk to local groundwater resources. Although perhaps small scale and very localised in accidental occurrence, certain contaminants have the capacity to pollute large aquifer blocks, potentially for very large periods of time...it is important to recognise that all of the major and minor aquifers represent highly strategic water resources within this area of South East England.'

'Earthworks, drainage and general construction operations potentially generate polluted surface water runoff which could cause chronic and diffuse pollution and is a potential significant effects (*sic*) during construction.'

'There is also a risk of acute pollution arising from accidental spillage of slurries, chemicals, hydrocarbons etc., particularly at construction sites. Measures to control, contain and clean-up such a spillage are objectives of the Construction Assumptions for Environmental Assessment (CAEA) but the random

(a)

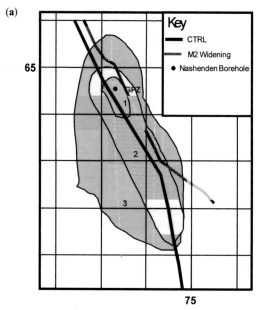

(b)

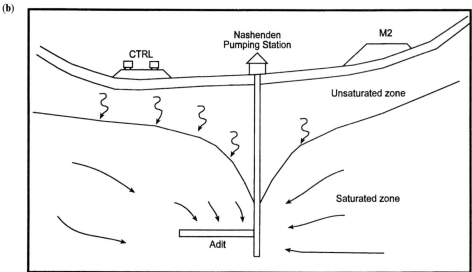

Fig. 2. Nashenden public supply source, GPZ and CTRL location.

and unpredictable nature of accidental spillage means that despite the assumed level of protection, a risk of effect from spillage will remain.'

'The high permeability of the underlying chalk, the presence of Nashenden Public Water Supply and associated Aquifer Protection Zone 1 strongly mitigate against the discharge of track drainage within the valley. Engineering report E12 states track drainage from the Nashenden Dry Valley (including the upper

valley in Route Window 19) will be conveyed by sealed carrier to discharge directly into the River Medway.'

(Assessment of Aquatic Effects, Final Report, Volume 1 of 4 Main Report, November 1994)

The CTRL Outline Railway Safety Case completed both a detailed deterministic and probabilistic safety assessment and addressed a range of issues including safety policy, the risk to members of the public from operation of the CTRL, the risk of train fires, etc., all based upon available information and well established techniques. The risk of groundwater contamination from the CTRL was not evaluated by the Outline Railway Safety Case specifically, but a judgement was made based upon assumptions of materials to be carried and the risk of collisions, derailments and fires.

The Promoters concluded from the work undertaken that no mitigating measures in terms of drainage to the aquifer would be required since 'The outcome of the exercise has established that the CTRL as an operational railway does not represent an appreciable pollution risk and will not therefore infringe the fundamental basis of the NRA's Groundwater Protection Policy.'

Concerns of the statutory water undertakers and the approach adopted

The Statutory Water Undertakers held serious concerns regarding the lack of protection of Groundwater Public Supply Sources from contamination during both the construction and operational phases of the CTRL. These concerns were not simply a function of commercial interests, but reflect their statutory duties/responsibilities. Statutory Water Undertakers were appointed by the Secretary of State for the Environment under the Water Act 1989 (now incorporated in the Water Industry Act 1991). This appointment contains legal obligations which are set out in the Instrument of Appointment. Parliament has imposed requirements on Statutory Water Undertakers to attain specific standards in respect to both quality and sufficiency of water. The statutory obligation to provide water of an acceptable quality is set out in Sections 68 and 69 of the Water Industry Act 1991 and the Water Quality Regulations (HMSO 1989). The statutory requirement to supply water for domestic purposes, non-domestic purposes and fire fighting, etc., are specified under Sections 52, 55, 57 and 59 of the Water Industry Act 1991. The seriousness which Parliament attaches to the protection of the water supply from pollution is detailed in Section 70 of the Act, and this indicates the severe penalties in respect to failing to comply with these statutory requirements.

The lease for the route of the CTRL is 999 years, while a groundwater abstraction site may continue to be utilized as a water resource *ad infinitum*, if contamination or derogation does not occur. Consequently, the Statutory Water Undertakers petitioned the Bill, over a number of issues, including the proposition that significant components of the public water resources for southeast England should not unnecessarily be put at risk, when cost-effective measures, in line with commonly perceived best practice, are available. Failure to

incorporate adequate mitigating measures was considered unprecedented in terms of contemporary design for a major transport link, which impact upon the most essential and vulnerable resources for both the economic and social health of the nation.

In order to define the most suitable mitigating measures and in preparation for Proof of Evidence, at All Party Parliamentary Select Committee, a structured approach was developed by the Statutory Water Undertakers working closely with the Agency. This approach included the definition of Groundwater Protection Zones, implementation of the Groundwater Protection Policy with hazard identification, risk assessment/legal precedents and cost–benefit analysis of a range of potential mitigation measures.

The identification of vulnerable groundwater resources and definition of public supply borehole Groundwater Protection Zones is the initial step in the evaluation of appropriate mitigating measures for any major construction or infrastructure development in the UK. In view of the size and complexity of the task of modelling GPZs for all the potentially impacted sources along the CTRL route, both the Statutory Water Undertakers and the Agency undertook numerical modelling to define source protection zones and subsequently agreed final zones along the route.

The identification of potential hazards (track side drainage, use of fill material, spillages, construction activities, weed killer, etc.) then enabled the interpretation of the Groundwater Protection Policy in terms of likely mitigation measures and codes of practice.

The use of risk assessment in order to define a quantitative statement of the probability of an adverse effect occurring and a judgement regarding its acceptability or tolerability is the natural progression of the Groundwater Protection Policy. A risk assessment for a major transport link such as the CTRL should consider both the probability of an adverse effect occurring and its consequences in both the construction and operational phases. In relation to the risk of groundwater contamination an adverse effect can be defined as a failure to meet Water Quality Regulations (HMSO 1989) drinking water standards and the population exposed to that risk for a public supply groundwater source.

The Statutory Water Undertakers completed a comprehensive review of the Promoters' risk assessment, which identified a number of important areas where the inclusion of additional information would enhance the risk assessment's level of rigour and therefore enable a more confident interpretation. Furthermore, with regard to the risk of public supply contamination the promoters based their decision making process on the application of an analysis of the probability of spillage with no consideration of consequences.

In terms of the probability of certain scenarios the Promoters' risk assessment was detailed and rigorous, but had been misapplied with regard to the potential for

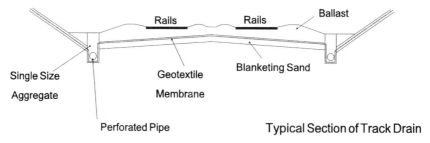

Fig. 3. Positive track drainage.

groundwater contamination. Consequently, in order to maintain continuity the Promoters' risk assessment was used by the Statutory Water Undertakers as a starting point, but was completed in terms of contamination risk to groundwater sources.

The Promoters stated an estimated total frequency of spillage of materials with the potential to cause groundwater pollution of between 1 in 10 000 years/route km and 1 in 3000 years/route km. However, since the CTRL passes across 88 km of vulnerable aquifers exploited for public water supply, a more correct expression of the frequency is between 1 in 114 years and 1 in 34 years at some point on the aquifer. However, careful scrutiny of the promoters' risk assessment identified a number of areas requiring refinement. These included freight traffic frequencies, possible non-compliance with the Eurotunnel Hazardous Goods Policy and the non-inclusions of certain accident types (i.e. fires) which may also result in the spillage of hazardous materials. Incorporating this series of factors in order to refine the original risk assessment and removing inappropriate assumptions, a conservative spillage frequency of between 1 in 34 and 1 in 8 years becomes apparent.

Although the risk was demonstrated to be significantly higher, the question of what constitutes a significant risk to an aquifer, and is therefore a suitable reference level, is clearly important in the context of this assessment and the necessity for judgements. No government guidance is available on this matter and precedents are essentially the only reliable mechanism available to determine suitable reference levels.

In 1990, a public inquiry into a planned waste treatment centre in Doncaster resulted in dismissal of the appeal on the grounds that a risk of 1 in 1000 years of contamination of an aquifer was too great. The Health and Safety Executive (HSE) guidelines state that, for land use planning purposes, the risk to an individual that a 'dangerous dose or worse' will be received should be less than ten in a million years.

In light of the above, the Statutory Water Undertakers judged a spillage frequency of between 1 in 1000 and 1 in 100 per year to be significant. Consequently, the revised risk assessment based entirely on the Union Rail Safety Case, augmented, where necessary, with informa-

tion from other Union Rail documentation and the HSE, indicated that the CTRL would represent a significant risk to certain public supply groundwater sources adjacent to the route, without adequate mitigating measures.

The final stage in the procedure is the completion of a cost–benefit analysis, in order that a suitable balance, or optimization, between required design features and cost may be compared. Sealed drainage, shown in Fig. 3, was identified as a principle design feature for the mitigation of potential groundwater contamination from either acute or chronic sources. The most rigorous requirements for positive drainage amounted to approximately £2.9 million. The loss of a single groundwater source as an asset only, may be in the region of £10–20 million. A complex optimization procedure was developed, which clearly demonstrated the long-term cost effectiveness of mitigation measures in reducing potential clean-up operations, fines and compensation pay outs.

Conclusions

The approach developed by the CTRL Promoters in order to evaluate the requirement for groundwater contamination mitigating measures focused on interpretation of the detailed risk assessment. The promoters concluded that 'the outcome of the exercise established that the CTRL as an operational railway did not represent an appreciable pollution risk and would not therefore infringe the fundamental basis of the Agency's Groundwater Protection Policy'.

The Statutory Water Undertakers and Environment Agency considered that while risk assessment methodologies should be an integral component of the decision making process, their use in isolation would be misleading. It was demonstrated that the promoters' own risk assessment could be further refined in order to show that the CTRL would constitute a major long-term risk to water resources, if suitable cost-effective mitigation measures were not incorporated within the design. In addition, no clear statements with regard to what constitutes an acceptable or tolerable risk existed, from either government or bodies with responsibilities for development planning. Therefore, in view of the nature of potential impacts to public health the precautionary principle should be adopted.

The Promoters ultimately recognized the case made by the Statutory Water Undertakers and the Environment Agency. Groundwater protection mitigating measures broadly in line with the Groundwater Protection Policy have been adopted by the main parties involved. The CTRL Bill represented one of the first applications of the Groundwater Protection Policy with regard to major transportation links and its vindication through this process has enhanced its status and is an important precedent for the future.

Finally, the CTRL Bill has highlighted the apparent paradox which exists with regard to statutory duties responsibilities and the protection of groundwater from contamination. Statutory Water Undertakers have a duty to attain specific standards in respect to both quality and sufficiency of water. However, the Statutory Water Undertakers have no statutory role with regard to protecting groundwater from contamination although they are responsible for the quality of water entering the public supply system.

Acknowledgements: The views expressed are those of the authors and not necessarily those of Thames Water Utilities Ltd or Southern Water Services. The authors are also grateful to Bob Edmunds of the Southern Region Environment Agency, and Mike Quint of Danes and Moore for the co-operation, advice and support in preparing both the work leading to, and drafting of, this paper.

References

HMSO 1989. *The Water Supply (Water Quality) Regulations 1989.* Statutory Instrument No. 1147. HMSO, London.

NRA 1992. *Policy and Practice for the Protection of Groundwater.* NRA Midlands Region, Solihull.

SECTION 3
SITE INVESTIGATION TECHNIQUES

Delineating the horizontal and vertical extent of hydrocarbon contamination using laser induced UV fluorescence

J. P. Hughes[1] & A. D. Taer[2]

[1] Chevron Research and Technology Company, Room 10-3650, PO Box 1627, Richmond, California 94802-0627, USA
[2] Fugro Geosciences, Inc., 6105 Rookin, Houston, Texas 77074, USA

Abstract. Before we can hope to successfully conduct a risk assessment, or select the proper technology for remediation at a contaminated site, we must first have a thorough understanding of the nature of the impacts at that site. This paper will present an overview of a field-proven, *in situ* site assessment technique based on laser induced UV fluorescence, that provides continuous, real time information on the distribution of hydrocarbons in the subsurface. The system can detect hydrocarbons regardless of whether they are located above or below the water table, and it gathers the data without generating any cuttings that could require costly disposal. This technology can also provide a qualitative 'fingerprint' of the hydrocarbons present at the site. Since the data are available in real time, adjustments to the site assessment programme can be made in the field. Examples of applications of this technology include using it as a screening tool to delineate both the horizontal and vertical extent of hydrocarbon contamination; estimating the volume of contaminated soil that may have to be addressed; or helping to select locations for more expensive confirmatory soil samples or permanent monitoring wells. Actual data from a number of sites will be presented to illustrate some of these applications.

Introduction

All of the currently available remedial technologies have some inherent limitations which tend to reduce their effectiveness in cleaning up contaminated sites. In addition to these inherent limitations, however, we often find that our problems are compounded by the fact that we poorly understand the nature and distribution of the contaminants in the subsurface. Although some sort of site assessment is typically conducted before remediation efforts begin, these site assessments are often limited to providing information on the general extent and distribution of contaminants. As an example, it is common in the US, during the various phases of site assessment, for soil samples to be collected, described and analysed, every 5 feet (1.5 m) during the installation of soil borings or monitoring wells. This protocol is obviously less expensive – in terms of analytical costs alone – than a continuous coring effort.

The drawback, of course, is that this technique could theoretically miss one or more contaminated zones, each as much as 5 feet (1.5 m) in thickness. Since these 'missing' zones might not be targeted by the selected remedial technology, an unknown source of contamination could remain in the aquifer. This could result in continual impacts to monitoring wells at the site, requiring the remediation system to stay in operation for decades.

In the US there has recently been an increased effort to incorporate a risk assessment step in the decision making process regarding remediation of impacted sites. This movement has resulted from a recognition by many, that not all contaminated sites generate the same level of risk to human health or the environment. Given that condition, an effort is being made to prioritize work at sites based on the risk they present. The driving mechanism is the desire to focus our time and resources where they are most needed.

A risk assessment involves a number of steps, including identifying the presence of chemicals of concern, identifying the presence of completed pathways to potential receptors, identifying the concentrations of those chemicals that the receptors could be exposed to, and finally, comparing the risks resulting from that exposure, to generally agreed upon levels of 'acceptable' risk. The information needed to conduct such a process can only be gathered during a complete assessment of the site.

Before we can hope to either successfully conduct a risk assessment, or select the proper technology for remediation at a contaminated site, we must therefore have a thorough understanding of the nature and distribution of the hydrocarbons in the subsurface. The focus of this paper is to describe an assessment technique designed to cost-effectively provide the kind of detailed information necessary to make these decisions.

HUGHES, J. P. & TAER, A. D. 1998. Delineating the horizontal and vertical extent of hydrocarbon contamination using laser induced UV fluorescence. *In*: LERNER, D. N. & WALTON, N. R. G. (eds) 1998. *Contaminated Land and Groundwater: Future Directions*. Geological Society, London, Engineering Geology Special Publications, **14**, 111–117.

UV fluorescence and hydrocarbons

Petroleum-based substances containing aromatic hydrocarbons (compounds that contain single, double or multiple rings) will fluoresce when excited by ultraviolet light. Petroleum fuels such as gasoline, diesel, kerosene and heating oils, as well as other petroleum substances such as coal tar, creosote and crude oils, all contain these aromatic hydrocarbons and will therefore fluoresce. The intensity of this fluorescence will be proportional to the contaminant concentration. Commercial laboratories have long taken advantage of this phenomenon to identify, and to some extent, fingerprint crude oils and certain refined products. In the oil production industry, fluorescence has been widely used to identify the presence of hydrocarbons in soil samples brought to the surface while drilling both exploratory and development wells. In spite of its potential usefulness, however, fluorescence, with very few exceptions, has not been routinely used by the environmental industry as a site assessment technique. Two factors have probably contributed to the limited use of this technology. The first is the general lack of awareness of potential benefits of using fluorescence by workers in the environmental field. The second factor has probably been the lack, until recently, of a commercially available field tool, designed to apply this technology.

The ROST^{tm} system

General background and applications

This paper describes a commercially available technology designed to rapidly collect real time, *in situ* data on the distribution of hydrocarbons in the subsurface, using laser induced fluorescence (LIF). The Rapid Optical Screening Tool (ROST^{tm}) system is a field-rugged fluorescence spectrometer, which in its current configuration, is designed to be coupled with a conventional cone penetrometer (CPT) rig. Since September 1994, ROST systems have completed more than 50 000 linear feet of LIF–CPT testing to assess subsurface contamination at more than 50 commercial sites in 16 states in the US and in five foreign countries, including the UK. A ROST system is currently stationed in England.

This technology can provide a number of benefits. First, the availability of real time data means that the scope of the delineation work may be adjusted in the field, so that site characterization can be completed often with a single mobilization, saving both time and money. Secondly, since the LIF data can accurately identify both the horizontal and vertical distribution of petroleum hydrocarbons in the subsurface, one can use the data either to support a risk assessment effort or, if necessary, to help select an appropriate remediation system designed to target the zone of impact. In addition, an accurate picture of the distribution of hydrocarbons in the subsurface can allow you to accurately estimate the volume of impacted soil that may have to be either excavated or remediated *in situ*. Finally, the data generated by the LIF–CPT system can also be used to pick the most appropriate locations to collect soil samples for analysis, or to place permanent monitoring wells. Examples of several of these applications are given in a later section.

Cone penetrometer testing

The cone penetrometer test (CPT) is performed simultaneously with each ROST sounding. The CPT soundings are performed in accordance with ASTM Standard D 3441 to identify site statigraphy. Testing is performed by hydraulically pushing an electronically instrumented probe into the subsurface, using the weight of the CPT vehicle. CPT trucks typically range in capacity from under 10 to greater than 30 tonnes.

The small-diameter CPT probe has a conical tip at the end, which typically consists of a 10 cm^2 base area with an apex angle of 60°. A friction sleeve with a standard area of 150 cm is located above the tip. The cone is pushed into the ground at a constant rate of 2 cm s^{-1}. Signals from the cone tip (tip resistance) and friction sleeve (friction) are sent to the surface through cables located within the centre of the push rods. The signals are processed by a computer in the CPT rig and real time data are displayed on a computer screen in the vehicle as the sounding proceeds. The data are evaluated by the computer using a soil behaviour classification chart (Robertson & Campanella 1986), to produce a stratigraphic log of the sounding. A paper copy of both the CPT data and stratigraphic chart can be printed in the field at the completion of each sounding. An example of the stratigraphic log is included in Fig. 1.

Laser induced fluorescence

Fluorescence versus depth. The ROST laser induced fluorescence system consists of a tuneable laser mounted in the CPT rig. The laser is connected via a fibre optic cable, to a small-diameter sapphire window mounted flush with the side of the cone penetrometer probe. The laser and associated equipment transmit 50 pulses of light per second through the fibre optic cable to the window. The laser light passes through the window and is absorbed by any aromatic hydrocarbon molecules on the soil in contact with the window as the probe is advanced. A portion of the fluorescence emitted from any contaminants encountered is returned through the sapphire window and conveyed by a second fibre optic cable to a detection system within the CPT rig. The emitted fluorescence resulting from the pulsed laser light is averaged into one reading per 2.5 cm interval, and is reported continuously on a computer monitor as fluorescence versus depth (FVD). Vertical resolution is

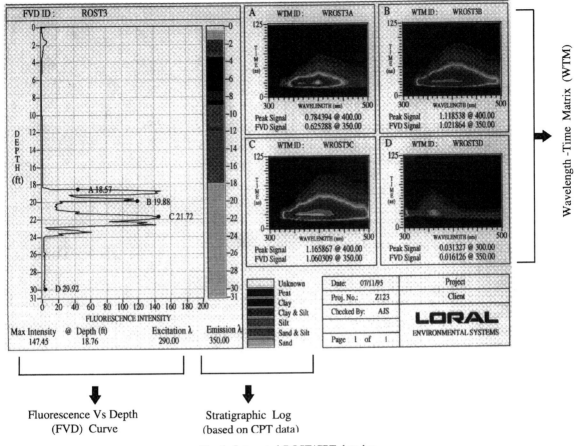

Fig. 1. Integrated ROST/CPT data log.

therefore on the order of 2.5 cm. A hard copy of the FVD log can be printed in the field immediately following the completion of each sounding (Taer 1996). An example of a FVD log is also included in Fig. 1.

Wavelength–time Matrix. In addition to the FVD plot, the ROST system also has another main data acquisition and display mode, called the wavelength–time matrix (WTM). In the FVD mode the emission response of the formation is monitored at a single wavelength. WTMs, on the other hand, are acquired by stopping the advancement of the CPT–LIF probe and measuring the emission response of the fluorescing hydrocarbons over a range of wavelengths – typically between 300 nm and 500 nm – in 10 nm increments. It takes roughly two minutes to stop and acquire data for a WTM.

WTMs provide a three-dimensional representation that relates fluorescence intensity to both emission wavelength and to fluorescence decay time, following the pulsed excitation. In the display mode, the emission wavelength is shown on the x-axis and fluorescence decay time on the y-axis. The intensity information is represented by line contours or their colour-coded equivalents. Many common fuel products exhibit characteristic WTM signatures which can be used for qualitative analysis and identification purposes (St Germain & Gillispie 1995). In effect then, the WTM mode of the ROST system has the ability to produce a fingerprint, of sorts, of the petroleum encountered in the subsurface. WTMs from your site can be compared with WTMs of common petroleum products (some examples of which are shown in Fig. 2), or else correlated to WTMs generated from soil or hydrocarbon samples that have already been recovered and fingerprinted from that site.

The wavelength at which the maximum fluorescence occurs (peak signal) on the WTM is a general indicator of the petroleum hydrocarbon composition. With increasing molecular weight, the peak signal of aromatic hydrocarbons shifts to higher wavelengths (Berlman 1971). When fresh hydrocarbons weather or biodegrade, they typically begin to lose their lighter ends first. When this occurs, the peak signal on the WTM tends to shift to the

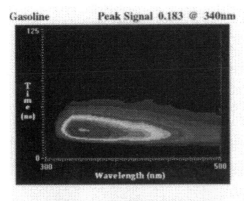

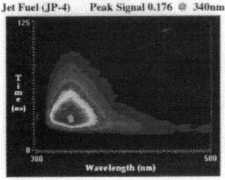

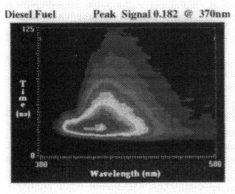

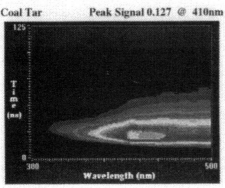

Fig. 2. WTM signatures of common petroleum products.

right (i.e. to a higher wavelength). WTMs can therefore sometimes be used to distinguish between fresh (or newer) and weathered (or older) spills.

Field data and applications

Vertical distribution of the hydrocarbons

Figure 3 shows two real time, field-generated LIF plots collected during a recent site assessment. Figure 3(a) shows a plot of fluorescence versus depth from the surface. Note that two distinct zones of contamination were discovered, one from roughly 5 to 18 feet (1.5–5.5 m), and the other from 26 to 35 feet (8.0–10.7 m). The contamination in the upper zone had been anticipated based on other data from the site. The presence of petroleum products in the lower zone, however, was unexpected, and indicated a larger problem existed at this site. Looking at the FVD curve in Fig. 3 consider for a moment the data that would have been generated from a conventional boring programme, with samples collected at 5 foot intervals. Since the sample taken at a depth of 5 feet (1.5 m) from the surface would probably have shown no petroleum impacts, the first indication of contamination with a conventional programme would have been at a depth of 10 feet (3 m). The sample taken at a depth of 15 feet (4.6 m) would also have indicated contamination, although the more highly impacted zone between 11 and 14 feet (3.4 and 4.3 m) would not have been apparent. Based on clean samples at depths of 20 and 25 feet (6.1 and 7.6 m), the conventional boring programme would probably have been terminated. The conclusion from such a programme would have been that, at this site, we only had some low level petroleum impacts from a depth of roughly 10 to 15 feet (3.0 to 3.7 m).

Selecting a remediation technology

A more conservative interpretation of the data shown in Fig. 3 would admit that the contamination probably started somewhere between 5 and 10 feet (1.5 and 3.0 m), and most likely extended to somewhere between 15 and 20 feet (4.6 and 7.6 m). Even with such an interpretation, however, the variations in hydrocarbon concentrations between 5 and 15 feet (1.5 and 4.6 m) would not have been noticed. More importantly, the lower zone of impact from 26 to 35 feet (7.9 to 10.7 m) would have been completely missed altogether. It is very unlikely that any remedial system selected for this site would have been designed to target this lower zone. Even if the technology had been successful in remediating the upper zone, the lower zone would have remained, providing a long-term source of contaminants.

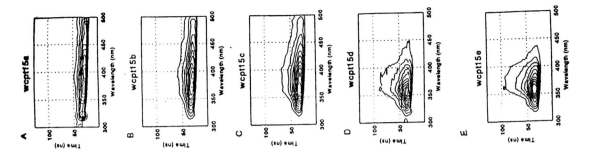

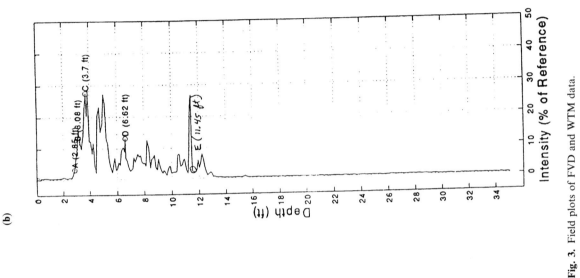

(b)

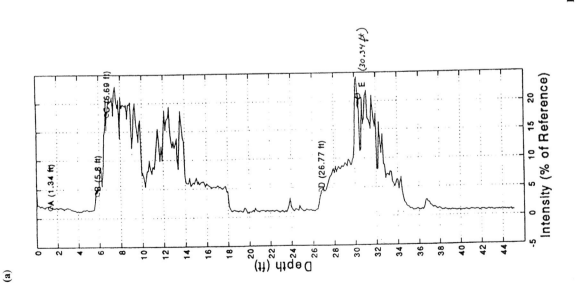

(a)

Fig. 3. Field plots of FVD and WTM data.

Let us assume, for example, that the upper (detected) zone was above the water table, and that the lower (undetected) zone lay below the water table. In that case, we might have selected some sort of vapour extraction system as our remedial technology, since the only contaminants that we were aware of, resided in the unsaturated zone. Since a vapour extraction system would not be able to remove hydrocarbons from the lower (saturated) zone, they would have remained as a long-term source of contaminant mass.

As an alternative, we might also imagine a case where a conventional sampling effort might have missed a contaminated interval in the unsaturated zone, but detected a second contaminated interval in the saturated zone. In such a case, we might select a pump and treat remediation system. While we might be able to clean up the lower (saturated) zone with such a technology, the hydrocarbons in the unsaturated zone would have remained as a long-term source of contaminants that could migrate into basements or later leach into, and thereby recontaminate the saturated zone.

Field decisions

For the purposes of this discussion, let us imagine a field programme designed to install a series of ten, equally spaced step out probes, looking for the edge of a hydrocarbon plume. With a conventional boring programme, all ten locations would be drilled, and for each, samples would be collected and analysed. The data would then be examined to determine the boundaries of the plume. Let us look at two of the possible outcomes of such a programme. If all ten of the borings show petroleum impacts, then the field effort would probably have to be remobilized later, in order to finally locate the plume boundaries. At the opposite end of the spectrum, we might imagine a data set which showed a very small impacted zone, with a number of the step out wells being clean. In such a case, some of those wells would, in hindsight, have been unnecessary. If LIF–CPT real time logs had been available in the first example, a decision could have been made in the field to expand the delineation effort until the edge of the plume (both horizontally and vertically) had been located. The cost of an additional field mobilization, and the associated time loss could then have been avoided. In the second example the real time LIF–CPT logs would have shown that the plume was much smaller than anticipated. In this situation, a field decision could have been made to drop the unnecessary probes once the edge of the plume had been reached, thus resulting in a potential cost savings.

Variations in hydrocarbon composition

Figure 3(b) shows another field plot, showing the FVD curve on the left and a series of WTMs on the right. The individual WTMs are marked A through E. The depths at which they were run are shown on the FVD curve. The site at which these data were collected is a former oil field. Because of problems associated with producing the heavy crude in this field, diesel fuel was pumped downhole to lower the viscosity of the crude. At the beginning of the site assessment, a crude oil problem was suspected, but it was unknown if the diesel pipelines had leaked. The WTM marked 'A' shows a signature characteristic of crude oil. The WTM at the bottom (E), on the other hand, shows a signature more characteristic of diesel fuel. As you go deeper from the surface, the WTMs show that the composition of the petroleum contaminant slowly changes, from mostly crude (A), to a progressive mixture of crude and diesel (B through D), to mostly diesel (E). WTMs would also be able to differentiate between different product types in a horizontal plane, as well as a vertical direction. At some sites, WTMs have been used to differentiate between adjacent or overlapping plumes of different hydrocarbon types.

Summary

When the contaminants of concern at a site consist of aromatic hydrocarbons, the ROST technology can provide a way of rapidly collecting cost-effective, high-resolution information on both the horizontal and vertical distribution of those contaminants in the subsurface, without generating any cuttings that may require costly disposal. This information can be used for a variety of purposes, including the following:

- using the data to support a risk assessment effort;
- modifying the site assessment data gathering efforts while still in the field, (based on the real time results being generated), in order to eliminate either unnecessary fieldwork or the likelihood of having to remobilize to the field later to collect additional data;
- making accurate estimates of the volume of impacted soil that will either have to be excavated, or remediated *in situ*;
- using the information gathered on the vertical distribution of hydrocarbons in the subsurface to help select an appropriate remedial technology that is capable of targeting all of the contaminated zones;
- using the 'fingerprinting' capabilities of the WTM plots to either help distinguish between impacts caused by adjacent plumes of different hydrocarbon types, or to help distinguish between plumes of fresh or weathered hydrocarbons;
- using the screening information to help select locations for a limited number of borings to collect soil samples for confirmatory analysis, or to accurately place and optimally screen, a limited number of groundwater monitoring wells.

References

BERLMAN, I. B. 1971. *Handbook of Fluorescence Spectra of Aromatic Molecules*. Academic, New York.

ROBERTSON, P. K. & CAMPANELLA, R. G. 1986. *Guidelines for the Use, Interpretation, and Application of the CPT and CPTU*. Soil Mechanics Series No. 105, University of British Columbia, Vancouver, BC.

ST GERMAIN, R. W. & GILLESPIE, G. D. 1995. Real-time continuous measurement of subsurface petroleum contamination with the rapid optical screening tool (ROST^{TM}). *Proceedings of Field Screening Methods for Hazardous Wastes and Toxic Chemicals*, 467–477.

TAER, A. D. 1996. In-situ hydrocarbon delineation using laser-induced fluorescence. *Proceedings of the Sixth West Coast Conference on Contaminated Soils and Groundwater, Part III*. Newport Beach, California, 11–14 March, Session VII.

Evaluation of inter-organisational sampling trials on contaminated land: comparison of two contrasting sites

A. Argyraki & M. H. Ramsey

Environmental Geology Research, Department of Geology, Imperial College, London SW7 2BP, UK

Abstract. The measurement process in environmental studies on contaminated land comprises sampling and analysis with the objective of estimating the values of the analyte concentrations. The estimated mean concentration has a real variation but also a variation due to errors originating from sampling and analysis. Inter-organizational trials, in the form of collaborative trials and proficiency testing, is a well established methodology for the estimation of the analytical uncertainty. However, such trials applied to sampling are in a very early stage of development. The objectives of inter-organisational sampling trials are to reveal discrepancies due to sampling at a particular site, to estimate measurement uncertainty on the estimates of mean metal concentrations at the site and ultimately to improve reproducibility of the participants' results. The very first pilot sampling trial was conducted on a smelter-contaminated site in Derbyshire. The results showed the feasibility of conducting sampling trials and also that errors originating from sampling tend to be much greater than the analytical errors. A second inter-organizational sampling trial was conducted on Hounslow Heath, West London, which is an old landfill site with different contamination characteristics. The results from both trials have shown large discrepancies in estimates of mean metal concentrations in soils by factors up to 2.5 times. The role of heterogeneity of the distribution of the contaminants is a limiting factor when conducting such trials and their usefulness in measuring uncertainty of metal concentration at a particular site has been demonstrated.

Introduction

Inter-laboratory trials are an essential part of analytical quality assurance. There are three kinds: the collaborative trial (essentially for validating analytical methods) the proficiency test (for testing the performance of laboratories) and the certification trial (to assign certified values to a reference material). It has been proposed that all three have an equivalent in the estimation of sampling quality (Thompson & Ramsey 1995).

This paper reports the results of the first two inter-organizational sampling trials, each one of them comprising a collaborative trial and a proficiency test. They were conducted for the purpose of showing the general feasibility of the approach, on two sites with different contamination characteristics, i.e. on an area of land contaminated by smelting in Derbyshire and on a landfill site with a lower level of contamination in West London. The significance of the first trial to the general principles of sampling quality have been discussed elsewhere (Argyraki et al. 1995; Ramsey et al. 1995b). In this paper a comparison of the results from the two sites has been made.

Two types of trials were tested at both sites: a collaborative trial in sampling (CTS) and a sampling proficiency test (SPT). For the CTS the participants separately visited the sites and applied the sampling protocol supplied to collect top-soil samples, to quantify within sampler variability. The samples were then analysed in duplicate under randomized repeatability conditions (i.e. in a single run in one laboratory). The resultant data were analysed statistically by nested analysis of variance (ANOVA) (Analytical Methods Committee 1989) to provide estimates of the analytical repeatability standard deviation, the sampling repeatability standard deviation and the between-sampler standard deviation. In this way the within- and between-sampler precision of the estimates of the mean concentration of selected metals over the sites could be quantified. The estimation of the mean concentration of metals in top-soil was selected as the objective in these sampling trials to give a simple statistic for comparison. More realistic yet more complicated objectives such as spatial locations of contamination hot spots should be possible in future trials.

With the SPTs the performance of the participants was assessed when they were using sampling protocols of their choice for the estimation of the average metal concentrations in the sampling targets. The analytical results of this trial were converted to z-scores, as recommended by the International Harmonised Protocol for Proficiency Testing (Horwitz 1988), using appropriate values of assigned value and target standard deviation selected on the basis of fitness-for-purpose.

ARGYRAKI, A. & RAMSEY, M. H. 1998. Evaluation of inter-organisational sampling trials on contaminated land: comparison of two contrasting sites. *In*: LERNER, D. N. & WALTON, N. R. G. (eds) 1998. *Contaminated Land and Groundwater: Future Directions.* Geological Society, London, Engineering Geology Special Publications, **14**, 119–125.

Methodology

Site descriptions

The contaminated land used as a sampling target for the first inter-organizational trial is a sub-rectangular field about 60×150 m near Wirksworth in Derbyshire, UK. The heavy metal pollution derives from the use of the site for lead smelting between the 14th and 16th centuries (Maskall & Thornton 1993), with lead concentrations reaching a maximum of 30 000 $\mu g\,g^{-1}$. Intensive sampling of the top-soils at this site and an adjoining area has been discussed for the comparison of different sampling protocols (Ramsey *et al.* 1995*a*). The field has not been ploughed for at least 45 years and is currently used as pasture for grazing horses. There are no visible signs of the ancient contamination, but there are possible minor modern sources in the form of an old shed with a galvanized roof and some abandoned agricultural machinery.

The second sampling trial on contaminated land took place in a 100×100 m square on Hounslow Heath, West London. The site has a long history of potential contamination due to its use for gravel extraction followed by back-filling of the pits with largely domestic wastes during the 1950s and 1960s. The particular sampling square selected is a part of Hounslow Heath which is currently used for general recreation.

Samplers

Nine organizations listed below from commerce, government, local authority and university departments sent samplers to the sites over a period of time. The samplers were given an explanation of the aims and intentions of the project before the sampling period, and the exact protocol for the collaborative trials immediately before commencing sampling. No sampler observed any other during the sampling exercise to maintain statistical independence.

Preparation and chemical analysis of the samples

The collected samples from all the trials were prepared for chemical analysis at Imperial College, except for the samples from the first proficiency test in Derbyshire. Each aggregate sample was dried at 65°C and broken down to individual grains with a pestle and mortar. The fraction passing a 2 mm plastic sieve was subsampled using a splitter to produce a 50 g sample. This sample was ground in a Tema mill to $<100\,\mu$m to comprise the laboratory sample.

The test portions (0.1 g) were treated with a mixture of nitric and perchloric acids to solubilize the analytes that were presented for analysis in dilute hydrochloric acid solution (Thompson & Walsh 1989). Twenty-five elements were determined in the solutions by ICP-AES.

Internal analytical quality control was provided by the inclusion of reagent blanks, six appropriate certified reference materials and duplicate analysis of samples.

The samples from the proficiency test in Derbyshire were prepared and analysed by the participants using analytical methods of their choice. The analytical bias was studied separately by distributing a matrix-matched reference material (HRM 31) to be analysed by the participants in the same analytical run with their samples.

Results and discussion

First sampling trial in Derbyshire

First CTS. The sampling protocol used by all the samplers for this trial was a 'W' shaped design, collecting the sample increments at the vertices, at three equidistant points along each leg (MAFF 1979). This sampling protocol is frequently used by soil samplers and can be quickly and simply executed. The statistical analysis of the results focused on two elements with contrasting characteristics in respect to their concentrations in top-soil. Lead has high concentrations reaching a maximum of 30 000 $\mu g\,g^{-1}$ and great variability across the site, but copper has concentrations closer to the natural background (20 $\mu g\,g^{-1}$). The concentrations for lead and copper determined in the laboratory samples are presented in Table 1. The statistics are given in Table 2.

The data for copper show that the element is evenly distributed throughout the field. The sampling standard deviations are small and comparable with the analytical error. The sampling reproducibility ($s_{R(s)} = 2.2\,\mu g\,g^{-1}$), which expresses differences between the samplers, is higher than the sampling repeatability ($s_{r(s)} = 1.4\,\mu g\,g^{-1}$), which represents variations in the performance of a single sampler. This is similar to the analogous situation encountered in collaborative trials in chemical analysis. The sampling relative standard deviations are reasonably small (3.7% analytical RSD, 4.7% sampling repeatability RSD) and the sampling protocol could therefore be regarded as 'fit-for-purpose'.

This is not the case for lead, for which the results reflect extreme variations in the concentrations. The analytical RSD of 3.7% gives good precision; however, differences between duplicate samples dominate giving sampling repeatability RSD of 25.4%. The fitness-for-purpose of this sampling protocol for lead at this site is therefore questionable.

First SPT. The nine participants collected top-soil samples from the field by applying sampling protocols of their own choice. No sampler observed the actions of any other during sampling and no particular depth of sampling was defined by the organizers. The participants

Table 1. *Data from the first CTS, Derbyshire* $(\mu g\,g^{-1})$

Participant	S1A1 Cu	S1A1 Pb	S1A2 Cu	S1A2 Pb	S2A1 Cu	S2A1 Pb	S2A2 Cu	S2A2 Pb
1	35	5871	33	6114	30	6842	29	6 541
2	31	7366	30	7152	28	6079	29	5 890
3	32	6113	35	6369	33	9826	33	10 451
4	28	6707	29	6867	26	5647	28	5 582
5	29	5218	28	5102	28	5953	27	5 642
6	30	7016	29	7015	31	7978	29	7 455
7	26	4779	25	4869	29	8166	29	8 015
8	32	3771	31	3964	33	8271	30	8 359
9	33	6043	31	5977	31	7915	29	7 851

S1, S2: sampling duplicates A1, A2: analytical duplicates.

were asked to analyse the samples and to report the values for lead and copper concentrations to the organizers, along with the analytical determination of the common reference material (HRM 31).

The estimation of bias between participants that is described in the International Harmonised Protocol (Horwitz 1988) uses z-scores. This requires the definition of an assigned value of concentration, X, and a target standard deviation, s. The X value for this sampling target was derived from the pilot study of this field in which a high density sampling scheme was employed, collecting samples every 10 m on average (Fig. 1). The assigned values were calculated to be 6296 $\mu g\,g^{-1}$ for lead and 28 $\mu g\,g^{-1}$ for copper. These values of the mean concentrations of the metals in top-soil of the field were the best estimates of the 'true' values since the 'consensus of experts' suggested by the harmonized protocol was unavailable to be used as the assigned value. Any error in the assigned value, would not substantially affect the degree of scatter measured between the concentration values reported by the participants, but would affect estimates of bias for

each participant. The target standard deviation, s, was arbitrarily set at 20% of the assigned value based on a broad estimate of fitness-for-purpose (i.e. 1259 $\mu g\,g^{-1}$ for Pb and 5.6 $\mu g\,g^{-1}$ for Cu).

The z-score is given by $z = (x - X)/s$, where x is the participants' reported result, X is the assigned value and s is the target value for standard deviation (Table 3). For lead, participant number 6 had a score that falls outside the range ± 2 ($z_6 = 4.2$), so the performance of this organization is considered to be unsatisfactory. For copper, participant number 2, with $z_2 = -3.2$, has the most unsatisfactory performance.

The estimates of concentration reported by the participants were also assessed for agreement with the assigned values for the field and the bias was calculated. Four of the participants reported results significantly different from the assigned mean concentration for lead, and three of the participants reported results significantly different for copper using the t-test with a 95% confidence interval.

The estimates of mean Pb concentrations for the site show a wide range, varying by a factor of 2.8. This

Table 2. *Statistics from the first CTS* $(\mu g\,g^{-1})$

Statistic	Cu Classical	Cu Robust	Pb Classical	Pb Robust
Grand mean	30	30	6618	6575
$S_{r(a)}$	1.1	1.1	245	165
$S_{r(s)}$	1.4	1.2	1683	1822
S_{bs}	1.7	2.1	0	0
$S_{R(a)}$	2.2	2.4	1683	1822
$RSD_{r(a)}$	3.7%	3.7%	3.7%	2.5%
$RSD_{r(s)}$	4.7%	4.0%	25.4%	27.7%
$RSD_{R(s)}$	7.3%	8.0%	25.4%	27.7%

$S_{r(a)}$, analytical repeatability standard deviation; $S_{r(s)}$, sampling repeatability standard deviation; s_{bs}, between-sampler standard deviation; $S_{R(s)}$, sampling reproducibility standard deviation; $RSD_{r(a)}$, $RSD_{r(s)}$, $RSD_{R(s)}$, relative standard deviations.

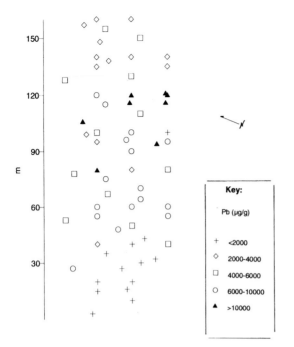

Fig. 1. Map showing the sample locations and concentrations of Pb in soil from the pilot study of the field. Average spacing of sampling points is approximately 10 m.

due to the analysis of one participant (number 6). The robust mean of the lead results on the field samples ($6171 \mu g\, g^{-1}$) is close to the assigned value ($6296 \mu g\, g^{-1}$) so there is no evidence for overall bias, when the information from all the participants is combined.

Second sampling trial on Hounslow Heath

The study of the results of this trial focused on four elements: lead, zinc, cadmium and cobalt. The first three of these elements showed high concentrations in soil, as might be expected from the previous use of the land as a landfill site. Cobalt, on the other hand, had concentrations on the Heath that were within the normal range in soils ($0.5–65 \mu g\, g^{-1}$) (Alloway 1995) and could be used for comparisons with the contaminated elements in the interpretation of the results.

Second CTS. The common sampling protocol used by the nine participants on Hounslow Heath was a regular grid, taking a total of 36 sample increments every 20 m. This protocol was applied in duplicate to produce two composite soil samples from the field. Subsequently the samples were analysed in duplicate within a single batch and the resultant data were analysed statistically using nested ANOVA. The elemental concentrations determined in the laboratory samples are recorded in Table 4. The statistics are given in Table 5.

The data for cobalt suggest that this element is evenly distributed across the site. The sampling standard deviations are comparable with the analytical error. The differences between samplers are greater than the variations in the performance of a single sampler. This is described statistically with the sampling reproducibility standard deviation, $s_{R(s)} = 0.9$, being greater than the

clearly indicates that for Pb there is a severe problem of inter-organizational reproducibility in the measurement of contaminated land at this site. The analytical aspect of the bias shown by the analysis of HRM 31 also shows a wide disparity between participants, but this is mainly

Table 3. *Analytical data ($\mu g\, g^{-1}$), % bias from the grand mean and z-scores from the first SPT, Derbyshire*

Participant	Cu			Pb		
	Reported value	% bias	z-score	Reported value	% bias	z-score
1	29	7	0.3	4 595	−26	−1.4
2	<10	−63	−3.2	4 650	−25	−1.4
3	31	15	0.6	6 532	6	0.2
4	27	0	−0.3	5 185	−16	−0.8
5	27	0	0	5 936	4	−0.3
6	29	7	0.3	11 571	88	4.2
7	–	–	–	5 968	−3	−0.3
8	31	15	0.6	4 203	−32	−1.7
9	31	15	0.6	6 900	12	1.5
Mean	27			6 171		
St. Dev.	7			2 223		
Tar. St. Dev.	5.6			1 259		

Table 4. *Data from the second CTS, London* $(\mu g\,g^{-1})$

| Participant | S1A1 | | S1A2 | | S2A1 | | S2A2 | |
	Cu	Pb	Cu	Pb	Cu	Pb	Cu	Pb
1	13	230	16	224	14	329	15	340
2	13	1074	13	1017	14	314	14	330
3	14	284	14	359	16	310	15	302
4	15	333	16	306	14	234	13	233
5	16	308	14	298	16	482	14	558
6	13	311	13	262	13	325	14	326
7	13	285	13	276	13	269	13	287
8	13	273	13	471	13	260	13	257
9	14	413	15	608	14	283	13	309

S1, S2: sampling duplicates A1, A2: analytical duplicates.

sampling repeatability standard deviation, $s_{r(s)}=0.6$ (using the robust estimates). The sampling relative standard deviations are reasonably small (4.3% within samplers and 6.6% between samplers). The sampling protocol could be regarded therefore as fit-for-purpose for this element at this site.

On the other hand, the results for lead reflect extreme variations in its concentration. The analytical precision is reasonably good ($RSD_{r(a)}=8.33\%$ for the robust results) but variations between duplicate samples are so great ($RSD_{r(s)}=33.9\%$) that they obscure the difference between the samplers. In this instance the sampling protocol is not fit-for-purpose due to the great heterogeneity of the site in respect to the lead concentration.

The zinc and cadmium data reflect boundary conditions with very small differences between the between-sampler and within-sampler variations. The heterogeneity of the field in respect to the concentrations of these elements is just on the limit for judging the sampling protocol as fit for purpose by this criterion.

Second SPT. The analytical measurements from the proficiency test on Hounslow Heath are recorded in Table 6. The general levels of contamination for lead are below the ICRCL trigger concentration for gardens and allotments of $500\,\mu g\,g^{-1}$. The results for zinc and cadmium range from below to above the regulatory limits. For zinc, only one participant (number 2) gave a result lower than the phytotoxic concentration limit of $300\,\mu g\,g^{-1}$. For cadmium only, participant number 8 gave a concentration estimate higher than the regulatory limit of $5\,\mu g\,g^{-1}$. Good agreement between the participants can be observed for cobalt, with maximum bias for participant number 3 of -8.9% from the grand mean.

In terms of the proficiency test the assigned values for the conversion of the results to z-scores were calculated to be $13.5\,\mu g\,g^{-1}$ for cobalt, $358\,\mu g\,g^{-1}$ for lead, $365\,\mu g\,g^{-1}$ for zinc and $4.7\,\mu g\,g^{-1}$ for cadmium. These values are the grand means of the metal concentrations in soil from all the participants. They were the best estimates of the 'true' values since the 'consensus of experts' suggested by the

Table 5. *Statistics from the second CTS, London* $(\mu g\,g^{-1})$

| Statistic | Cu | | Pb | |
	Classical	Robust	Classical	Robust
Grand mean	13.9	13.9	363	336
$S_{r(a)}$	0.6	0.6	52	28
$S_{r(s)}$	0.5	0.6	186	114
S_{bs}	0.6	0.7	0	0
$S_{R(s)}$	0.78	0.92	186.00	114.00
$RSD_{r(a)}$	4.3%	4.3%	14.33%	8.3%
$RSD_{r(s)}$	3.6%	4.3%	51.2%	33.9%
$RSD_{R(s)}$	5.6%	6.6%	51.2%	33.9%

$S_{r(a)}$, analytical repeatability standard deviation; $S_{r(s)}$, sampling repeatability standard deviation; S_{bs}, between-sampler standard deviation; $S_{R(s)}$, sampling reproducibility standard deviation; $RSD_{r(a)}$, $RSD_{r(s)}$, $RSD_{R(s)}$, relative standard deviations.

Table 6.   *Analytical data ($\mu g\,g^{-1}$), % bias from the grand mean and z-scores from the second SPT, London*

Participant	Cu			Pb		
	Reported value	% bias	z-score	Reported value	% bias	z-score
1	13.8	2.2	0.11	372	3.9	0.20
2	12.8	−5.2	−0.26	294	−17.9	−0.89
3	12.3	−8.9	−0.44	311	−13.1	−0.66
4	14	3.7	0.19	465	29.9	1.49
5	13.8	2.2	0.11	441	23.2	1.16
6	13.3	−1.5	−0.7	293	−18.2	−0.91
7	13.8	2.2	0.11	311	−13.1	−0.66
8	14.3	5.9	0.30	444	24.0	1.20
9	13.3	−1.5	−0.07	294	−17.9	−0.89
Mean	13.5			358		
St. Dev.	0.6			73		
Tar. St. Dev.	2.7			71.7		

harmonized protocol was unavailable to be used as the assigned value. The target standard deviation, s, was arbitrarily set at 20% of the assigned value based on a broad estimate of fitness-for-purpose.

For most of the elements z-scores were within the ±2 range, except for participant number 8 with high z-scores for Cd and Zn. However, it should be noted that a z-score outside the ±2 range does not necessarily mean bad performance because of the high heterogeneity in this particular site. Unlike proficiency testing for analytical laboratories, it seems logical to introduce a factor to allow for the heterogeneity of the sampling target, in the selection of a fitness-for-purpose criterion.

Comparison of trials at the two sites

From the results of the two CTSs at the two sites there are clearly very wide discrepancies for each site in the estimates of the mean concentration of lead made by the nine participants, varying by a factor of up to 2.5 (first CTS). The reasons for this may include the variations in interpretation of the sampling protocol that were observed by the organizers. The accuracy of the marking out of the site varied from those who paced out the intervals, judging directions by eye, and those who used measuring tapes and canes to interpret the protocols more rigorously.

Probably the main cause of the bias, however, was caused by the susceptibility of the protocols to heterogeneity in the distribution of lead in both sampling targets. Relatively small variations in the exact location of the sampling points could easily result in a small 'hot spot' of contamination being included or excluded, thus affecting the composition of the composite sample. The 'W' design used in the first trial is more susceptible to heterogeneity. The large differences in the orientation of the 'W' would be expected to have such an effect, but

there was no clear systematic variation of mean concentration with particular orientation.

The regular grid used in the second CTS was expected to increase the agreement between the results because it covers the sampling area more evenly and with a higher sample density. However, the degree of heterogeneity on a landfill site is likely to be greater, so that small scale variation in lead concentration may still have been the dominant factor. The contrasting agreement of the Cu and Co mean values for the smelter and the landfill site respectively and the lack of spatial variation in these elements further support this idea. The CTS has been shown therefore to be a useful method for testing suitability of sampling protocols for a particular purpose at a particular site, rather than testing the performance of the participants.

Individual organizations, however, do show bias outside the assigned values as shown by the z-score plots of both proficiency tests. Scores can be considered satisfactory between −2 and +2, which is equivalent to being within 20% of the assigned value. For the estimation of mean lead at the smelting site, four out of the nine organizations failed to meet this 'fitness for purpose' criteria. For organization 6 this is dominantly an analytical problem (mirrored in analysis of HRM 31) but for organizations 1, 2 and 8 this failure seems to arise from the field sampling. At the landfill site all the participants 'scored' within the ±2 z-score range for lead and the general level of agreement ($s = 20\%$) was improved from the first SPT in Derbyshire ($s = 36\%$).

Conclusions

The methodology of sampling trials which were first applied to a site in Derbyshire heavily contaminated by smelting (Argyraki *et al.* 1995; Ramsey *et al.* 1995*b*) are equally applicable to a landfill site in Hounslow with different distribution and intensity of metal contamination.

The extremely heterogeneous nature of the lead contamination at both sites is a limiting factor in the sampling precision that was achievable in the collaborative trials. In the landfill site the effect of heterogeneity is more intense, reflecting on the precision of 68% (at 95% confidence) being greater than that measured at the Derbyshire site (51%). In general, site heterogeneity is a major contributing factor in sampling error and has to be taken into account when inter-organizational trials are applied on a contaminated site.

Both sampling protocols chosen for the collaborative trials ('W' design at the rural site and 20 m regular grid at the urban site) were not fit-for-purpose of estimating mean concentrations (to within 20%) for Pb, Zn and Cd, but were fit-for-purpose for more evenly distributed elements across the sites such as Cu in Derbyshire and Co in Hounslow.

It has been shown that the effectiveness of sampling protocol at a particular site can be evaluated using a CTS. Such a conclusion is obviously site-specific and cannot be generalized. When this technique is applied more widely it may become possible to derive generalization about potential suitability of particular protocols at contaminated sites.

The general level of agreement in the second proficiency test for lead ($s = 20\%$) was improved from the first SPT in Derbyshire ($s = 36\%$). This improved performance is especially notable when the heterogeneity of the second site has been shown to be greater than the former.

z-Scores in SPTs reflect the ability of the participants for effective sampling and the heterogeneity of the contaminated sites. More detailed work is needed to allow for this heterogeneity in assigned values for the mean and the target standard deviation used in z-scoring.

Acknowledgements. We wish to thank the following people and organizations for participating in this study:

First sampling trial in Derbyshire: P. Nathanail of Wimpey Environmental; J. Nathanail of Delta Environmental; M. J. Brown of British Geological Survey; M. Hill of the Department of Environmental Sciences, University of Bradford; J. Ray of the Postgraduate Institute for Sedimentology, University of Reading; P. Abrahams of the Department of Geography, University College of Wales; J. Cotter-Howells of the Department of Geology, University of Manchester; and A. Mehra of the School of Environmental and Applied Sciences, University of Derby.

Second sampling trial in Hounslow Heath, West London: M. Hill of University of Bradford; Aradhana Mehra of Derby University; J. Ray of Reading University; M. Thompson of Birkbeck College University of London, C. Dawes of Walsall MBC; J. Trick of British Geological Survey; J. Jones of British Gas; and D. Barry of W. S. Atkins Environmental.

We also wish to thank R. Wood and his staff at the London Borough of Hounslow for their support of this work.

References

ALLOWAY, B. J. 1995. *Heavy Metals in Soils* (2nd edition). Blackie, Glasgow.

ANALYTICAL METHODS COMMITTEE 1989. *Analyst*, **114**, 1693.

ARGYRAKI, A., RAMSEY, M. H. & THOMPSON, M. 1995. Proficiency testing in sampling: pilot study on contaminated land. *Analyst*, **120**, 2799–2803.

HORWITZ, W. 1988. Protocol for the design, conduct and interpretation of collaborative studies. *Pure and Applied Chemistry*, **60**, 855.

MASKALL, J. & THORNTON, I. 1993. Metal contamination of soils at historical lead smelting sites. *Land Contamination and Reclamation*, **1**, 92.

MAFF 1979. *Leaflet 655, Sampling Soils for Analysis*. Ministry of Agriculture, Fisheries and Food, London.

RAMSEY, M. H., ARGYRAKI, A. & THOMPSON, M. 1995*a*. Estimation of sampling bias between different sampling protocols on contaminated land. *Analyst*, **120**, 1353–1356.

——, —— & —— 1995*b*. On the collaborative trial in sampling. *Analyst*, **120**, 2309–2312.

THOMPSON, M. & RAMSEY, M. H. 1995. Quality concepts and practices applied to sampling – an exploratory study. *Analyst*, **120**, 261.

—— & WALSH, J. N. 1989. *A Handbook of Inductively Coupled Plasma Spectrometry*. Blackie, Glasgow, 143–144.

Integration of environmental assessment indicators into site assessment procedures

P. Tucker,[1] C. Ferguson[2] & J. Tzilivakis[3]

[1] Department of Chemistry and Chemical Engineering, University of Paisley, Paisley PA1 2BE, UK
[2] Centre for Research into the Built Environment, Nottingham Trent University, Nottingham NG1 4BU, UK
[3] Division of Environmental Sciences, University of Hertfordshire, Hatfield, Hertfordshire AL10 9AB, UK

Abstract. The amount of information that can be gathered for contaminated site assessment is often limited by the cost of making measurements. Effective decisions on site management rely heavily on this information. Lower cost measurements or more effective use of the diverse information already available should increase the quality of these decisions, provided that final data quality is not compromised. However, fundamental problems can arise from interpreting the reliability, uncertainty and significance of the raw measurements or other indicators. Such problems are paralleled in Environmental Impact Assessment and Life Cycle Analysis methodologies. Drawing on the work undertaken within these disciplines may help clarify the solution for site assessment. Scoring, ranking and valuation techniques have been used successfully in providing decision support for the design of sampling strategies for contaminated sites through maximizing the use of desk study data and site reconnaissance observations.

Introduction

Owners of contaminated sites, site developers and organizations involved in site investigation have indicated a need for reliable, fast and cost-effective methods of site investigation. The balance between adequacy of statistical coverage and cost is a major issue. The drive towards a more cost-effective solution has focused attention on site investigation techniques other than sampling and laboratory analysis. These techniques include non-invasive methods such as geophysics, remote sensing and rapid screening methods using, for example, field test kits, immuno-assay and bio-sensors. Such techniques can provide good indication of potential contamination but many are not fully validated and some have proved difficult to interpret in terms of the data quality objectives of the investigation. Another problem relates to the detection of small-scale heterogeneities on contaminated sites. Experimentally, a dense sampling pattern is necessary to pick up such heterogeneities and may lead to high costs. Lower cost interpolation methods such as geostatistics and small-scale modelling may not delineate these heterogeneities with confidence.

The site investigator does not necessarily suffer from a lack of information or lack investigative tools. The problem is how to reconcile the wealth and diversity of available information into a form from which statistically reliable decisions can be made. This means ensuring a sufficiency of evidence and aggregating that evidence, without losing important details, until it is tractable for the human decision maker. In this respect, the support needed for site investigation parallels the support methods now being developed for Environmental Impact Assessment (EIA) and Life Cycle Analysis (LCA).

The paper assesses how the totality of information can be structured and investigates the role of EIA and LCA methods within site assessment. These methods might be automated and standardized through 'intelligent' software. Reference is made to the Site-ASSESS software as an early working example of intelligent software for site assessment.

Environmental assessment

Site assessment is aimed at providing information on the contaminant, geotechnical and water environment of a site. This can determine the nature and extent of contamination, identify hazards, pathways and targets (for risk assessment), inform decisions on remedial action and monitor the performance of remedial works (see e.g. CIRIA 1995). In many ways these actions parallel those within EIA. The following section explores some of the commonalities and highlights common problems which need to be addressed.

TUCKER, P., FERGUSON, C. & TZILIVAKIS, J. 1998. Integration of environmental assessment indicators into site assessment procedures. *In*: LERNER, D. N. & WALTON, N. R. G. (eds) 1998. *Contaminated Land and Groundwater: Future Directions*. Geological Society, London, Engineering Geology Special Publications, **14**, 127–133.

Measurement and indexation

Many parameters can be measured but due to the complexity of the environment, technological limitations, time and/or budget constraints, there is a limit on the number of measurements that can be made. Therefore assumptions are necessary and the measurement becomes an indicator. The indicator can either point to a particular parameter of interest or represent a number of parameters. The development of environmental indicators has received much attention recently and a number of criteria have been developed for their selection. The following is a distillation of criteria from OECD (1994) and Parker (1991):

> scientifically and technically based; **low error; standard** method of measurement; **reliable; representative; comparable** against a reference value; **responsive** to changes in the environment; **appropriate** to the scale of the pollution; **cost-effective; unambiguous**ly related to an assessment end-point; **readily available data; simple** to measure interpret and understand; **applicable** to issues of national significance.

Indicators have also evolved for site assessment. The desk study and site reconnaissance phases are implicitly based on indicators (Ferguson *et al.* (1996) provide a typical list). These indicators usually serve simply as checklists for the site investigator and are rarely quantified. To the authors' best knowledge, no attempt has been made to rationalize the indicators against objective selection criteria. Most would fail to satisfy many of the above-listed criteria. In particular, many are ambiguous in their interpretation. This needs to be addressed if they are to be more formally integrated into the decision making process.

OECD (1994) defines three main types of indicator:

- *pressure* indicators, which relate to human activities that cause stress on the environment;
- *state* indicators, which provide information on the condition of the environment and natural resources;
- *response* indicators, which relate to societal responses.

The desk study phase of site assessment essentially provides a suite of pressure indicators. Site reconnaissance provides the complementary state (or condition) indicators. Response indicators would be more appropriate to later stages of site assessment, e. g. monitoring remediation.

The image of reality provided by the primary indicators, however, is generally too complex and too large to visualize in a form useful for decision making. To reduce it to a manageable size and complexity usually means amalgamation. Amalgamation can be viewed as simplification and clarification, though at the expense of losing detail and increasing uncertainty.

Amalgamation may be used to produce indices (representative of a number of environmental parameters) and as an aid to classification into impact categories. There are many problems with amalgamation and there have been extensive discussions on this topic in the literature. Hobbs (1985) provides one such account. In practice, amalgamation generally has to cope with combining information measured on different scales. This means normalizing the scales to a common denominator. Scoring techniques are often used. The end-point is generally a set of scores, equivalence factors or, in some cases, a single overall assessment score.

Scoring or weighting different types of information is inherently subjective and value-laden. A number of valuation methods have been devised which aim to provide some structure to the valuation process. A review of three such methods – 'Swiss eco-points', 'Dutch environmental performance indicators (EPIs)' and 'Panel judgements' – has been published in ENDS (1994). In an EPI-type approach to valuation in LCA, the Netherlands National Research Programme 'Reuse of Waste' (NOH 1995) introduces objectivity in the relative weighting of effects by relating effects to environmental damage. A damage–effect function is formulated for each environmental effect. A target effect level (T_i) is determined according to the critical damage level (D_k) that can be accepted. The contribution of each effect score to an indicator value is then represented in terms of T_i, D_k and the current levels. 'Distance [of current level] to target' forms the basis for indicator comparison (Fig. 1). Unfortunately the form of the curve in Fig. 1 is seldom known. However, it is conceptually believed to follow the sigmoidal shape which is often used as a model in toxicology.

The relative valuation of more widely differing indicators and indices is even more subjective. The trade-off between environmental, social and economic effects, for example, is often a political judgement. Techniques such as multicriteria analysis can provide a mathematical solution but the specification of the parameters behind this approach remain value-laden. If a structured approach

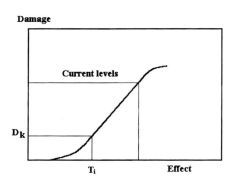

Fig. 1. Damage–effect correlation used in distance to target approach.

can be developed for setting these parameters, then multi-criteria methods could find application in methodically integrating social and economic factors with technical assessments.

Uncertainty

Uncertainty is one of the most difficult problems to deal with in decision making. It can compound complex issues, create ambiguity, be a source of conflict and prevent consensus. Friend & Jessop (1981) have identified three perceptions of uncertainty when it comes to decision making:

- uncertainties in the environment, i.e. uncertainties in the raw data;
- uncertainties as to appropriate value judgements;
- uncertainties pertaining to related decision fields, e.g. follow on actions.

Each is relevant to site assessment. Data are often missing, ambiguous or of poor quality, and there may be incomplete scientific understanding of contaminant transport, exposure pathways, dose–response relationships, etc. The relative significances of information are not known absolutely. Full integration of all investigation activities is rarely achieved in practice.

In the decision making process there is a need for techniques which make uncertainties more explicit, and more easily understood and more easily interpreted by the decision maker. However, there has been a general tendency, to date, to omit uncertain parameters from EIA investigations. One possible technique for dealing with uncertainty is the pedigree matrix (Constanza et al. 1992). This system employs the scoring system shown in Table 1 to assess the pedigree of the information and produce a score for the numeral used, the unit of measure used and the spread of the data. These scores are then averaged to provide an information pedigree rating.

Making value judgements on ordinal or nominal scales is inherently subjective and a natural spread in responses is usual. The information is thus inherently fuzzy. For example, different experts may differently rate a significance as high, medium and low respectively. The true significance is probably then best described as $x\%$ high and $y\%$ medium and $z\%$ low. The fuzzy membership values x, y and z are, in general, not easy to define. If they can be defined then fuzzy arithmetic rather than conventional arithmetic can be used in the assessment. Smith (1994) provides an example for environmental impact assessment. The value of this approach over conventional approaches has not yet been established; nevertheless it appears to offer some potential for handling uncertainty within environmental assessment.

A prototype approach applied to sampling design

The software package Site-ASSESS (Assessment of Sampling Strategies Expert Support System) provides a working example of some of the methodologies appropriate to decision support. The system assists the design of a sampling strategy to meet set data quality objectives. Specifically, it is targeted at locating contaminant hotspots utilizing the prior information gained from desk study and site reconnaissance activities. Descriptions of the overall methodology are given elsewhere (Ferguson et al. 1996; Tucker et al. 1996). This paper concentrates solely on the 'expert system' part of the methodology, addressing the development of indicators, their quantification (scoring) and aggregation through the use of expert value judgements.

Table 1. *Numerical estimate pedigree matrix (after Constanza* et al. *1992)*

Score	Theoretical quality of model	Empirical/quality of data	Social, degree of acceptance
4	Established theory – Many validation tests – Causal mechanisms understood	Experimental data – Statistically valid samples – Controlled experiments	Total – All but cranks
3	Theoretical model – Few validation tests – Causal mechanisms hypothesised	Historical/field data – Some direct measurements – Uncontrolled experiments	High – All but rebels
2	Computational model – Engineering approximations – Causal mechanisms approximated	Calculated data – Indirect measurements – Handbook estimates	Medium – Competing schools
1	Statistical processing – Simple correlations – No causal mechanisms	Educated guesses – Very direct approximations – 'Rule of thumb' estimates	Low – Embryonic field
0	Definitions/assertions	Pure guesses	None

Environmental assessment indicators

The pressure indicators in site assessment refer to past industrial stress on the site. This includes a description of the processes (production, storage, waste handling, etc.), their duration, the time since operation, the type and quantity of chemicals handled and their potential for attenuation in the ground. The significances of these indicators are effectively linked directly or inversely to their magnitudes, e.g. a high tonnage operation is potentially a more significant source of contamination than a lower tonnage operation *if* a spillage, leakage or accident occurs. If such a spillage did occur, contamination at the point of release is liable to be less significant when the released substance degrades rapidly or is rapidly leached, significance decreasing with elapsed time. Because of the interdependencies between the indicators, a more meaningful presentation is provided through aggregation into a compound index. This poses two main problems: (i) some data may be known with numerical precision (e.g. 10 years since operation) while other data (e.g. biodegradation potential) may be unknown, (ii) even when the raw data are known with precision, their significances are likely to be fuzzy (e.g. is 10 years a long or short time or both?). The expedient adopted within Site-ASSESS was to de-fuzzify these estimators at their lowest common resolution. In practice this meant limiting all responses to be one of three values: 'unknown/average', 'high' or 'low'. A compound index score (S) was then derived for each process:

$$S = \sum_j \phi(\text{response})_j / n$$

$$\phi(\text{unknown or average}) = 1, \quad \phi(\text{high}) > 1, \quad \phi(\text{low}) < 1$$

where $\phi(\text{response})_j$ is the score estimated for contributory indicator j and n is the number of indicators.

The condition indicators can, in the main, only be definable as binary indicators having a 'Yes' or 'No' response. These indicators essentially answer questions on the current state of the site, e. g. 'Is there vegetation stress?', 'Is there soil discoloration?', 'Is there a tarry odour?' In contrast, the format for recording actual condition measurements (e.g. preliminary sampling results) must vary according to the quality of data obtained. When measurements are based on unrepresentative sampling or on low precision analyses (some field test kits), they are probably best represented on a simple ordinal scale (e.g. 'high', 'medium' or 'low'). Immuno-assay measurements provide a natural binary response. Well-sampled and well analysed results can be used to provide an ordinal judgement on adjacent areas, though their actual locations can be excluded from further analysis, i.e. they need not be sampled again. Scores are calculated on a common basis: 2 = 'high', 1 = 'yes' or 'medium' , 0 = 'no' or 'low'.

Scores are compounded for all pressure indicators and condition indicators within defined sub-areas of the site,

$$T(r) = \sum_j S_j(r) \cdot w_j + \sum_k S_k(r) \cdot w_k$$

where $T(r)$ is the total score for sub-area r of the pressure indices j and the condition indicators k; w is a weighting factor describing the *relative* significance of each piece of information, i.e. 'Is a tarry odour more significant than a patch of dead grass?' Site-ASSESS makes the default value judgement that all data are equally significant, but it also allows the expert to impose personal judgements if so willed.

The framework for decision making

The sampling decision reduced to its simplest terms is 'How many samples do I put in each sub-area of the site in order to meet my data quality objectives?' As it is implicit that these data quality objectives are not already met (in which case there would be no point in further sampling), the decision effectively becomes 'What do I have to do to get from the current level in order to become as close as possible to the target?' This is analogous to the 'distance to target' model in LCA, and can be represented in a similar manner (Fig. 2).

By relating the arbitrary-scaled scores to an expectation of a hotspot existing, an experiment (i.e. sampling strategy) can be designed, the results of which would either locate the hotspot or, if failing to locate any hotspot, would decrease expectations that any hotspots do in fact exist. The theory behind this is well documented in the listed references to Site-ASSESS. In this paper, the prime interest is in how the above relationship is defined. Like its counterpart in LCA, its exact form is not known and must be set through expert value judgement based on physically realistic assumptions. It is assumed here that, as indicators are not unambiguous determinants of contamination, the presence of one or two will add little to one's expectation of contamination. They might have a quite separate cause, e.g. poor

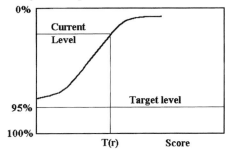

Fig. 2. Distance to target approach for sampling design.

vegetative growth could be due to a mineral deficiency in the soil. As more independent indicators are seen, the weight of evidence for a common contaminative cause rapidly increases. With a large number of positive indications, contamination becomes highly likely irrespective of the exact number of indicators seen. This interpretation remains consistent with its LCA analogy.

The data quality target in Site-ASSESS is expressed as a confidence level (the probability of failing to locate existing hotspots). This provides a usable format of direct and clear meaning to decision makers. The 95% target portrayed above is quite arbitrary. The appropriate target level should be set according to the decision being made.

Handling value judgements and uncertainty

Because of the ambiguity and uncertainty inherent within the indicator set, their 'scoring' and interpretation must remain flexible or fuzzy. It may eventually prove possible, by analysing large quantities of validated case study data, to develop empirical rules, fuzzy membership relations or case-based reasoning approaches to aid setting the unknowns (e.g. the relative weighting factors). More practically, preferred settings might be achieved from expert consensus. The latter approach was investigated here using the well documented Delphi technique (Martino (1972) provides a good description). In essence, Delphi comprises iteration towards consensus using controlled feedback and statistical group response. It is conducted remotely with the anonymity of the participating experts preserved throughout.

For this work, the experts comprised eight senior environmental consultants and leading researchers of contaminated land. They were asked to judge the significance of 12 pressure indicators and 27 condition indicators on a five-point scale. The most favoured ranking for each indicator was determined. Experts were then asked if they could accept the majority response. Results are shown in Fig. 3. These results indicate that when an indicator was judged to be most significant (Rank 5), there appeared to be little dispute over its

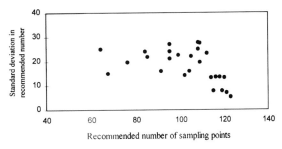

Fig. 4. Site-ASSESS sensitivity analysis based on the Delphi response. The recommended number is based on the mean Delphi response. The standard deviation is computed from the spread of responses from individual experts.

significance. Where indicators were judged less significant there appeared to be more uncertainty over what their significance was. The implications are seen in the resulting Site-ASSESS predictions (Fig. 4). The results refer to a site covered by a uniform distribution of a single indicator and show the number of sampling points recommended (based on the mean Delphi response) and the standard deviation of this recommendation based on the range of individual responses. Each point refers to a separate indicator. The absolute values of the scale numbers are not important to this argument and depend on a number of additional assumptions made about the sampling objectives. The form of the scatter plot, however, is of note. The lower significances lead to a lower recommended number of samples but also lead to increased uncertainty in how many this number should be. It is also interesting that the standard deviation appears to flatten towards the lower significances, i.e. a high relative error on a smaller number and a low relative error on a larger number are tending to produce much the same absolute errors.

Whilst these results need confirmation and much more extensive validation, they do indicate the possible relationship between perceived significance and uncertainty (or ambiguity).

Currently Site-ASSESS adopts a 'pragmatic' approach to uncertainty, giving uncertain data an intermediate significance.

Discussion and conclusions

A recent workshop organized by the Soil and Groundwater Technology Association (SAGTA) identified three priorities for research in site assessment (Bardos 1996).

1. non-invasive and rapid on-site screening techniques;
2. intelligent software tools to assist in the design of sampling strategies, data interpretation, data reconciliation and the modelling of processes in small volumes;

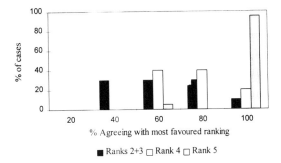

Fig. 3. Delphi consensus on indicator ranking.

3. sampling strategies and methodology, particular validation against objective criteria.

This paper primarily addresses priorities 2 and 3.

Site assessment, in many ways, needs similar decisions to those in Environmental Impact Assessment (EIA) and Life Cycle Analysis (LCA). Some problems (e. g. indicator selection, aggregation, ranking, scoring and valuation) are generic to all three applications. Whereas definitive solutions have not yet been found, much research has already been undertaken in the fields of EIA and LCA which can now benefit the development of site assessment methodologies.

The cost of making measurements on contaminated sites is seen as a major limiting factor. This not only flags the need for lower cost methods but also raises the possibility that such measurement techniques could potentially be integrated to some synergistic advantage (Bardos 1996). This paper illustrates how this may be done. Individual and diverse measurements (or indicators) are scored and aggregated onto a common scale, the scale being chosen to provide the necessary information in a form usable to the decision maker. A rapid-screening or non-invasive result could simply be treated as one indicator among many, the data adding synergistically to the weight of evidence. As an example, consider predictive modelling at the very local scale. Should such methods be neglected, just because the results are uncertain? Or could an approximate model (whose input data were of course cheap to obtain) serve usefully as an indicator? The quality of such a model might then be reflected by an assigned pedigree weighting.

While it is tempting to want to use all possible available information so that decisions can be made on the widest possible information base, there are in practice many trade-offs to consider. Apart from obvious cost–benefit considerations, trade-offs will arise from the inherent uncertainties in individual data and in their relative worth. This paper indicates that experts tend to disagree more over the actual value of data when these data had lower bearing on the problem. This generates increased uncertainty in the information presented to the decision maker. It may then be that inclusion of perceived weak indicators (e.g. geophysics) might seriously reduce precision for, perhaps, only marginal gains in accuracy. Thus when striving for synergy, care must be exercised. Choice of appropriate indicators and measurements is not yet obvious. Developing an indicator set for site assessment will need critical research into the available measurement methods: the value of the information they provide; the uncertainty in this information; and the ambiguity of moving from this information to a decision end-point.

The development of methods to handle uncertainty is another area where further research is required. Perhaps one key premise which needs further debate is the influence of uncertainty on perceived significance.

Table 2. *Possible consequences of uncertainty*

Treatment of uncertainty	Influence on decision
Neglect	None
Pedigree approach	Low
Pragmatic approach	Medium
Fuzzy approach	Medium
Precautionary principle	High

Table 2 illustrates this point through a conceptual picture of the possible consequences of different uncertainty assumptions.

In conclusion, intelligent software for site assessment is a recognized research need. Fulfilling this need will require research into data quality, data handling and decision methods. The potential for intelligent software has already been demonstrated with the Site-ASSESS system for sampling design. Can we now move on to a more fundamental and integrated approach for site assessment?

Acknowledgement. Development of Site-ASSESS was funded by the Department of the Environment. The views expressed are those of the authors and do not necessarily represent those of the Department.

References

BARDOS, P. 1996. Conclusions on the Parallel Workshop on Site Assessment. *Land Contamination and Reclamation*, **4**(3), 217–218.

CIRIA 1995. *Remedial Treatment for Contaminated Land. Volume III. Site Investigation and Assessment.* Construction Industry Research and Information Association, London.

CONSTANZA, R., FUNTOWICZ, S. O. & RAVETZ, J. R. 1992. Assessing and communicating data quality in policy relevant research. *Environmental Management*, **16**, 121–131.

ENDS 1994. *The Elusive Consensus on Life Cycle Assessment.* The ENDS Report, **231**, Environmental Data Services, London.

FERGUSON, C. C., TUCKER, P., NATHANAIL, P. & ABBACHI, A. 1996. *Design of sampling strategies for site investigation.* Report prepared for the Department of the Environment. Nottingham Trent University. DoE, London.

FRIEND, J. K. & JESSOP, W. N. 1981. The nature of planning. *In*: Open Systems Group (eds) *System Behaviour.* (3rd edition). Open University, Milton Keynes, 236–245.

HOBBS, B. F. 1985 Choosing how to choose: comparing amalgamation methods for environmental impact assessment. *Environmental Impact Assessment Review*, **5**, 301–319.

OECD 1994. *Environmental Indicators. OECD Core Set.* OECD, Paris.

MARTINO, J. P. 1972. *Technological Forecasting for Decision Making.* Elsevier, New York.

NOH 1995. *The Eco-Indicator 1995 Final Report.* NOH Report 9523. Novem: PO Box 8242, Utrecht, The Netherlands.

PARKER, J. D. E. 1991. *Environmental Reporting and Environmental Indices*. PhD Dissertation, University of Cambridge.

SMITH, P. N. 1994. Fuzzy applications in project appraisal: discrete fuzzy sets. *Project Appraisal*, **9**(2), 99–109.

TUCKER, P., FERGUSON, C., ABBACHI, A. & NATHANAIL, P. 1996. A decision support system for designing sampling strategies for potentially contaminated sites. *Proceedings of the 7th International Symposium on Spatial Data Handling, SDH '96*, Delft, The Netherlands, 12–16 August.

SECTION 4
POLLUTANT BEHAVIOUR ON FIELD SITES

The importance of understanding groundwater flow history in assessing present-day groundwater contamination patterns: a case study

Ian Jones, Ruth M. Davison & David N. Lerner

Groundwater Protection and Restoration Research Unit, University of Bradford, Bradford, West Yorkshire BD7 1DP, UK

Abstract. Locating and delineating suspected or known groundwater contamination is often a difficult and costly task. Prior to drilling the first borehole or taking the first sample it is standard practice to undertake a desk study. This is likely to involve investigating the history, geology and hydrogeology of the site. Often, only present-day groundwater flow patterns are used to assess the current situation and plan a site investigation. This paper uses a recent experience to illustrate the importance of understanding the history of groundwater flow in planning a successful and cost-effective groundwater investigation.

The site of an old coal carbonization (coking) plant in the UK East Midlands was selected as a field site to undertake research into coal tar related contamination in sandstone aquifers. From the evidence of previous studies, contamination was known to exist in the aquifer, although its exact location and extent was unknown. A comprehensive desk study, extensive surface geophysics and a solute transport modelling exercise were undertaken prior to doing any drilling. Based on the results of this work a number of monitoring wells were installed and samples taken. Results from these initial wells confirmed the original hypothesis. As more wells were completed it became evident that our understanding was not entirely correct and that the evolution and distribution of the contamination was more complex than the initial investigations indicated.

Ongoing investigations have revealed a complex groundwater flow and contaminant history. This paper intends to illustrate how limited information can be made to fit and 'prove' expectations, whereas in reality an entirely different situation may exist.

Introduction

This paper presents a case study of a site investigation into the extent and nature of contamination released from a former coal carbonization plant and associated colliery activities at a site in the UK East Midlands. The work is part of an ongoing European Union (EU) funded research project entitled 'Processes underlying the remediation of creosote (coal tar) contaminated groundwater in fractured sandstone' (University of Bradford 1995). During the investigation it became apparent that the distribution and nature of contamination were not as expected from the initial desk study. As work proceeded, a complex site history was unveiled, which led to a reappraisal of the initial findings. This paper intends to briefly highlight some of the complexities inherent in site investigation of contaminated groundwater and to give some pointers to help avoid potentially costly mistakes.

A detailed procedure, involving a desk study, groundwater flow modelling, surface geophysics and preliminary sampling of groundwaters was undertaken. As the investigation is part of a large research project, data acquisition and computer modelling were more detailed than could normally be expected in a commercial setting.

Approach to delineating the contaminant plume

Desk study

Site history. An initial desk study revealed that the coal carbonization plant (referred to from here on as 'the plant' or 'the coking plant') was in operation for approximately 15 years from the early 1950s to the late 1960s. In addition to smokeless fuel, the plant produced waste products of coal tar and approximately 20 000 litres of liquor per day (Anon 1987). An analysis of a local waste liquor from a similar process to that at the site has recently been undertaken (Table 1 in Broholm et al. 1998). At an unknown date, storage tanks used to store the liquor are known to have fractured and leaked waste product (Anon 1987). The liquor was encouraged to migrate along a drain adjacent to a rail track and into a small lagoon 700 m to the east (Fig. 1). This drain and the lagoon were used for disposal of the waste liquor until the works closed. Based on the above details and data from Broholm et al. (1998), it is possible that as much as 90 000 tonnes of liquor, containing 900 tonnes of ammonium, 693 tonnes of phenols, 583 tonnes of cresols and 161 tonnes xylenols, leaked into the subsurface.

JONES, I., DAVISON, R. M. & LERNER, D. N. 1998. The importance of understanding groundwater flow history in assessing present-day groundwater contamination patterns: a case study. *In*: LERNER, D. N. & WALTON, N. R. G. (eds) 1998. *Contaminated Land and Groundwater: Future Directions*. Geological Society, London, Engineering Geology Special Publications, **14**, 137–148.

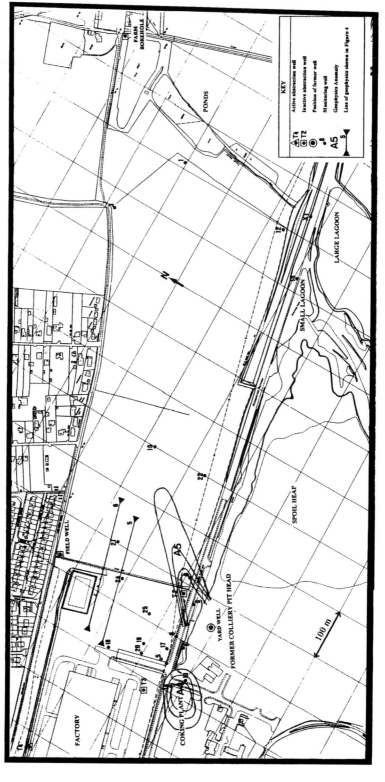

Fig. 1. Plan of fieldsite.

Table 1. *Some groundwater chemistry data for selected boreholes*

Chemical indicators of contamination from plant	Groundwater chemistry data $(mg\,l^{-1})$ from some local boreholes			
	YW	FARM	T2	T3
Ammonium	27.8	353	100	BD
Phenols	NR	77	BD	BD
Sulphates	NR	560	83	129
Chlorides	NR	1610	110	108

Note: YW, yard well (1977); FARM, farm well (1986); T2–T2 well (1993); T3–T3 well (1993) used to represent background quality. NR, not recorded; BD, below detection.

In 1986, approximately 20 years after the coking plant closed, a borehole was sunk by a local farmer to provide water for crop irrigation (Farm BH on Fig. 1). During the initial pumping test the water from this borehole was black and foamed on the surface (Anon 1987). An analysis of the water revealed elevated levels of a variety of compounds, particularly ammonium, phenols, sulphate and chloride (Table 1). This contamination was attributed to the former coking plant. In 1988, after 84 years of production, the adjacent colliery closed (Fig. 1). In the early 1990s, as part of a redevelopment package, a new factory was built near to the former pit head. Part of the attraction of the site was the availability of large quantities of high quality groundwater, which the factory required for part of its production process. Accordingly a number of abstraction wells were sunk, pump tested and sampled for chemical quality. Water from Well T2 (Fig. 1) was found to be contaminated with $100\,mg\,l^{-1}$ ammonium (Table 1) (Anon undated), was blue-black and foamed on the surface (engineer in factory on site, pers. comm.). As a result of this contamination the company engaged the services of an environmental consultant in an attempt to assess the risk to present and future water supplies. Meanwhile the local council undertook a site investigation of the area to assess its suitability for an industrial estate. As part of this investigation and the subsequent reclamation works, the site of the coking plant was excavated and capped with an impermeable surface. During the excavation, tanks containing liquor and coal tar were found and coal tar saturated sandstone down to the base of the excavation (6 m) was observed.

The above details confirm that contamination from the former coking plant was present and had entered the groundwater. This paper will focus on contamination entering the subsurface at the site of the coking plant. Groundwater contaminated via the drain and small lagoon will not be discussed.

Geology and hydrogeology. The aquifer geology consists of approximately 80 m of Triassic Sherwood Sandstones overlying Permian Marls and Lower Magnesian Limestone (Table 2). The sandstones form the main aquifer of the region with the marls and limestone forming an effective aquitard where extensive fractures and solution features are not present. There is very little drift over the area, with the possible exception of isolated patches of glacial sands and gravels on the higher ground and some recent river deposits.

The Permo-Triassic Pebble Beds form a high yielding inter-granular aquifer unit. With increasing depth the sandstones become harder and less weathered and fractures are thought to play an increasingly important role in groundwater flow.

Data from pumping tests and groundwater modelling indicate a regional hydraulic conductivity of between

Table 2. *Brief description of aquifer geology*

Name	Description	Thickness (m)	Depth to base (mbgl)
Permo-Triassic Pebble Beds	Weathered sandstone, with pebbles and marl nodules	20–30	20–30
Lower Mottled Sandstone	Compact medium to fine grained sandstone, silty with marl bands	20–30	40–60
Lower Mottled Sandstone	Sandstones of variable hardness with thin layers of mudstone and marl	10–20	50–80
Middle Permian Marl	Marls with very compact well cemented sandstones	0–15	approx. 80

2 and 6 m day^{-1}. The regional groundwater flow over the field site area is in a northeasterly direction.

Groundwater flow and solute transport modelling

Groundwater flow, particle and solute transport models were developed using MODFLOW (McDonald & Haraugh 1988), MODPATH (Pollock 1989) and MT3D (Zheng 1990), respectively. The modelling was used as a reconnaissance tool to aid in delineating the contamination and to provide possible locations for the initial monitoring wells. The model is a single layered, finite difference model, composed of a 14 × 24 km irregular mesh, with grid spacings of 20 m in the central area of interest expanding to 1000 m at the model boundaries. The model is well calibrated against a number of observation wells, both at local and regional scales (residuals <2 m). The

initial modelling study confirmed a local groundwater flow direction towards the northeast (Fig. 2).

Geophysical survey

As part of the reconnaissance a geophysical survey was conducted. This included resistivity soundings, electrical imaging and ground conductivity measurements. Since the most highly contaminated groundwater has an electrical conductivity of between three and six times background levels, electrical techniques were expected to indicate the location of any contamination. Due to large scale landscaping works at the time of the survey and various surface and subsurface features, coverage of the site was not as good as hoped. The relevant subsurface anomalies located by the geophysics survey are shown in Fig. 1. Anomalies A4 and A5 confirm our

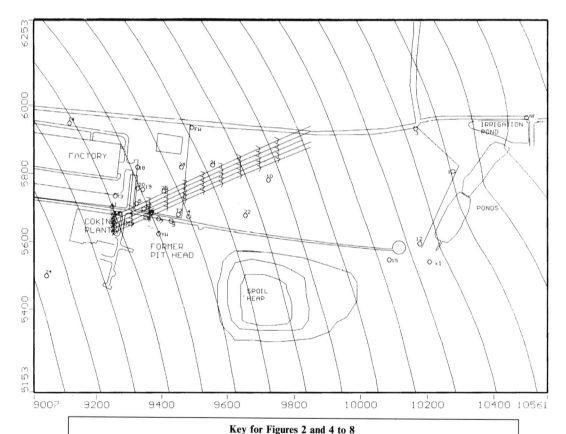

Key for Figures 2 and 4 to 8
Plot axes shown in metres   Groundwater contours at 1 m intervals   ₁° Borehole, refer to Figure 1 for further details   ✷ Particles position at end points of pathlines from previous modelled time period   Pathlines, with flow direction arrows at 1 year intervals, represent unretarded advective contaminant transport for the time period indicated

Fig. 2. Modelled steady-state groundwater head contours and pathlines for the period 1955–1965.

initial understanding of contamination emanating from the coking plant and travelling in a northeasterly direction with groundwater flow. The contours in Fig. 1 indicate the areas of low resistivity.

Monitoring well installation and groundwater sampling – phase one

Based on evidence from the desk study, early modelling and geophysics, a number of monitoring wells were installed at the site. Table 3 lists the different phases of monitoring well installation and other work in the site investigation period. Boreholes (BHs) 5, 6, 7 and 8 were located directly down-gradient of the former coking plant in an attempt to assess the character of the contamination. These BHs were screened from near the water table to approximately 6–8 m below the water table (mBWT), as the contamination was expected to be near to the water's surface close to the source. Table 4 gives the ammonium concentrations measured in each of the monitoring wells. No organic coal tar compounds were found in wells 5, 6, 7 and 8 despite high levels of ammonium being found. The presence of high concentrations of ammonium ($>150 \, \mathrm{mg \, l^{-1}}$) is indicative of contamination by the waste liquor (Broholm *et al.* 1998). The lack of any organic compounds is a mystery.

Table 3. *Relevant chronology of site investigation*

Approx. date	Work undertaken	Reasons for work	Principal findings
October 1994	Initial desk study	Scope out site history, gather information on site	Contamination from former coking plant is present
December 1994	Geophysics survey	To locate contamination as indicated by increased electrical conductivity	Various anomalies, but of main interest was low resistivity body extending in a NE direction from position of former coking plant
May 1995	Installation of four monitoring wells (BHs 5, 6, 7 and 8)	To locate and assess nature of contamination from former coking plant	Up to $174 \, \mathrm{mg \, l^{-1}}$ ammonium, but no coal tar organics found
June 1995	Installation of a further five monitoring wells (BHs 9, 10, 11, 12 and 13)	To establish extent of contamination and to try and locate organic coal tar compounds	Low ammonium in BHs 9, 10, 11 and 13. $130 \, \mathrm{mg \, l^{-1}}$ in BH 12. No organic coal tar compounds
July 1995	Surveyed site	To establish accurate groundwater heads and determine present groundwater flow directions	Pumping from factory wells has a severe effect on groundwater flow. Flow near former plant is to NW
September 1995	Installation of five multilevel wells (BHs 16, 17, 18, 19 and 20)	To characterize the local redox chemistry related to ammonium and assess the vertical distribution of the contamination	Plume extends to the NW as far as BH 18 and to 10–15 m below the water table. No organics, but up to $352 \, \mathrm{mg \, l^{-1}}$ ammonium
March/April 1996	Further geophysics and logging of T2 well	Using enhanced data processing capabilities to assess any movement in the position of the plume	Contamination confirmed to have moved to the N and to occupy the top 15 m of saturated aquifer
May 1996	Installation of five more monitoring wells, some multilevels. (BHs 21, 22, 23, 24 and 25)	To confirm the broader understanding of the contaminant distribution and findings of recent geophysics	Confirmed movement of ammonium contamination to the north and findings of geophysics. More contamination than originally envisaged
June 1996	Reassessment of contaminant movement	using modelling and repeated desk study exercise using all data to understand history of contaminant movement	Revealed further complexities in site history. Contaminant movement and distribution complex

Table 4. *Ammonium concentrations in selected monitoring wells*

Well number	5	6	7	8	9	10	11	12	13	16	17	18	19	20	21	24	25
$NH_4\,(mg\,l^{-1})$	141	147	45	174	7	7	0	130	6	146	352	9	132	153	334	77	308

Note: Where more than one monitoring level exists data have been taken from a level consistent with the mean depth of the majority of the single level wells (approx. 2 to 5 mBWT).

Provisional conclusions following phase one of the investigation

After examining the current data it is easy to conclude that the initial understanding was correct: a plume from the coking plant extending in a northeasterly direction with regional groundwater flow (Fig. 2). However, at this stage in the investigation, the longitudinal and vertical extents of the plume and the explanation for the lack of organic compounds are not known. It is possible that the organics were less retarded than the ammonium and have, therefore, travelled beyond wells 5, 6, 7 and 8. They may have also been preferentially attenuated in the vadose zone and aquifer. The question of the disappearing organics will be put aside, as it is a separate issue to

that covered by this paper. A companion paper by Broholm *et al.* (1998) discusses the issue of the lack of coal tar organics.

Monitoring well installation and groundwater sampling – phase two

In an attempt to define the lateral limits of the ammonium contamination and to try and locate organic coal tar contamination, a further five monitoring wells were installed: BHs 9 10, 11, 12 and 13 (see Table 3 and Fig. 1). The data from these monitoring wells (Table 4) indicate that the contaminant plume has shifted in a northerly direction away from BHs 9 and 10. Data from BHs 11 and 13 suggest that the reclamation of the site

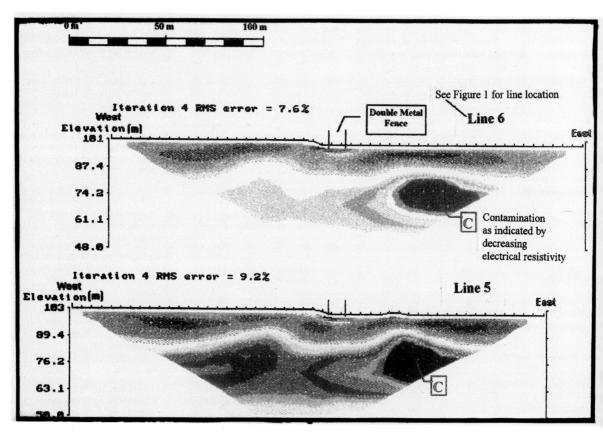

Fig. 3. Electricity resistivity survey results – lines 5 and 6.

Table 5. *History of local groundwater abstractions*

Period	Known abstractions	Relevant figure
1955 to 1965	No local wells	2
1965 to 1988	Yard well and field well active; actual annual abstractions recorded, but daily pumping rates and timing unknown	4
1988 to July 1992	No local wells	5
July 1992 to February 1993	T2 and T3 wells active with limited activity from other factory wells up groundwater gradient; monthly abstraction data available	6
February 1993 to February 1995	T4 well dominates local absractions, with some from T3 and other up-gradient factory wells	7
February 1995 to present day	T4 well dominates with increasing abstractions from up-gradient wells	–

of the coking plant has successfully prevented further contamination from entering the groundwater. Borehole 12 confirms that the small lagoon (now dry) which received coal tar liquor is still a source of ammonium. Groundwater heads measured in the monitoring wells showed the groundwater flow direction to have shifted to the northwest. Recent groundwater abstraction data obtained from the factory on site allowed the flow model to be updated for present-day conditions.

Subsequent, more detailed modelling shows local variations due to present pumping regimes from the factory wells. Five multilevel monitoring wells (BHs 16 to 20) confirmed that the ammonium contamination had begun to migrate to the northwest about as far as BH 18 (Table 4 and Fig. 1). These multilevel wells also confirmed that the ammonium contamination was confined to the upper 15 m of the aquifer, with peak concentrations at approximately 5 mBWT.

Conclusions following phase two

Although it seems safe to conclude that the contaminant plume is located in the upper 15 m of the aquifer, smearing in a northwesterly direction in response to the change in groundwater flow direction, its exact lateral extent is still not known.

Most recent assessment

In a final attempt to establish the distribution and travel history of the ammonium plume the desk study exercise was repeated with hindsight, more precise modelling carried out and further geophysics, with more advanced data processing capabilities, undertaken. Following this work a further five boreholes (some multilevel) were drilled (BHs 21 to 25) and sampled (Table 4 and Fig. 1). The desk study, combined with modelling, revealed a more complex site history than originally envisaged; principally caused by varying rates and times of pumping from the two colliery wells (yard well and field well on

Fig. 1) and the factory wells. Geophysics confirms that contamination was indeed smearing to the north (Fig. 3).

Final evaluation

The investigations detailed above have revealed a complex site history which has produced a distorted and smeared contaminant plume. Table 5 lists the major changes in local groundwater abstractions since the coking plant began production in the early 1950s. It is important to note that the exact timing and rates of both the groundwater abstractions and contamination releases are unknown; this makes it extremely difficult to predict accurately the travel history of the groundwater and contamination in the field site area. This is not an unfamiliar problem.

Below is an outline of what is believed to have occurred at the site from the early 1950s to the present day. Table 5 and a number of model plots (Figs 2 and 4–8) accompany this outline.

According to available data, there were no wells active in the vicinity of the fieldsite until 1965, at which time the colliery began to abstract water for coal washing from two shallow wells (yard well and field well shown on Fig. 1). It should be noted that 1965 is the start of licensing for water abstractions in the UK; it is possible that the colliery wells operated prior to this date. For the purposes of this case study, however, we shall use available data and assume no abstractions prior to 1965. Until 1965 the groundwater flow was to the northeast in the direction of the regional gradient. If it is assumed, as the evidence suggests, that the contaminant release began in 1955 then this will allow particles to be tracked from this date. This will enable some of the possible positions of the contamination to be seen over time. Advection without any retardation or dispersion will be used for this illustration, as the attenuation and dispersion of the contaminants are not yet quantified. Figures 2 and 4–8 show particles released at the start of

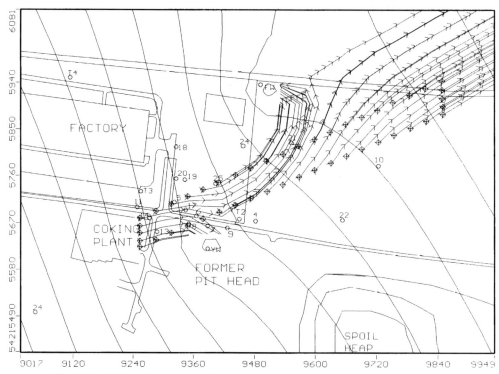

Fig. 4. Modelled steady-state groundwater head contours and pathlines for the period 1965–1988.

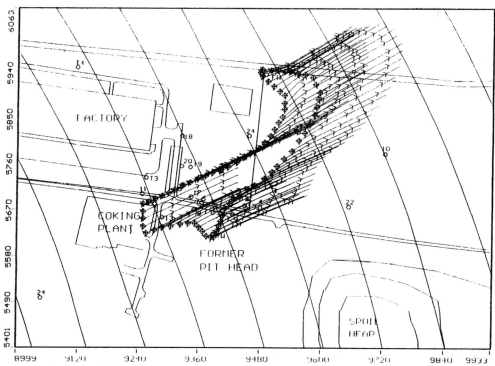

Fig. 5. Modelled steady-state groundwater head contours and pathlines for the period 1988–1992.

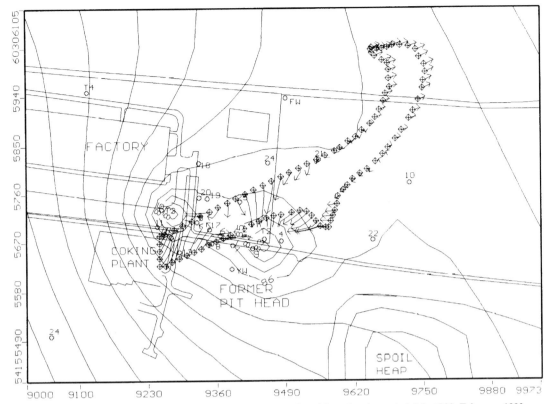

Fig. 6. Modelled transient groundwater head contours and pathlines for the period July 1992–February 1993.

each time period indicated. The pathlines show the travel history of the contamination (minus retardation and dispersion) over that time period. For each new time period, particles are positioned at the end points of the pathlines from the preceding time period. As the contaminant source at the coking plant must be assumed to be active from 1955 to 1994 (in the absence of any data to the contrary) then the five particles at the coking plant are released at the start of each and every new time period from 1955 to 1994.

In summary, from 1955 to 1965, groundwater, and by inference contamination from the coking plant, travelled in a northeasterly direction as shown on Fig. 2. Between 1965 and 1988, yard well (YW) and field well (FW) were used to abstract water for the colliery. Figure 4 shows a model plot with both FW and YW pumping concurrently. The exact timing and daily pumping rates of the two wells are unknown; however, it is likely that for much of the period use of the two wells was alternated, so only one well would be in use at any one time. During this period it is probable that much of the contamination was captured by these wells. Water quality data from YW confirms this idea (Table 1). The section of the plume down-gradient of FW's capture zone would then

'breakaway' and continue towards the northeast (Fig. 4). From 1988 until 1992 no local abstractions were present and so the ammonium plume moved to the northeast with the regional groundwater flow (Fig. 5). In 1992 local groundwater flow became severely disrupted when a newly constructed factory began to abstract groundwater from a number of fully penetrating wells (Table 5). Figures 6–8 outline the history of the contaminant plume from 1992 to the present day.

From July 1992 until February 1993, wells T2 and T3 were operational, causing the plume near to the former coking plant to thin out as T2 acted as a clean-up well (Fig. 6 and Table 1). Due to ammonium contamination T2 was decommissioned in February 1993. T3 continued to be used at a reduced rate until early 1995; however, from February 1993 the groundwater flow near to the former coking plant was dominated by abstractions from well T4. Pumping from T4 caused a shift in flow direction of 90° to the west (Fig. 7).

As the preceding summary illustrates, the groundwater flow history and, by association, the plume history, is extremely complex. It is important to reiterate that the contaminant movement and distribution is even more complex than groundwater flow alone would

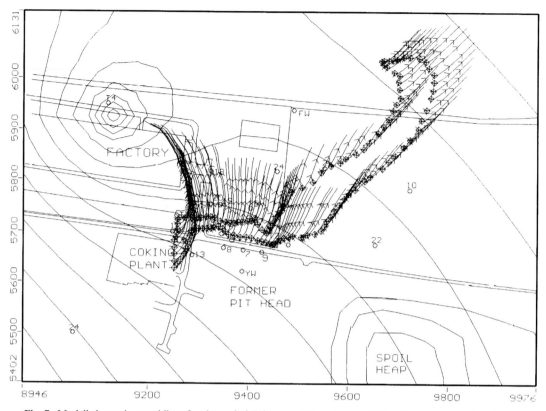

Fig. 7. Modelled transient pathlines for the period February 1993–February 1996 with groundwater head contours for February 1996.

indicate. Geological heterogeneities, including fracturing, and processes of contaminant dispersion and retardation, such as cation exchange (see Torstensson *et al.* 1998), biodegradation and biotransformations mean that the clear contaminant boundaries as indicated by advection alone are in reality very much blurred. Field evidence illustrates that the simple plume boundaries shown by modelling advection alone (Fig. 8) are unrealistic. Work is being undertaken on all these aspects in an attempt to fully understand the properties and processes controlling the movement and attenuation of contamination in this aquifer.

Conclusions

Now that one possible historical scenario of the groundwater flow and contaminant migration has been outlined for this fieldsite, we can use it as an example and return to the title and premise of this paper. Using this case study, we are able to clearly illustrate the importance of understanding groundwater flow history in assessing present-day groundwater contamination

patterns. A poor understanding of the subsurface and the groundwater flow history for a site is likely to result in an inadequate evaluation of the distribution of groundwater contamination.

Below are some recommendations resulting from this case study for anyone undertaking groundwater contamination investigations:

- Do not assume groundwater flow or well abstractions are constant over time: even short periods of two to three years can mean plumes are hundreds of metres off their expected position.
- Do not assume contamination will have a simple distribution in the vertical: geology, vertical flows, fracturing due to subsidence and so on can be very important. The screen depths of abstraction wells can strongly influence the depth at which contamination will travel in the aquifer. In this example, both colliery wells are very shallow (< 10 mBWT); if this were not the case then it is probable that the ammonium contamination would be found deeper in the aquifer.
- Do not assume a contaminant source is constant over time.

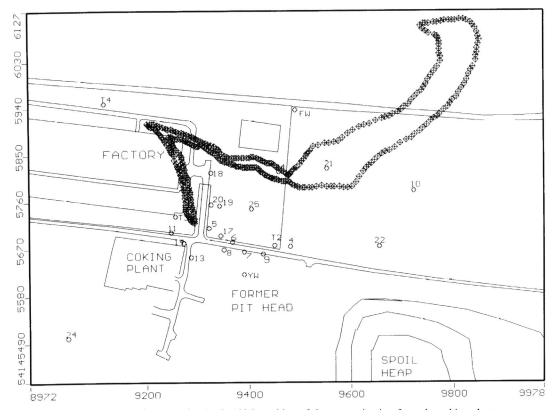

Fig. 8. Modelled present-day (early 1996) position of the contamination from the coking plant.

- Always undertake a thorough desk study: check for the presence of former wells and get as much detail as possible, including screen depths and the abstraction data, if any exist.
- Prior to drilling the first borehole, if at all possible, produce a simple groundwater flow model. This can be a considerable time saver, particularly on larger projects. A model will not provide all the answers, but it can provide a real insight into the groundwater system. A model can help with positioning of monitoring wells and the subsequent interpretation of the field data. In particular, it can be used to assess the range of possibilities (e.g. sensitivity analysis).
- Monitoring wells should include some wells positioned in a triangular or similar distribution and not only in a straight line down-gradient from the source. Also use wells to confirm areas assumed to be free of contamination, not just where contamination is expected. Monitoring well screen depths should be reasonably consistent over the investigation area for inter-well comparisons. When possible, at least one multilevel well or set of wells should be installed to confirm the vertical distribution of the contamination (Lerner & Teutsch 1995).

- Geophysics can be an excellent investigative tool for certain contaminant types.

Acknowledgements. This fieldsite investigation has involved a large number of people from many organizations. The authors would like to thank the following people and organizations who have all contributed to this paper: O. Baines, D. Hay, P. Cannon, L. Amalric, S. Nema, M. Broholm, C. Thomas, J. Clark, D. Tor-stensson, R. Barker, J. Tellam, Mansfield District Council, Nottinghamshire Council, the engineering section of the on-site factory, Specialist Drilling and Testing, The Environment Agency, Seven Trent Water, The British Geological Survey and, of course, The European Union for funding the work.

References

BROHOLM, M. M., JONES, I., TORSTENSSON, D. & ARVIN, E. 1998. Groundwater contamination from a coal carbonisation plant. *This volume.*

ANON 1987. *Pollution of the Triassic Sherwood Sandstones east of Mansfield.* Technical Services Groundwater Report No. 33. File cat. 414.124.03.

—— undated. *Borehole quality data for the area around the factory site.*

LERNER, D. N. & TEUTSCH, G. 1995. Recommendations for level-determined groundwater sampling in wells. *J. Hydrol.*, **171**, 355–377.

MCDONALD, M. G. & HARBAUGH, A. W. 1988. *A modular three-dimensional finite, difference groundwater flow model.* US Geol. Surv. Open File Report 83–875.

POLLOCK, D. W. 1989. MODPATH. *Documentation of computer programs to compute and display pathlines using results from the USGS modular three dimensional finite difference groundwater flow model.* USGS Open File Rep. 89–381. US Geological Survey, Denver, CO.

TORSTENSSON, D., THORNTON, S. F., BROHOLM, M. M. & LERNER, D. N. 1997. Hydrochemistry of pollutant attenuation in groundwater contaminated by coal tar wastes. *This volume.*

UNIVERSITY OF BRADFORD 1995. *First year annual report: Processes underlying the remediation of creosote contaminated groundwater in fractured sandstone.* Directorate General XII, Commission of the European Communities, Contract No. EV5V-CT94–0529.

ZHENG, C. 1990. *MT3D. A modular three-dimensional transport model.* SS Papadopulos and Associates.

Hydrochemistry of pollutant attenuation in groundwater contaminated by coal tar wastes

Daniel Torstensson,[1,2] Steven F. Thornton,[3] Mette M. Broholm[4] & David N. Lerner[3]

[1] AB Jacobson and Widmark, Water and Environment, Stjärnvägen 2 SE-18183 Lidingö, Sweden
[2] Now at Department of Civil and Environmental Engineering, Royal Institute of Technology, SE-100 44, Stockholm, Sweden
[3] Groundwater Protection and Restoration Research Unit, Department of Civil and Environmental Engineering, University of Bradford, Bradford, West Yorkshire BD7 1DP, UK
[4] Department of Environmental Science and Engineering, Technical Universtiy of Denmark, Lyngby, Denmark

Abstract. This paper describes a preliminary hydrochemical study of a Triassic Sandstone aquifer in the UK East Midlands which is contaminated by coal tar waste products from a former coal-carbonization plant. Processes controlling the attenuation of inorganic species within the identified plume are examined, supported by equilibrium and reactive transport modelling of contaminant fate. The study forms part of a more detailed research programme examining the long term fate of pollutants from this site in the aquifer. Groundwater beneath the site is polluted with NH_4 (up to $350\,mg\,l^{-1}$), SO_4 and NVOC from the plant and nearby coal mining operations. Concentrations of organic chemicals within the plume are not significant. The aquifer is calcareous, (Fe) oxide-rich and aerobic, and geochemical modelling suggests that the native groundwater chemistry is primarily controlled by carbonate equilibria. Anaerobic conditions are sustained within the plume by microbial oxidation of the NH_4 and NVOC load which is coupled to the reduction of native Fe oxides. Sulphate is transported conservatively within the plume. The NH_4 load is primarily attenuated by cation exchange reactions with the aquifer sediments. This is supplemented by nitrification at the plume margins under conditions of higher oxygen flux which generates locally elevated NO_3 concentrations and depressed pH in the contaminated groundwater. Elevated alkalinity within the plume is consistent with dissociation of the ammonia waste stream during groundwater transport and is an important control on the increased porewater Ca and Fe load mobilized by cation-exchange and redox reactions. A conceptual model of the key processes affecting contaminant fate within the plume is presented and the implications for aquifer clean-up are discussed.

Introduction

The behaviour of anthropogenic pollutants in groundwater has received considerable attention during the last 10 years, with respect to predicting both contaminant fate and the attendant risks to human health. Gasworks are a major source of soil and groundwater contamination by a suite of organic and inorganic compounds, including aromatic and polyaromatic hydrocarbons and ammonia (e.g. Berglind 1982; Lotimer *et al.* 1992; Raven & Beck 1992; Kiilerich & Arvin 1995). In many cases this has resulted in a need for remedial action and site clean-up.

An important prerequisite for the implementation of cost-effective clean-up strategies at such sites is an understanding of the processes regulating the distribution and form of contaminants in the subsurface environment. There is an increasing body of evidence suggesting that

anthropogenic pollutants may be effectively attenuated in groundwater by natural processes (e.g. Nicholson *et al.* 1983; Mather 1989; Christensen *et al.* 1994), and recent attention has focused on the important role of redox reactions in determining contaminant transformation and fate (Kehew & Passero 1990; Lyngkilde & Christensen 1992; Heron *et al.* 1994; Cozzarelli *et al.* 1994). The exploitation of the natural (or intrinsic) remediation capacity of an aquifer is economically attractive, as part of a management strategy for polluted groundwater, but there remains a need to verify its potential. This is necessary for reliable risk assessment and also for the planning and development of aquifer restoration programmes.

The study site comprises a former coal-carbonization plant in the UK East Midlands which produced coke for about 20 years (1950–1970). Leakage of coal-tar processing waste water from storage tanks at the site has

TORSTENSSON, D., THORNTON, S. F., BROHOLM, M. M. & LERNER, D. N. 1998. Hydrochemistry of pollutant attenuation in groundwater contaminated by coal tar wastes. *In*: LERNER, D. N. & WALTON, N. R. G. (eds) 1998. *Contaminated Land and Groundwater: Future Directions*. Geological Society, London, Engineering Geology Special Publications, **14**, 149–157.

resulted in extensive contamination of the underlying soil and aquifer by creosote and ammonia liquors. The area is also an historically important coal mining centre which has had a significant local impact on groundwater quality.

This paper examines the groundwater quality beneath the site and provides a preliminary interpretation of the key physico-chemical processes controlling plume hydrochemistry and inorganic contaminant attenuation. Processes controlling the fate of organic contaminants in groundwater at the site are examined in a companion paper (Broholm *et al.* 1998).

Site geology and hydrogeological setting

The site geology comprises ~80 m of Triassic Sherwood Sandstone underlain by Permian Marls and Lower Magnesian Limestone. The sandstone is the main aquifer in the region, with the marls and limestone forming an effective aquitard. Apart from some recent river deposits there is minor drift cover, although isolated patches of glacial sands and pebbles are found on higher ground (Anon 1995).

The sandstone is a high yielding intergranular aquifer which, with increasing depth, becomes less weathered and more compact, with fractures providing an increasingly important component of the groundwater flow. Regional-scale hydraulic conductivities range from 2 to 6 m day^{-1} and groundwater flows generally northeast through the fieldsite at approximately 0.18 m day^{-1} (Anon 1995). Groundwater modelling studies and abstraction well

data for the surrounding area highlight a complex history of changes in groundwater flow direction over the last 30 years which have produced a pollution plume that is convoluted in shape.

Fieldsite investigation and analytical procedures

Samples were collected from 20 monitoring wells using single level and multilevel sampling techniques (Schirmer *et al.* 1995). The samples were processed and analysed by standard methods (APHA 1985) using the procedures summarized in Table 1.

The following analytical detection limits (mg l^{-1}) were obtained for the inorganic determinands: Ca, 0.05; Mg, 0.05; Na, 0.2; K, 0.2; Fe, 0.1; Mn, 0.25; NH$_4$, 0.5; Cl, 1; SO$_4$, 1.5; NO$_3$, 10; NO$_2$, 0.1; S^{2-}, 0.2.

Results

The concentrations of selected species measured in the typical waste stream from a coal-carbonization plant, and uncontaminated and contaminated groundwater beneath the site are shown in Table 2. The background water quality is estimated from boreholes 4 and 11 (see Fig. 1).

The distributions of selected species in the ground-water beneath the site (Fig. 1(a)–(d)) generally illustrate a marked contrast between the uncontaminated ground-water and pollution plume. Solute concentration profiles for transect A–B, along a flowpath in the contaminated

Table 1. *Summary of processing and analytical procedures for groundwater samples*

Parameter	Preservation and measurement	Method of analysis
pH, Eh, dissolved oxygen, electrical conductivity	No filtration or preservation; measured immediately in the field using a flowcell	Probe
Alkalinity	No filtration or preservation; measured immediately in the field	Titration
Metals	Filtered (0.45 μm Whatman® membrane) and acidified to <pH 2 with HNO$_3$; measured in the laboratory	ICPS and flame photometry
NH$_4$, Cl, SO$_4$	Filtered (as above) but no preservation; measured in the laboratory	Colorimetry
NO$_3$/NO$_2$	Filtered (as above) and preserved with one drop of 0.25% HgCl$_2$; measured in the laboratory	Colorimetry
S^{2-}	Filtered (as above) and preserved with three to four drops of 2M ZnAc; measured in the laboratory	Colorimetry
Total organic carbon (TOC)	No filtration but acidified to <pH 2 with H$_2$SO$_4$; measured in the laboratory	TOC analyser
Dissolved gases	No filtration or preservation; samples collected in Venojet® glass ampoules and measured in the laboratory	Gas chromatography

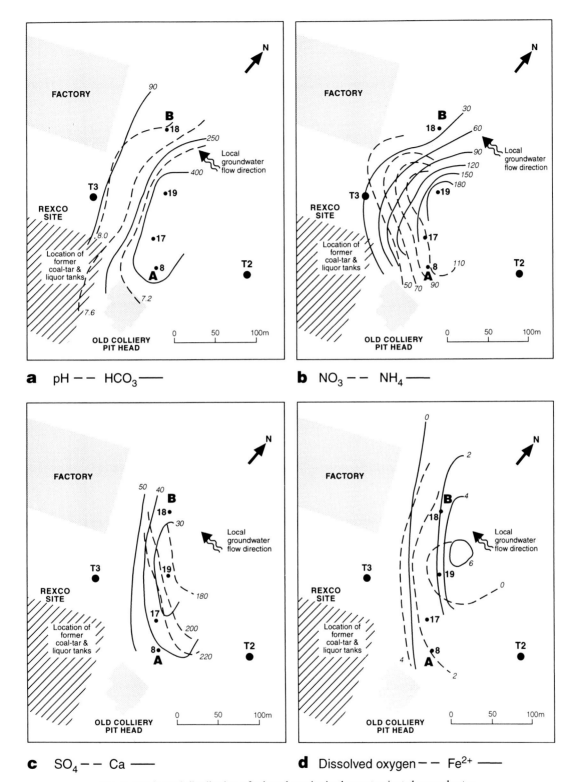

Fig. 1. Horizontal distribution of selected species in the contaminated groundwater.

Table 2. *Selected chemical parameters for a typical waste stream, uncontaminated and contaminated groundwater (Anon 1995)*

	pH	Cl	TOC	NO_3	NO_2	NH_4	Mn	Fe	SO_4	S^{2-}	O_2	CH_4
WS	9.2	nd	4400	nd	nd	1100	nd	nd	nd	115	nd	nd
BG	8–8.5	70–110	0–2	10	0–10	<1	<0.3	bdl	100	<0.2	8–10	0.5–2
CG	6.7–7.5	90–490	5–20	10–130	0–2	15–350	0–0.5	0–9	150–1000	<0.2	0–2	0.5–2

Notes: All data in milligrams per litre except pH; ND = no data available; BDL = below detection limit; WS = typical waste stream; BG = background groundwater; CG = contaminated groundwater.

groundwater, are also displayed in Fig. 2. From these data the main features of the plume chemistry at the site, relative to the uncontaminated groundwater, are as follows:

- Depressed pH, lower Ca concentration but higher alkalinity.
- High NH_4 concentrations plus locally high NO_3 concentrations in the upper part of the plume. The distribution of NO_2 is not unambiguous but is found inside the plume.
- Low or depleted dissolved oxygen concentration but elevated Fe concentration.
- SO_4 and Cl concentrations which show variable distribution.
- Absence of organic chemicals in significant concentrations downstream of the site.
- NVOC (as TOC) present in low concentrations (up to $20 \, \text{mg} \, \text{l}^{-1}$).

In composite, the water quality data suggest that the inorganic contaminants in the plume are primarily derived from the former gasworks site. The relatively high background concentration and distribution of Cl and SO_4 in the groundwater also probably reflect historical localized contamination of the aquifer from colliery workings adjacent to the site (Fig. 1). The source of the NVOC load is uncertain, possibly comprising contributions from both the ammonia waste stream and former mining operations (Broholm *et al.* 1997).

Geochemical modelling

Geochemical modelling of the groundwater quality data was undertaken to interpret in more detail the groundwater hydrochemistry at the site and to provide a dynamic insight into contaminant attenuation processes within the

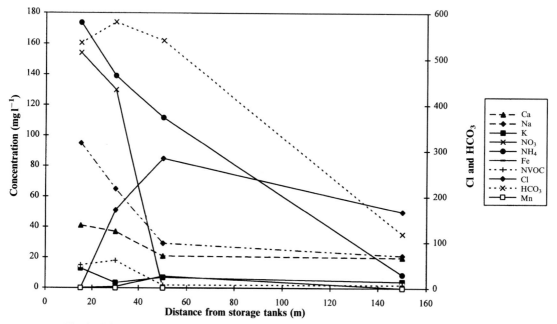

Fig. 2. Solute concentration profiles for selected parameters in the contaminated groundwater.

Table 3. *Saturation states for samples from the plume (5) and uncontaminated groundwater (11)*

Sample	Calcite (CaCO₃)	Siderite (feCO₃)	Mackinawite (FeS)	Rhodochrosite (MnCO₃)	Dolomite ((CaMg)CO₃)	Gypsum (CaSO₄)
5	0.03	0.006	1.288	−1.021	−0.346	−0.561
11	0.360	−	−	−	0.530	−0.715

plume. Static speciation and equilibrium saturation state modelling was performed using MINTEQA2 (Allison *et al.* 1990). Additional equilibrium batch-mixing and reactive transport modelling was undertaken using PHREEQM (Appelo & Postma 1993). In evaluating the saturation status of the groundwater, input values at the detection limit of the analyte were used for species which were not detected. This was done to determine whether aqueous concentrations of these species were controlled by equilibrium with mineral phases. Examples of modelled saturation indexes (SI) for samples from the groundwater and plume are presented in Table 3.

MINTEQA2 calculations indicate that metal cations in both the native and polluted groundwater are primarily bound up in carbonato- and sulphato complexes. The uncontaminated groundwater is generally saturated with respect to calcite and dolomite but undersaturated with respect to $CaSO_4$. In contrast, samples from the plume are in equilibrium with respect to calcite and siderite but undersaturated with respect to dolomite, rhodochrosite and $CaSO_4$. The model also predicted oversaturation with respect to iron monosulphide (mackinawite) in the plume, but this may reflect the high detection limit for sulphide used in the simulations and should therefore be viewed with caution. However, these data suggest that FeS would be expected to immediately precipitate in the plume to limit aqueous sulphide concentrations, and that siderite ($FeCO_3$) equilibrium is more likely to control ferrous iron levels than FeS.

The PHREEQM modelling code was used to evaluate interactions between the ammonia-rich waste stream and native groundwater which may be responsible for the observed hydrochemical characteristics of the contaminant plume. The processes expected to be of importance were oxidation of reduced N species, carbonate phase precipitation and dissolution, and cation-exchange reactions. Static batch mixing was used to simulate oxidation of the ammonia waste, via nitrification, for the following conditions:

1. nitrification in an open system ($ppCO_2 = 3.5$) in equilibrium with calcite;
2. nitrification in an closed system ($ppCO_2 \neq 3.5$) in equilibrium with calcite;
3. as case 1 but initial alkalinity based on dissociation of $350\,mg\,l^{-1}$ NH_3;
4. as case 2 but initial alkalinity based on dissociation of $350\,mg\,l^{-1}$ NH_3;
5. as case 3 but no equilibrium with respect to calcite.

The individual scenarios simulated in these modelling exercises were selected to evaluate possible conditions and reaction pathways in different parts of the plume. Emphasis was placed on evaluating their relative importance in contributing to pH, alkalinity and Ca variations in the groundwater. The initial alkalinity used in cases 3, 4 and 5 was calculated from dissociation of NH_3 in the waste stream. The results of these simulations are presented in Table 4.

The data in Table 4 indicate that ammonia dissociation can produce an order of magnitude higher increase in alkalinity than nitrification and suggest that the latter is a less important influence on the distributions of these species in much of the plume. However, in the absence of ammonia dissociation, nitrification may significantly influence the groundwater chemistry. The results also suggest that the aquifer is probably a closed system when pH in the contaminated groundwater is markedly lower than background values. PHREEQM was also used to simulate reactions affecting contaminant distributions in the plume during transport through the aquifer. Cation exchange reactions and mineral equilibrium were modelled for the following cases:

1. Calcite equilibrium but no initial equilibration with siderite which may precipitate later.
2. No initial equilibration with calcite and siderite (which may precipitate later).

Table 4. *Modelled changes in pH, alkalinity and Ca during nitrification under various conditions*

Case		pH	Total alkalinity ($mg\,l^{-1}$ HCO_3)	Total Ca ($mg\,l^{-1}$)
1	Initial	8.23	39.0	71.3
	Final	7.96	50.2	167
2	Initial	8.23	39.0	71.3
	Final	7.14	208	219
3	Initial	8.23	1215	71.3
	Final	9.11	719	1.12
4	Initial	8.23	1215	71.3
	Final	6.95	955	77.6
5	Initial	8.23	1215	71.3
	Final	6.93	936	71.3

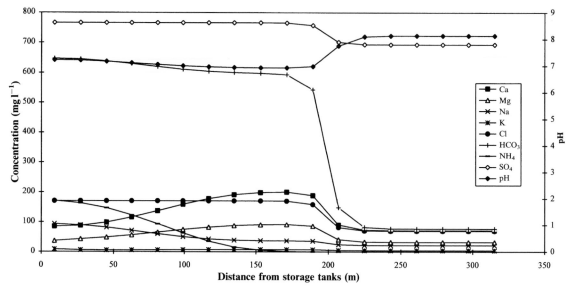

Fig. 3. Simulated groundwater composition for a plume transport time of 2.7 years (1992–1995).

3. Calcite equilibrium but no initial equilibration with siderite which may precipitate later, plus initial alkalinity calculated from dissociation of $350\,mg\,l^{-1}$ NH_3.

A representative model output of these simulations (case 3) showing changes in contaminant loadings with distance from the storage tanks is displayed in Fig. 3 for a transport time of 2.7 years.

The simulated NH_4 profile has been matched to the field data by adjustment of the ion-exchange coefficients and suggests that cation-exchange reactions effectively retard groundwater migration of NH_4 from the site. Downgradient changes in the modelled pH and alkalinity are also in general agreement with the field data, showing respectively depressed and elevated values within the plume compared with the uncontaminated groundwater. Calcium concentrations increase towards the edge of the plume, as recorded by the field survey, but the modelled distribution does not clearly replicate the relatively lower total observed concentrations. This probably reflects simplistic representation of the ion-exchange processes for this system. Further refinement of the model predictions will require experimental determination of selectivity coefficients for all cations in the waste liquor and more detailed characterization of the plume chemistry.

Discussion

Based upon the results of the hydrochemical survey and accompanying geochemical modelling, the key processes controlling inorganic contaminant attenuation in this system are as follows:

- N-compound transformations
- carbonate phase precipitation
- cation-exchange reactions
- redox reactions

The relative contributions of these processes in determining the hydrochemical evolution of the plume will vary according to spatial and temporal changes in the supply of reactants in the system. This must be evaluated with respect to understanding contaminant fate and future groundwater impacts from this site and will now be considered for the various species affected.

Batch mixing of the ammonia-rich waste stream with the native groundwater (data not shown) suggested that the high alkalinity recorded in the plume could arise from the following reactions:

$$NH_3 + H_2O \rightarrow NH_4 + OH^- \qquad (1)$$

$$OH^- + CO_2 \rightarrow HCO_3 \qquad (2)$$

This reaction is likely to be locally important in raising porewater pH above that of the native groundwater, with implications for the mobility of metallic species (see below). Further attenuation of the NH_4 load will occur via sorption to the aquifer substrate and biotic transformation. The presence of NO_3 and NO_2 at concentrations significantly above background levels in groundwater at the site (Table 2 and Fig. 1) suggests that such transformation occurs by nitrification, according to the following pathway:

$$NH_4 + 3/2O_2 \rightarrow NO_2 + H_2O + 2H^+ \qquad (3)$$

$$NO_2 + 1/2O_2 \rightarrow NO_3 \qquad (4)$$

Batch-mixing simulations (see cases 4 and 5 above) indicate that the theoretical pH and alkalinity produced by these nitrification reactions are in reasonable agreement with those measured in the contaminated groundwater. However, this process is likely to be restricted to the mixing zone between oxygenated and contaminated groundwater at the edge of the NH_4 front, as confirmed by the presence of high NO_3 levels adjacent to the site where upstream aerobic groundwater intercepts the plume (Fig. 1).

Reactions (3) and (4) produce net acidity which may be buffered in this system by dissolution of native carbonate phases. Batch-mixing simulations (cases 1 and 2) show that although this produces increased porewater alkalinity, it cannot account for the lower Ca concentrations observed within the plume. The simulation for case 5 suggested that this could be achieved if nitrification occurred in the absence of calcite equilibrium (Table 4). This is unrealistic on kinetic grounds and is not substantiated by the distribution of NO_3, alkalinity and Ca in the contaminated groundwater (Fig. 1). The depressed pH and Ca depletion can instead be explained by precipitation of authigenic calcite within the plume, under the high porewater alkalinities generated by ammonia dissociation (reactions 1 and 2), as in:

$$Ca + HCO_3 \rightarrow CaCO_3 + H^+ \qquad (5)$$

Reactive transport modelling has demonstrated that cation-exchange reactions may significantly retard NH_4 migration from the site. The simulations predict that NH_4 sorption should be accompanied by desorption of native Ca and Mg from the aquifer sediment (Fig. 3).

This feature is confirmed by locally higher groundwater concentrations of these species in the plume, downgradient of the NH_4 centroid (Fig. 1). It is expected that the porewater concentrations of Ca and Mg mobilized by exchange with NH_4 will be limited by carbonate precipitation (e.g. reaction (5)).

Elevated levels of Fe in groundwater beneath the site (Fig. 1) probably arise from the reductive dissolution of ferric oxyhydroxides on the aquifer sediments. This process is commonly coupled to the microbially catalysed anaerobic oxidation of organic matter (e.g. CH_2O), as in:

$$CH_2O + 4Fe(OH)_3 + 8H^+ \rightarrow CO_2 + 4Fe^{2+} + 11H_2O$$
$$(6)$$

and will be sustained by the supply of NVOC in the plume. Measured Fe concentrations in the groundwater are in good agreement with those predicted from this reaction, based on the NVOC load (up to $20\,mg\,l^{-1}$). Aerobic degradation of the NVOC load may also occur at the plume edges (Broholm *et al.* 1998), competing with nitrification for the available dissolved oyxgen supply. MINTEQA2 simulations predict that siderite precipitation will attenuate the ferrous iron mobilized by reaction (6) under the alkaline conditions prevailing within the plume:

$$Fe^{2+} + HCO_3 \rightarrow FeCO_3 + H^+ \qquad (7)$$

No sulphide and, by inference, SO_4 reduction was detected in the contaminated groundwater, and model calculations imply that concentrations of both species are

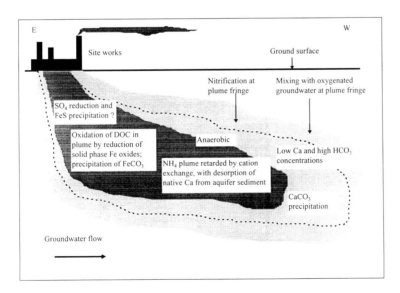

Fig. 4. Schematic of attenuation processes in the contaminated groundwater.

not constrained by mineral equilibria (e.g. FeS and $CaSO_4$) (Table 3). Precipitation of FeS may occur in the plume but it cannot be demonstrated with the present data. These data suggest that SO_4 behaves conservatively in the system, with advective mixing and dilution providing the major attenuation mechanism. The colliery workings immediately southeast of the site are probably the primary source of the locally high SO_4 load recorded in the groundwater (Fig. 1), although inputs from oxidation of the sulphide load present in the waste stream from the site (Table 2) may also be important. The relative contribution from these two sources cannot be evaluated with the data available.

A conceptual model for the aquifer, summarizing the key attenuation processes for inorganic contaminants within the pollution plume at this site, is presented in Fig. 4.

Conclusion

A hydrochemical investigation of a Triassic Sandstone aquifer polluted by wastes from former coal-carbonization plant and coal mining operations indicates that the contaminated groundwater is reducing and highly alkaline, with elevated concentrations of NH_4, SO_4, NO_3, Fe and dissolved organic carbon. The water quality data, supported by geochemical modelling, suggest that N-compound transformation, carbonate phase precipitation, cation-exchange reactions and redox reactions are primarily responsible for attenuating the inorganic contaminants within the plume identified. The key physico-chemical properties of the aquifer which control the attenuation of the contaminant suite examined are the pH buffering, oxidation and cation exchange capacity.

Although the aquifer has considerable potential for the intrinsic remediation of the polluted groundwater, the present loadings of reduced C- and N-compounds in the plume vastly exceed the dissolved oxygen supply in the system. This is principally mediated and constrained by mixing of the contaminant plume with aerobic groundwater, and limits the capacity for passive remediation of the residual NH_4 load which remains a long term problem under the present conditions. Sorption by the aquifer sediment is the main mechanism responsible for the attenuation of NH_4 within the plume. This is supplemented by nitrification at the plume margins.

A substantial supply of other oxidants such as dissolved SO_4 and Fe oxyhydroxides on the aquifer sediment is available within the system. These can in principle be used in the anaerobic oxidation of organic fractions in the plume, and there is some evidence, for Fe at least, that this is currently occurring. However, the present organic loadings in the plume are negligible in comparison to the reservoir of NH_4. Under these conditions the contaminated groundwater is likely to remain anaerobic and additional amendments of oxidants will be necessary to supplement the natural supply as part of an active restoration programme for the aquifer.

Acknowledgements. E. Arvin (Technical University of Denmark) is thanked for useful discussion of this paper, and the help of D. Hay and I. Jones (University of Bradford) with fieldwork and chemical analysis is gratefully acknowledged. This research is (partly) sponsored by the EU in the project 'Processes underlying the remediation of creosote-contaminated groundwater in a fractured sandstone'.

References

ALLISON, J. D., BROWN, D. S. & NOVO-GRADAC, K. J. 1990. *MINTEQA2 metal speciation equilibrium model for surface and groundwater, version 3.00.* Center for Exposure Assessment Modelling, USEPA, Athens, Georgia.

ANON 1995. *Processes underlying remediation of creosote contaminated groundwater in fractured sandstone.* 1st Year Annual Report, Directorate General XII, Commission of the European Communities.

APHA 1985. *Standard Methods for the Examination of Water and Wastewaters.*

APPELO, C. A. J. & POSTMA, D. 1993. *Geochemistry, Groundwater and Pollution.* Balkema, Rotterdam.

BERGLIND, L. 1982. *Determination of polycyclic aromatic hydrocarbons in industrial discharges and other aqueous effluents.* Norwegian Institute for Water Research Report.

BROHOLM, M. M., JONES, I., TORSTENSSON, D. & ARVIN, E. 1998. Groundwater contamination from a coal carbonisation plant. *This volume.*

CHRISTENSEN, T. H., KJELDSEN, P., ALBRECHTSEN, H. J., HERON, G., NIELSEN, P. H., BJERG, P. L. & HOLM, P. E. 1994. Attenuation of landfill leachate pollutants in aquifers. *Critical Reviews in Environmental Science & Technology,* **24**, 119–202.

COZZARELLI, I. M., BAEDECKER, M. J., EGANHOUSE, R. P. & GOELITZ, D. F. 1994. The geochemical evolution of low-molecular weight organic acids derived from the degradation of petroleum contaminants in groundwater. *Geochimica et Cosmochimica Acta,* **58**, 863–877.

HERON, G., CHRISTENSEN, T. H. & TJELL, J. C. 1994. Oxidation capacity of aquifer sediments. *Environmental Science & Technology,* **28**, 153–158.

KEHEW, A. E. & PASSERO, R. N. 1990. pH and redox buffering mechanisms in a glacial drift aquifer contaminated by landfill leachate. *Groundwater,* **28**, 728–737.

KIILERICH, O. & ARVIN, E. 1995. Groundwater contamination from creosote sites. *Groundwater* (in press).

LOTIMER, A. R., BELANGER, D. W. & WHIFFEN, R. B. 1992. Occurrences of coal tar and contaminated groundwater at three sites in Ontario. *In:* WEYER (ed.) *Subsurface Contamination by Immiscible Fluids.* Balkema, Rotterdam.

LYNGKILDE, J. & CHRISTENSEN, T. H. 1992. Fate of organic contaminants in the redox zones of a landfill leachate pollution plume (Vejen, Denmark). *Journal of Contaminant Hydrology,* **10**, 273–289.

MATHER, J. D. 1989. The attenuation of the organic component of landfill leachate in the unsaturated zone: a review. *Quarterly Journal of Engineering Geology*, **22**, 241–246.

NICHOLSON, R. V., GILLHAM, R. V. & REARDON, E. J. 1983. Migration of contaminants in groundwater at a landfill: a case study, 6. Hydrochemistry. *Journal of Hydrology*, **63**, 131–176.

RAVEN, K. G. & BECK, P. 1992. Coal tar and creosote contamination in Ontario. *In*: WEYER (ed.) *Subsurface Contamination by Immiscible Fluids*. Balkema, Rotterdam.

SCHIRMER, M., JONES, I., TEUSTCH, G. & LERNER, D. N. 1995. Development and testing of multiport sock samplers for groundwater. *Journal of Hydrology*, **171**, 239–257.

Groundwater contamination from a coal carbonization plant

Mette M. Broholm,[1] Ian Jones,[2] Daniel Torstensson[3] & Erik Arvin[1]

[1] Department of Environmental Science and Engineering, Technical University of Denmark, Denmark
[2] Department of Environmental and Civil Engineering, University of Bradford, Bradford, U.K.
[3] AB Jacobson & Widmark, Water and Environment, Lidingö, Sweden

Abstract. The Rexco coal carbonization plant near Mansfield in the UK East Midlands produced coke by the process known as 'Rexco' in the 1950s to early 1960s. In the process gas and coal-tar were also produced. The gas was cooled with water whereby ammonia and coal-tar in the gas were dissolved/condensed. Ammonia liquor and coal-tar are known to have leaked into the subsurface from cracked tanks at the site. Based on this, a large plume of ammonium and coal-tar compounds was expected to be present in the aquifer. Effluent compositions have been determined, and an extensive reconnaissance study of the groundwater contamination in the sandstone aquifer has been carried out. The coal-tar contained phenols, naphthalenes and BTEXs, and low levels of PAHs. The ammonia liquor contained very high concentrations of phenols and ammonium. Extensive contamination with ammonium has been encountered, indicating the ammonia liquor as the primary source of contamination. No significant contamination with specific organic coal-tar compounds is present today in spite of the extensive leaks of coal-tar and ammonia liquor in the past. The organic coal-tar compounds released with the ammonia liquor have likely been degraded/transformed in the saturated part of the aquifer as well as in the vadose zone.

Introduction

Gas and coke production by coal carbonization is a well known source of soil and groundwater contamination with organic coal-tar compounds. The Rexco coal carbonization plant located east of Mansfield in the UK East Midlands produced coke by a process known as 'Rexco'. This paper concentrates on the groundwater contamination with specific organic compounds from process effluents. Groundwater flow history and non-reactive solute transport modelling is presented in a companion paper by Jones *et al.* (1998) and the hydrochemistry of the aquifer and plume is presented in a companion paper by Torstensson *et al.* (1998).

The coal carbonization plant and the Rexco process

The Rexco plant was in operation in the 1950s and 1960s (Mansfield District Council 1987). A site plan is shown in Fig. 1. Coke was produced by the low temperature carbonization process known as 'the Rexco process'. Weakly caking coal was carbonized in cylindrical vertical retorts. The coal was heated directly by hot gases drawn down through the retort. The process was intermittent. A flow diagram of the Rexco process is shown in Fig. 2. The crude gaseous products of the carbonization were taken away from the bottom of the retort through a curtain of re-circulated aqueous cooling liquor. Most of the tar and ammonia was removed from the gas in this wash-box, and the remainder was removed in a cyclone tar-extractor. The tar was separated from the aqueous ammonia liquor in a tank, and the ammonia liquor was transferred to other tanks. The gas was used as process gas or burned to waste. The intermittent process was later replaced by a continuous process (Utah Conservation and Research Foundation 1939; Gibson & Gregory 1971).

Rexco produced around 5000 gallons ($20 \, m^3$) of liquor a day. At an unknown date, a storage tank for ammonia liquor cracked and liquor migrated along the railway track drain to a small lagoon approximately 800 m east of the plant. The drain was open along at least part of its length. The company apparently continued to use the drain and lagoon for the disposal of liquor (Mansfield District Council 1987).

The site has since been reclaimed. The tanks and part of the contaminated soil at the part of the site located on the west side of the access road were removed in 1994. Several tanks full of aqueous liquor and two tanks with coal-tar were encountered. At least one of the coal-tar tanks had leaked, and free phase coal-tar was observed in fractures in the sandstone. Below the bottom of the excavation (approximately 7 m deep) free phase coal-tar was still present in the fractures. The part of the site west of the access road was capped to prevent rainwater infiltration through the remaining coal-tar. The coal-tar tanks were situated near the retort; the approximate

BROHOLM, M. M., JONES, I., TORSTENSSON, D. & ARVIN, E. 1998. Groundwater contamination from a coal carbonization plant. *In*: LERNER, D. N. & WALTON, N. R. G. (eds) 1998. *Contaminated Land and Groundwater: Future Directions*. Geological Society, London, Engineering Geology Special Publications, **14**, 159–165.

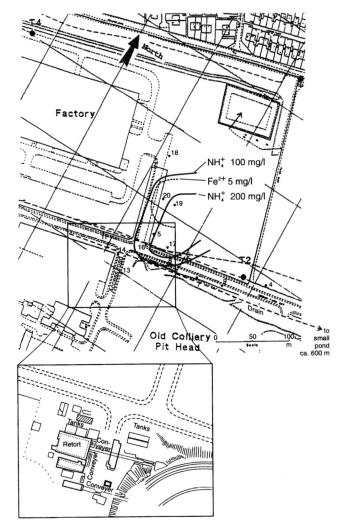

Fig. 1. The Mansfield site and the distribution of ammonium and dissolved iron in the groundwater. The insert shows the Rexco coal carbonization plant, with the hatched area indicating the approximate location of the coal-tar tanks.

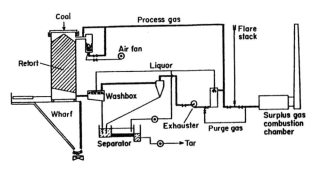

Fig. 2. Process diagram for the Rexco process (Gibson & Gregory 1971).

location is indicated on the insert in Fig. 1. Two wells were installed approximately 2 m apart, where the coal-tar leak was observed, and one of the boreholes was cored through the coal-tar (Nottingham County Council 1995). In the water sample from one of the wells high concentrations of coal-tar compounds (940 ppb total naphthalenes and polyaromatic hydrocarbons) were found, while the water sample from the other well was free of coal-tar compounds. Analysis of sandstone samples from these two wells contained ammonium (5–330 ppm) and phenol(s) (12–53 ppm) above the water table. The highest concentrations were encountered 17–20 m below the ground surface (analytical results supplied by Nottingham County Council).

Geology and groundwater flow

The site is situated east of Mansfield in the UK East Midlands on Triassic Sherwood Sandstone. The sandstone is highly porous and fractured and serves as the primary aquifer in the region. The water table is situated approximately 20 m below the ground surface at the site. The direction of flow has changed over the past 30 years as water extraction in the area has varied. The predominant direction of flow in the past has been to the north-northeast, and since 1992 it has been to the west. The regional-scale hydraulic conductivity is 2–6 m day^{-1}. The history of water extraction, hydrogeology and flow directions are presented in the companion paper by Jones *et al.* (1998). The sandstone aquifer is aerobic. The hydrochemistry of the aquifer is presented in the companion paper by Torstensson *et al.* (1998).

Investigations

Coal-tar and ammonia liquor analysis

A coal-tar sample and an ammonia liquor sample from a low temperature carbonization process very similar to the Rexco process were analysed for organic coal-tar compounds. The coal-tar was diluted in an ether (85%)–pentane (15%) mixture with 1-bromo-naphthalene as internal standard, and analysed by gas chromatography with flame ionization detection (GC-FID). For the coal-tar the dominating organic compounds were identified by GC with mass-spectrometric detection (MS) of a sample. The ammonia liquor was diluted in tap-water and extracted with the ether–pentane mixture. The analytical method used for coal-tar and ammonia liquor was a slightly modified version of the method described below for groundwater samples. The oven temperature increase was changed to 10°C min^{-1} to improve compound separation. Standards of a mixture of phenols and naphthalenes in the ether–pentane mixture and standards of 22 coal-tar compounds including all major groups were prepared and used for quantitative calibration.

The ammonia liquor was analysed for pH by indicator paper and ammonium by an Aquamerck test-kit method.

Groundwater sampling and analysis

The study has included the sampling and analysis of groundwater from about 20 wells (including existing sampling wells and extraction wells in the area) and seven multilevel samplers. This presentation concentrates on the contamination which has entered the ground at the former Rexco site. Data from eight wells and six multilevels and two existing extraction wells (T2 and T4) were selected because these wells and multilevels were the ones closest to the former Rexco site. The locations of the boreholes are given in Fig. 1. The wells and multilevel not included in this paper are located outside the area included in Fig. 1. Boreholes 4, 5, 6, 7, 8, 9, 11 and 13 are equipped with a single well-screen. Boreholes 14, 16, 17 and 18 are equipped with multilevels with a sock-packer system with 5–10 sampling points; in addition boreholes 16, 17 and 18 are equipped with a narrow piezometer pipe. Boreholes 19 and 20 are equipped with three narrow piezometer pipes screened at different depth intervals. The wells were purged (minimum 100 l) and sampled with a MP1 submersible pump, the narrow piezometer pipes were purged (minimum 10 l) and sampled with a Waterra pump and the multilevels with sock-packers were purged (chamber emptied three to five times) and sampled by application of nitrogen gas pressure. The drilling techniques and borehole installations are described in more detail by Jones *et al.* (1998). Boreholes 8, 5, 17, 19 and 18 are placed along the present flow-lines and perpendicular to the previously predominant flow direction.

Prior to sampling, the wells and multilevels were purged untill free of fines and until constant conductivity and pH measured in a flow-cell was obtained. Samples for organic compounds were obtained from an unbroken waterstream overflowing the 100 ml dark sampling bottles with teflon-lined screw-caps. The samples were preserved with phosphoric acid. Immediately prior to extraction the samples were neutralized with sodium hydroxide.

The majority of the samples were analysed for specific organic coal-tar compounds. A gas-chromatographic method for coal-tar compounds in groundwater, including 37 organic compounds, was developed. A 10 ml water sample was extracted with 1 ml of an ether (85%)–pentane (15%) mixture with 1-bromonaphthalene as internal standard. Complete extraction efficiencies were found for BTEXs, naphthalenes and PAHs. Phenol had an extraction efficiency of 38% and the other phenolic compounds had extraction efficiencies ranging from approximately 60% to 85%. For O- and S-heterocyclic compounds tested, between 80% and full extraction efficiencies were found. N-heterocyclic compounds were not selected for quantification, the extraction yields for quinoline and pyrrole respectively were of the order of

40% and 22%. The extract was analysed on a Shimatzu gas chromatograph 14A (GC) with flame ionization detector (FID) and 25 m Wcot fused silica 32 mm ID CP-sil 19CB Chrompack column. An oven temperature programme of 45°C for 2 min, 20°C min^{-1} to 280°C, and holding for 5 min was used. Data collection and peak integration were performed with MAXIMA. An internal standard calibration method was used, and the standard curve was obtained by best-fit linear regression through the origin of six to eight calibration standards concentration versus relative peak area. Detection limits for most of the organic compounds (including phenols and naphthalenes) were in the low ppb range.

A standard was occasionally analysed for verification of retention times. Minimum duplicate blank samples of tap-water were prepared and analyzsed with every set of samples, and great care was taken not to cause laboratory contamination of samples.

The tubing (nylon) used for the multilevels with sock-packers caused severe contamination (ppm level) of the samples with *one* organic compound (likely a plasticizer) and ppb level contamination with several other organic compounds. Therefore, samples for organic analysis from boreholes with multilevels were obtained from the piezometer pipes, except for multilevel 14. Of the samples for which data for organic analysis are reported in this paper, only the samples from multilevel 14 had been exposed to the nylon tubing. These samples contained the ppm-level compound from the nylon tubing. As a simple batch leaching test revealed the compound to be from the tubing (extremely high concentration in the leaching test, over-scale peak) and as it is not a process effluent compound, it is not included in Table 2. The two peaks with retention times 7.73 and 8.36 reported in Table 2 were observed at ppb level in the leaching test and correspond to the retention time of two of the 37 compounds included in the analysis. It can therefore not be excluded that the low ppb contamination (below or near the quantification limit) might be from the tubing.

Subsequently, all tubing materials used were tested in simple batch leaching tests. This revealed that it could also not be excluded that the tubing used for the sampling of wells with a submersible pump might have caused the low ppb level contamination (below or near the quantification limit) with the two peaks with retention times 7.73 and 8.36. The samples from piezometer nests and piezometer pipes of multilevels were sampled with Waterra pumps and tubing (HDPE), for which the leaching test did not indicate any cross-contamination to water samples.

Selected samples were analysed for total non-volatile organic carbon (NVOC) by a standard method on a Dohrmann DC-80 TOC analyser. Selected samples were analysed by High Performance Size Exclusion Chromatographic (HP-SEC) analysis of the molecular weight distribution with UV detection to determine the nature of the NVOC content.

In addition analyses were carried out for ammonium and the redox-parameters oxygen, nitrate, nitrite, sulphate, sulphide, iron, manganese and methane, major ions, pH, conductivity and alkalinity. The techniques are described in Torstensson *et al.* (1998).

Soil sample analysis

A surface soil sample from the small lagoon was dispersed in water and extracted with ether. The extract was analysed by the GC-FID method. The extraction efficiency is unknown and the analysis therefore only qualitative. Compound identification is based on retention-times alone.

Results

Coal-tar and ammonia liquor composition

The pH of the ammonia liquor was approximately 9 and the concentration of ammonium was approximately 10 000 mg N l^{-1} (or 1%). This corresponds well with the ammonium concentration of 12 800 mg N l^{-1} determined in a sample of ammonia liquor taken at the plant in 1955 (Mansfield District Council 1987).

Table 1. *Comparison of coal-tar and organic coal-tar compounds in ammonia liquor*

Compounds	Coal-tar (wt%)	Ammonia liquor (mg l^{-1})	Compounds	Coal-tar (wt%)	Ammonia liquor (mg l^{-1})
Phenol	1.31	7700	Naphthalene	0.46	1
o-Cresol	1.36	2400	Benzene	0.04	10
m-, p-Cresol	1.86	4100	Toluene	0.12	20
2,6-Xylenol	0.30	100	Ethylbenzene	0.09	10
2,4- 2,5-Xylenol	1.33	780	o-Xylene	0.12	10
3,4-Xylenol	0.38	220	m-, p-Xylene	0.17	10
2,3-, 3,5-Xylenol	1.15	690	Phenanthrene	0.27	nd
1-Methyl-naphthalene	0.18	nd	2-Methyl-naphthalene	0.39	nd

The results of coal-tar and ammonia liquor analysis are given in Table 1 for selected organic compounds.

In addition to the compounds listed in Table 1 the following compounds have been identified in the coal-tar: C3-alkylbenzenes, C3-alkylphenols, C3-alkylnaphthalenes, antracene, methylphenanthrene, methylfluorene, methylthiophene, methyldibenzofurane and various aliphatic hydrocarbons. The chromatograms for the coal-tar show a high concentration of phenolic compounds and a relatively low concentration of naphthalenes. Lower contents of mono-aromatic hydrocarbons (BTEXs) are observed. Individual polyaromatic hydrocarbons (PAHs) and heterocyclic compounds (NSOs) are scarce and present in low concentrations. The overall picture does not resemble that of a typical gas-work coal-tar but rather a (distillation) fraction of a coal-tar dominated by phenols and naphthalenes without the coal-tar compounds of high and low boiling-points.

The chromatograms for the ammonia liquor resemble the coal-tar, but the phenols dominate and the relative content of naphthalenes and PAHs is very low. The composition compares well to the expected composition in water in contact with the coal-tar analysed. The dominating individual phenols in the ammonia liquor as well as the coal-tar are phenol, m- and/or p-cresol, o-cresol, 2,4- and/or 2,5-xylenol, and 2,3- and/or 3,5-xylenol. The total concentration of phenols in the ammonia liquor is very high and corresponds well with referenced values for ammonia liquor from coal carbonization plants (Needham 1961; Nichols undated).

Groundwater contamination

Ammonium plume. A plume of ammonium with concentrations of up to $352 \, mg \, l^{-1}$ has been located emanating from the drain or from the part of the site east of the access road. The plume might partially originate from the part of the site located west of the access road, if after the reclamation of this part of the site contaminants are no longer leached to the groundwater. The distribution of ammonium in the aquifer based on water sample analysis by September 1996 is illustrated in Fig. 1. The contours are based on the highest concentration measured at the location independently of depth of sampling location (e.g. multilevel point). The points sampled in multilevel 14 are deeper relative to the water table than the section sampled in other wells and multilevels. Ammonium contamination has been found to about 15 m below the water table. The highest concentrations are found in the upper approximately 5 m of the saturated zone. Recent geophysical investigations and groundwater flow modelling indicate that the plume extends much further northeast (Jones *et al.* 1998). As no non-reactive tracer has been found, ammonium appears to be the parameter best describing the extend of the plume.

Organic coal-tar compounds and NVOC. The results of the organic analysis of samples are summarized in Table 2. As the concentrations were too low for MS identification of compounds found by GC-FID analysis, the compound names given in Table 2 are based on

Table 2. *Organic contaminants in groundwater samples ($\mu g \, l^{-1}$)*

Well multilevel	RT 4.42 (toluene)	RT 7.73 (C4-alkyl-benzene)	RT 8.36 (phenol)	RT 12.61 (fluorene) RT 13,66	NVOC	NH_4^+ conc. in sample ($mg \, l^{-1}$)
4	6–8	(5–8)	(8–38)	nd	–	3
5	nd	(nd–2)	(3–8)	8	4 100–5 800	144
6	nd–3	(nd–2)	(nd–13)	nd	–	106
7	nd	(1)	(1–5)	nd	–	43
8	nd	nd	(nd–3)	nd–152	15 000	122
9	1	(1)	nd	10	–	7
11	nd	nd	nd	nd	–	0.8
13	nd	(1)	nd	nd	–	6
14–6	5	nd	nd	nd	–	0.6
14–7	7	(7)	(14)	nd	–	0.4
14–8	6	(1)	(5)	nd	–	35
14–9	3	nd	nd	nd	–	0.7
14–10	8	nd	nd	nd	–	0.2
16	–	–	–	–	–	146
17-pz	nd	nd	nd	nd	16 000	352
18-pz	–	–	–	nd	2 100	9
19-pz2	5	nd	nd	nd	6 400–9 700	132
T2	nd	nd	nd	nd	–	–
T4	nd	nd	nd	nd	1 100	nd

RT, retention time of compound peak in GC-FID analysis; –, not analysed; nd, not detected.
Concentrations $< 10 \mu g \, l^{-1}$ are at or below normal detection limits and below quantification limits. Parentheses indicate that low ppb level contamination from tubing cannot be excluded.

retention time alone. As mentioned previously, contamination from tubing occurred in multilevel 14 and possibly in some of the wells. Results that may be related to contamination from tubing are marked.

In general the concentrations of specific organic compounds in the groundwater were insignificant, for most samples lower than or of the same order of magnitude as the detection and quantification level for the compounds. This was verified by analysis at independent laboratories.

Elevated NVOC concentrations were encountered in the plume. The NVOC content appears (based on the HP-SEC analysis) to consist primarily of humic-like substances.

Redox conditions

The aquifer is aerobic. Within the ammonium plume, depletion of oxygen is observed, indicating anoxic conditions in the plume. Closest to the site single samples have increased levels of nitrate indicating nitrification of ammonium, whereas single samples further downstream in the plume indicate nitrate reduction. Dissolved iron is present in the plume (illustrated in Fig. 1). This indicates the occurrence of iron reduction in the plume. Sulphate is generally high due to coal mining activities in the area. The hydrochemistry including the redox conditions in and at the perimeter of the plume are described in more detail by Torstensson *et al.* (1997).

Soil contamination in lagoon

The surface soil sample contained organic coal-tar compounds, dominated by naphthalenes. The overall picture resembled that of a weathered coal-tar with a very low PAH content, and corresponds relatively well with the expected composition of a weathered contamination from ammonia liquor (weathered meaning with the most soluble compounds leached out, most volatile compounds evaporated, and some compounds potentially degraded aerobically).

Discussion

The high concentrations of ammonium in the groundwater strongly indicate that the source of the contamination is the aqueous ammonia liquor from the Rexco process. The aqueous ammonia liquor is based on the analysis of liquor from a similar process believed to have contained high concentrations of organic coal-tar compounds, in particular phenolic compounds. The results of organic analysis of groundwater samples have revealed that no significant contamination with organic coal-tar compounds is present in the plume defined by the ammonium. This means that either the compounds have been degraded/transformed in the aquifer and/or

unsaturated zone, or they have been separated from the source and the ammonium plume.

The contamination of the topsoil in the small lagoon indicates that the ammonia liquor released did contain organic coal-tar compounds and that naphthalenes and BTEXs were retarded relative to phenols in the topsoil. The presence of coal-tar compounds in the surface topsoil also indicates that complete degradation of the compounds has not occurred.

All of the phenols can potentially be degraded under aerobic conditions (Mueller *et al.* 1991; Nielsen & Christensen 1994). Degradation of phenol, o-cresol, m-cresol, p-cresol, 2,4-xylenol and 3,4-xylenol has been observed under anoxic (nitrate and/or iron reducing) conditions in laboratory experiments (Lovley & Lonergan 1990; Flyvbjerg *et al.* 1993; Nielsen *et al.* 1995) whereas 2,3-, 2,5-, 2,6- and 3,5-xylenol were persistent under nitrate reducing conditions (Flyvbjerg *et al.* 1993). In a field experiment within a leachate plume phenol was degraded under anoxic conditions (nitrate and iron reducing) after a long lag-phase, but o-cresol was persistent (Nielsen *et al.* 1995).

If oxygen is present, nitrification of ammonium occurs. However, as nitrifying bacteria grow slowly relative to heterotrophic bacteria responsible for degradation of organic compounds, available oxygen may be utilized in the degradation of organics thereby preventing nitrification (Henze *et al.* 1995). Hence, there appear to be a good potential for degradation of the organic compounds outside and at the perimeter of the ammonium plume in the groundwater as well as in the unsaturated zone. For phenol, the cresols and some of the xylenols there also appears to be a potential for degradation within the anoxic plume whereas other xylenols would be expected to persist. However, the number of sites for which degradation experiments with aquifer material have been conducted is limited. Laboratory experiments with sandstone material from the site can provide information on the degradation potential under anoxic as well as aerobic conditions in this aquifer.

Phenols have been observed to be polymerized or incorporated in humic materials enzymatically (Lassen *et al.* 1994) in laboratory experiments. It is unknown whether polymerization is likely to occur in this aquifer.

Geochemical modelling (Torstensson *et al.* 1997) has indicated that ammonium may be strongly retarded by ion-exchange to the sandstone. However, laboratory determinations of the ion-exchange capacity for the sandstone is essential in order to evaluate the transport of the phenols relative to ammonium.

The amount of ammonia liquor released from the plant while it was still in operation was very large. Concentrations of phenols were apparently very high. Therefore, in spite of the potential for aerobic degradation of phenols in the large unsaturated zone, it does not seem likely that the plume never contained phenols.

The lack of contamination with phenols within the ammonium plume in the sandstone aquifer may well be a result of a combination of aerobic degradation or transformation of phenols outside and at the perimeter of the ammonium plume and in the vadose zone in combination with retardation of the ammonium; and degradation or transformation of phenols under nitrate and/or iron reducing conditions.

Free phase coal-tar is known to have been present in fractures in the vadose zone below the former coal-tar tanks. There have been liquor tanks all around this part of the site and previous analysis of sandstone samples from the vadose zone below the coal-tar tanks indicates contamination with ammonia liquor. Therefore, coal-tar compounds eluted from the free phase coal-tar by infiltrating water is likely to have entered the saturated zone in an area where ammonium also entered the saturated zone. However, it is unknown where the bulk of the ammonia liquor entered the subsurface or reached the water table. Based on the ammonium plume encountered it may have been over the entire Rexco site and from the drain along the Rexco site. It appears likely that coal-tar compounds leached from the free phase coal-tar would have migrated in the same direction as the ammonium plume. It is unknown if the amount of coal-tar compounds eluted from free phase coal-tar with infiltrating water has been significant relative to the amount of coal-tar compounds infiltrating with ammonia liquor.

The plume of NVOC appears to be related to the ammonium plume. The NVOC primarily consists of humic-like substances and not organic coal-tar compounds such as phenols. This indicates that the humic substances have been eluted by the ammonia liquor. This may be a result of transformation of naturally occurring humic substances by enzymatical incorporation of phenols or of degradation of biomass formed by degradation of phenols in the unsaturated zone.

Conclusions

In spite of extensive leaks of coal-tar and ammonia liquor with high concentrations of phenols in the past, no significant groundwater contamination with specific organic coal-tar compounds is present within the ammonium plume in the aquifer at the Rexco site near Mansfield today. These findings indicate a good potential for natural attenuation of organic coal-tar compounds in contamination related to the coal carbonization process in the aquifer as well as the unsaturated zone of the sandstone deposit. A large plume of ammonium has resulted from the activities on the site.

Acknowledgements. The data presented in this paper constitute part of the research project, 'Processes underlying remediation of creosote contaminated groundwater in fractured sandstone', sponsored by the European Union. C. Grøn, RISØ National Laboratories, is greatly acknowledged for performing and evaluating the HP-SEC analysis for speciation of the NVOC content.

References

FLYVBJERG, J., ARVIN, E, JENSEN, B. K. & OLSEN, S. K. 1993. Microbial degradation of phenols and aromatic hydrocarbons in creosote contaminated groundwater under nitrate reducing conditions. *Journal of Contaminant Hydrology*, **12**, 133–150.

GIBSON, J., & GREGORY, D. H. 1971. *Carbonization of Coal.* Coal Research Establishment, National Coal Board. Mills and Boon, UK.

HENZE, M., HARREMOES, P., JANSEN, J. C. & ARVIN, E. 1995. *Waste Water Treatment. Biological and Chemical Processes.* Springer, Berlin.

JONES, I., DAVISON, R. & LERNER, D. 1998. The importance of understanding groundwater flow history in assessing present-day groundwater contamination patterns: a case study. *This volume.*

LASSEN, P., RANDALL, A., JØRGENSEN, O., WARWICK, P. & CARLSEN, L. 1994. Enzymatically mediated incorporation of 2-chlorophenol and 4-chlorophenol into humic acids. *Chemosphere*, **28**, 703–710.

LOVLEY, D. R. & LONERGAN, D. J. 1990. Anaerobic oxidation of toluene, phenol and p-cresol by the dissimilatory iron-reduction organism, GS-15. *Applied Microbiology*, **56**, 1858–1864.

MANSFIELD DISTRICT COUNCIL 1987. *Pollution of the triassic Sherwood sandstones east of Mansfield.* Technical Services Groundwater Report No. 33. File cat. 414.124.03.

MUELLER, J. G., MIDDAUGH, D. P., LANTZ, S. E. & CHAPMAN, P. J. 1991. Biodegradation of creosote and pentachlorophenol in contaminated groundwater: chemical and biological assessment. *Applied Environmental Microbiology*, **57**, 1277–1285.

NEEDHAM, C. E. 1961. Reactive fuels and chemicals from coal. *I. P. Review*, 165–171.

NICHOLS, R. undated. Effluent problems associated with the coking process. Internal memo by R. Nichols, Chief Scientist for National Smokeless Fuels, Great Britain. Courtesy of Coal Products Limited.

NIELSEN, P. H., ALBRECHTSEN, H-J., HERON, G. & CHRISTENSEN, T. H. 1995. In situ and laboratory studies on the fate of specific organic compounds in an anaerobic landfill leachate plume, 1. experimental conditions and fate of phenolic compounds. *Journal of Contaminant Hydrology*, **20**, 27–50.

—— & CHRISTENSEN, T. H. 1994. Variability of biological degradation of phenolic hydrocarbons in an aerobic aquifer determined by laboratory batch experiments. *Journal of Contaminant Hydrology*, **17**, 55–67.

NOTTINGHAM COUNTY COUNCIL 1995. Personal communication with administrator involved in the Rexco site remediation.

TORSTENSSON, D., THORNTON, S., BROHOLM, M., & LERNER, D. 1998. Hydrochemistry of pollutant attenuation in groundwater contaminated by coal tar wastes. *This volume.*

UTAH CONSERVATION AND RESEARCH FOUNDATION (President J. L. Gibson) 1939. *Low temperature carbonization of Utah coals.* A report to the Governor and State Legislator by the Utah Conservation and Research Foundation, USA.

Modelling biodegradation in a groundwater environment: choosing an appropriate method

Ruth M. Davison & David N. Lerner

Groundwater Protection & Restoration Research Unit, University of Bradford, Bradford, West Yorkshire BD7 1DP, UK

Abstract. The transport of contaminants through aquifers is a complex issue affected by advection, dispersion, sorption and biodegradation. Biodegradation is the only process which allows the contaminant mass naturally to be physically reduced. Due to the quantity of contaminated sites and the expense of remediation schemes it is essential to understand the natural attenuation provided by biodegradation. Modelling of the biodegradation processes provides not only the means to a fuller understanding of a plume's development but also the facility to test potential remediation schemes. A two-tier classification system is presented which summarizes the current literature regarding the modelling of biotransformations in saturated porous media. The first relates to the treatment of the physical microbial setting and the second tier relates to the reaction approach. The physical setting tier is discussed in the context of biofilms. The basic theory and various types of biofilm are summarized while discussing the evidence for and against the necessity of representing biofilms in biotransformation models. The techniques implemented to model biofilms are summarized, including the limitations and previous and potential applications. The reaction tier constitutes four sections: first-order decay models, instantaneous reaction models, Monod kinetic models and Michaelis–Menton kinetics. For each of the reaction approaches a physical and mathematical description is provided with an explanation of its relevance for the modelling of biotransformations. An approach for selecting the appropriate modeling techniques is illustrated for a contaminated site.

Introduction

Biodegradation is the only process by which contaminants, in particular organic contaminants actually lose mass within an aquifer. In this way biodegradation can actually help to restore groundwater quality. During biodegradation, compounds are chemically transformed through the agency of microbes.

Bacteria and other micro-organisms require four things to function:

- a substrate or energy source,
- an electron acceptor,
- some essential nutrients including nitrogen and phosphorus, and
- a suitable environment.

The substrate takes the form of either an inorganic or an organic compound, depending on the bacteria type. The substrate is used in the process of respiration (Equation (1)) as the electron donor and, once oxidized, produces energy which can be used by the bacteria.

$$CH_4 + 2O_2 \rightarrow CO_2 + 2H_2O + energy \qquad (1)$$

Equation (1) illustrates respiration, i.e. the consumption of a substrate (CH_4) to provide energy. In the conversion of CH_4 to CO_2 in Equation (1) the carbon atom changes from an oxidation state of -4 to $+4$, which implies the transfer of eight electrons. These transfer to the oxygen atoms which change between oxidation states of zero and -2 (Schwarzenbach *et al.* 1993). This illustrates another essential component of a biodegradation reaction for pollutants: the presence and utilization of electron acceptors. Therefore a redox reaction occurs where the electron acceptor is reduced by the number of electrons increasing and the substrate is oxidized by the number of electrons decreasing. Other electron acceptors can be used, such as nitrate and sulphate, but oxygen is used preferentially when present because it has the highest energy return.

The reaction illustrated in Equation (1) only proceeds if conditions are suitable for the bacteria. As well as substrate, bacteria and electron acceptors being available, the pH must be within a suitable range (conventionally 5.5–8.5), inhibitory compounds must not be present and nutrients such as nitrogen and phosphorous must be available for biomass creation. Assuming that these conditions are met, modelling of biodegradation becomes a simulation of the interplay between the substrate, electron donor and bacterial population.

Biofilms

A biofilm occurs when micro-organisms become attached to and colonize a surface. These bacteria can form a single

DAVISON, R. M. & LERNER, D. N. 1998. Modelling biodegradation in a groundwater environment: choosing an appropriate method. *In*: LERNER, D. N. & WALTON, N. R. G. (eds) 1998. *Contaminated Land and Groundwater: Future Directions*. Geological Society, London, Engineering Geology Special Publications, **14**, 167–177.

 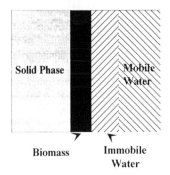

Fig. 1. Schematic representation of the structure of a biofilm at two scales. Adapted from Baveye & Valocchi (1989).

or multilayer of cells. In some cases, the organisms ultimately occupy the entire surface but patchy growth is often observed (Characklis & Wilderer 1989).

The structure of a biofilm as presently understood is illustrated in Fig. 1. The biomass itself is attached to the solid phase and between this and the mobile pore water is an immobile water phase (Baveye & Valocchi 1989). A biofilm model assumes that the process of diffusion is dominant for electron acceptors such as oxygen and substrates such as phenol to pass from the flowing groundwater across the immobile layer to the micro-organisms.

Non-biofilm models

A non-biofilm model recognizes that the bacteria are attached to surfaces but does not involve local-scale transport as a controlling factor. Rather it is based on the assumption that advection and dispersion are the dominant transport mechanisms required for the dissolved solids to reach adhering bacteria (Zysset *et al.* 1994*a*, *b*).

Reactions

The microbially mediated reactions have been simulated in four main ways: Monod kinetics, Michaelis–Menton kinetics, instantaneous reactions and first-order reactions. The Monod equation (Equation (2)) was originally formulated in 1949 to represent the growth of bacterial cultures as a function of a limiting nutrient concentration. Monod assumed that more food (substrate) means more growth, at least up to a certain point where the maximum growth rate is reached (Schwarzenbach *et al.* 1993).

$$\mu = \mu_{\max}\left[\frac{S}{K_{\mathrm{m}} + S}\right] \qquad (2)$$

where μ is the specific micro-organism growth rate (day^{-1}), $\mu_{\max}$ is the maximum specific growth rate obtained in the absence of any substrate limitation

(day^{-1}), K_{m} is the half saturation constant (mg l^{-1}), which is the concentration of growth limiting substrate that allows the micro-organisms to grow at half the maximum specific growth rate, and S is the substrate concentration (mg l^{-1}).

Lawrence & McCarty (1970) adapted the Monod equation to simulate the utilization rate of a primary substrate, making it applicable to the kinetics of biodegradation. Equation (1) was adapted to become a substrate utilization equation by considering a yield function which gives a ratio between the number of cells grown and the amount of substrate used. Using the yield information, the production rate of new cells can be related to the disappearance rate of the chemical of concern. The substrate utilization equation can be written in two ways (Equations (3) and (4)), which are equivalent as $k = \mu_{\max}/y$ and $B = M_{\mathrm{t}}$.

$$\frac{\mathrm{d}s}{\mathrm{d}t} = \mu_{\max} B Y^{-1}\left(\frac{S}{K_{\mathrm{m}} + S}\right) \qquad (3)$$

$$\frac{\mathrm{d}s}{\mathrm{d}t} = M_{\mathrm{t}} k\left(\frac{S}{K_s + S}\right) \qquad (4)$$

where S is the substrate concentration (mg l^{-1}), $\mathrm{d}s/\mathrm{d}t$ is the substrate utilization rate (mg l^{-1} day^{-1}), M_{t} is the microbial concentration (mg$_{\mathrm{microbes}}$ l^{-1}), k is the maximum specific substrate utilization rate (mg mg$_{\mathrm{microbes}}^{-1}$ day^{-1}), and K_s is the half saturation coefficient (mg l^{-1}). The intrinsic coefficients k and K_s characterize Monod's empirical equation but are system-specific and therefore care should be taken when extrapolating data between sites (Alvarez *et al.* 1991).

The dual Monod equation (Equation (5)), which is a further adaptation from the Monod equation, was developed by Kissel (1986). This has been used to calculate the concentration of substrate per unit time consumed in the presence of an adapted microbial population and an electron acceptor.

$$\frac{-\mathrm{d}S}{\mathrm{d}t} = M_{\mathrm{t}} k\left(\frac{S}{K_s + S}\right)\left(\frac{A}{K_A + A}\right) \qquad (5)$$

where A is the mass concentration of electron acceptor $(mg\,l^{-1})$ and K_A is the electron acceptor concentration at which the utilization rate is half its maximum $(mg\,l^{-1})$.

Michaelis–Menton kinetics are used when the microbial population does not respond to the substrate. The Michaelis–Menton equation (Equation (6)) is derived from a mechanistic analysis of enzyme catalysed reactions whereas Monod's equation is entirely empirically based. (Chapelle 1993).

$$\frac{-\mathrm{d}S}{\mathrm{d}t} = k\,\frac{S}{K_s + S} \qquad (6)$$

In the presence of the essential nutrients, an electron acceptor and the substrate, an instantaneous model assumes that a reaction will proceed instantaneously from its reactants to its products. Such a model is unable to simulate slow degradation. If a reaction is considered to be fast relative to the transport processes which are working to change the concentrations then a instantaneous reaction should be considered. However if the reaction is comparatively slow then a kinetic reaction should be applied (Domenico & Schwartz 1990).

Microbial setting

Biofilm models

Baveye & Valocchi (1989) present three conceptual models on which to base the mathematical description of the concurrent growth of bacteria and transport of biodegradable substrates in saturated porous media:

1. The aquifer material is uniformly covered by a biofilm in which consumption of the substrate and electron acceptor takes place (e.g. Rittman & McCarty 1980; Bouwer & Cobb 1987).
2. Bacteria grow in small discrete colonies or microcolonies attached to particle surfaces (e.g. Molz et al. 1986).
3. No assumptions are made about the configuration and distribution of bacteria in pores, and the way in which organisms are grouped together on solid surfaces is considered irrelevant for the macroscopic description of their growth and metabolism (Baveye & Valocchi 1989).

Baveye & Valocchi (1989) concluded that technique 3 is the most preferable for modelling biodegradation as it does not make any unwarranted assumptions regarding the spatial distribution of the biomass. This model assumes that the bacteria are attached to and growing on aquifer solids but requires no detailed information regarding grouping patterns or dimensions of such groups.

Molz et al. (1986) used a microcolony approach for the simulation of biofilms, representing them as disks of uniform radius and thickness attached to the aquifer sediments. The microcolonies were assumed to be surrounded by a boundary layer across which oxygen and the substrate were transported by diffusion. The advection, dispersion, adsorption and biodegradation model was used in a preliminary manner to simulate biodegradation and microbial growth in a one-dimensional column of porous media, and indicated that biodegradation would have a major effect on contaminant fate when suitable growth conditions exist.

Widdowson et al. (1988) extended the work of Molz et al. (1986) to include nitrate and oxygen based respiration. The 1D model remained a microcolony biofilm with a Monod kinetic reaction and was once more applied to laboratory column experiments. A large number of parameters related to the microbial population were required as inputs to the model. Many were estimated from literature or during the calibration process. Widdowson et al. (1988) suggested that the model could be increased from 1D to 2D or 3D and that the model could be used to simulate enhanced or natural biodegradation in a polluted aquifer. It is unlikely that in a field situation the many parameters required to quantify the model would ever be known with any accuracy.

Zysset et al. (1994a, b) developed a model to simulate the transport of solutes in a groundwater biofilm system. The model conceptualizes the diffusion dominated transport processes within the biofilm. No assumptions are made regarding the structure of the biofilm as Baveye & Valocchi (1989) suggested. The model divides the system into three compartments – the aqueous, the solid and the biofilm – and a method of dominant transport is assigned to each: advection, negligible and diffusion respectively. A simplified form of Monod kinetics simulates the biodegradation. The 1D model of Zysset et al. is capable of reproducing the results of column experiments for the transport of nitrate and sulphate, both of which act as electron acceptors.

Kinzelbach et al. (1991) have presented a numerical model that simulates nitrate as both the electron acceptor and the contaminant. A series of hypotheses were tested to compare modelling techniques, including (1) the only source of substrate and electron acceptor is recharge, and Monod kinetics govern nitrate reduction dynamics; (2) substrate and electron acceptors are supplied through recharge, and diffusion between mobile water and the bacteria control the nitrate supply; and (3) the substrate and electron acceptor were also provided by dissolution from the aquifer matrix and diffusion is not limiting. After the model was applied to a field situation, diffusion between the pore water and the biophase was observed to be important. The model was applied to the testing of remedial technologies at a field site contaminated with nitrate and the authors concluded that accurate predictive modelling of a field situation is unlikely to be possible.

A complete sequence of biologically mediated redox processes has been modelled by Lensing et al. (1994) to simulate field data from a natural subsurface flow path, and to demonstrate the influence of microbially catalysed redox reactions on the aquifer's chemistry. The model included a formless biofilm as suggested by Baveye & Valocchi (1989) and a series of Monod equations to simulate the growth and metabolism of the various sets of bacteria. The biofilm approach was used as field studies have shown that exchange between various phases in an uncontaminated aquifer can be limiting to the microbial activity (Kinzelbach *et al.* 1991). The model performed reasonably well for oxygen, nitrate and sulphate. Iron and manganese were not well represented but this was expected due to the simplified modelling approach. The modelling results suggested that dissolved organic carbon (DOC) was the limiting factor for the growth of micro-organisms and that this was caused by the diffusion limited supply to the biofilm. The model was unusual in its application to a natural uncontaminated aquifer and confirmed the theory proposed by Kindred & Celia (1989) that in uncontaminated aquifers the rate of biodegradation is limited by the availability of organic carbon.

Biofilm models have been applied extensively to laboratory-scale investigations. They provide more parameters to give an adequate calibration to the column data. Two other examples of the biofilm models have been presented, both of which are used to simulate field-scale problems with inorganic contaminants.

Biofilm versus non-biofilm calculations

A set of calculations have been developed which can be used to determine whether diffusion between the mobile pore water and the attached bacteria is rate limiting. A contaminated field site on the East Midlands Triassic Sandstone will be used as an example with which to demonstrate the calculations. Ammonium is the main contaminant and substrate, and oxygen will be assumed to be the only electron acceptor (Broholm *et al.* 1998).

The method compares the characteristic time for the oxygen and ammonium to diffuse across a biofilm to the bacteria to the characteristic time for transport by advection and dispersion. If the characteristic time for transport across the biofilm were short compared to the characteristic time for transport by advection and dispersion then the biofilm aspect can be assumed to be non-limiting.

An equation for characteristic time, Equation (7) (Barker 1985), was adapted to create three new equations:

$$t_c = \frac{a^2}{2D^*} \tag{7}$$

where t_c is the characteristic time, a is a characteristic length, and D^* is the diffusion coefficient. The first (Equation (8)) gave the characteristic time for diffusion

across the biofilm, $t_{cbiofilm}$, for both ammonium, $t_{cNH4+biofilm}$, and oxygen, $t_{cDObiofilm}$.

$$t_{cbiofilm} = \frac{x_{bio}^2}{2D^*} \tag{8}$$

where x_{bio} is the diffusion length (biofilm thickness), and D^* is the diffusion coefficient for transport across a biofilm. The second (Equation (9)) assessed the characteristic time for oxygen to be input to the system by dispersion, t_{cDO}. The plume within the Triassic Sandstone is completely anaerobic and oxygen is input by mixing with uncontaminated oxygenated groundwater around its periphery:

$$t_{cDO} = \frac{x_{mix}^2}{2D_T} \tag{9}$$

where x_{mix} is the thickness of the mixing zone between the plume and uncontaminated groundwater and D_T is the transverse dispersion coefficient. The third equation (Equation 10) gives a characteristic time for ammonium transport by advection (t_{cNH4+}):

$$t_{CNH_4^+} = \frac{L}{V} \tag{10}$$

where L is the distance to a point in the plume and V is the groundwater velocity.

Calculations were made for column experiments as well as for the field site to assess how applicable it would be to model biofilms at different scales. The characteristic time for the transport of oxygen and ammonium across a theoretical biofilm was calculated for two biofilm thicknesses, a minimum of 0.01 mm and a maximum of 1 mm (Characklis & Wilderer 1989). It is unlikely that a biofilm would reach the maximum thickness in the Sherwood Sandstone aquifer as no visible signs of a biofilm are present and the pore space is unlikely to allow this kind of covering. The thickness of the biofilm in the column experiments is unknown; however, the porosity in each experiment is more than double that found in the Sherwood Sandstone aquifer (0.39 compared to 0.15), allowing the possibility for a thicker biofilm.

From the results contained in Tables 1 and 2 it can be seen that the minimum (and most likely) characteristic time for transport of ammonium and oxygen across the biofilm in the Triassic Sandstone is ten orders of magnitude less than the characteristic time for ammonium and oxygen transport within the aquifer. The large gap between the characteristic times indicates that the transport across the biofilm is not limiting the rate the bacteria receive substrate and electron acceptor.

The calculations of characteristic time for the column experiments show that advective time can reach the same order of magnitude, as the diffusive time (Tables 1 and 3). As the characteristic times can reach the same order of magnitude, the two processes could both prove

Table 1. *The characteristic time for the transport of oxygen and ammonium across a theoretical biofilm with a minimum thickness of 0.01 mm and a maximum thickness of 1 mm*

Case	Equation	D^* $(m^2 day^{-1})$	x_{bio} (m)	Characteristic time (days)
Min. for ammonium	(8)	1.1×10^{-4}	0.00001	4.4×10^{-7}
Min. for oxygen	(8)	1.9×10^{-4}	0.00001	2.6×10^{-7}
Max. for ammonium	(8)	1.1×10^{-4}	0.001	4.0×10^{-3}
Max. for oxygen	(8)	1.9×10^{-4}	0.001	3.4×10^{-3}

Table 2. *The characteristic time for oxygen transport by dispersion and ammonium transport by advection. The characteristic time for ammonium is calculated at two points in the plume*

Case	Equation	x_{mix} (m)	α_T (m)	$V (m\,day^{-1})$	L	Characteristic time (days)
Oxygen dispersion	(9)	1	0.43	0.168	n/a	6.92
NH_4^+	(10)	n/a	n/a	0.168	20	119
NH_4^+ far from source	(10)	n/a	n/a	0.168	100	595

to be limiting the biodegradation rate, and should be accounted for in the modelling. Both column experiments were described with models which included a term for diffusional exchange across the biofilm.

The results show that it is not necessary to model biofilms at the scale of the field site in this example but for the two column experiments biofilms should be considered. The results also indicate that during column experiments different processes are limiting biodegradation than in the field and therefore care should be taken when up-scaling the data obtained from such procedures.

Reaction approach

Monod kinetics

Over the past decade Monod kinetics have become well established as the most popular technique for representing the reactions involved in biodegradation.

Kissel (1986) adapted the theory proposed by Monod (1949) to give the dual Monod equation (Equation (3)) which has been used in most subsequent models

including that of MacQuarrie *et al.* (1990). The dual Monod equation represents the utilization of the primary substrate in the presence of an adapted microbial population and an electron acceptor.

Sudicky & MacQuarrie (1989) used the dual Monod relationship combined with a two-dimensional form of the advection dispersion equation, to represent the biological and physical processes affecting the organic solute, electron acceptor and microbial population. Sudicky & MacQuarrie (1989) used the model with a synthesized random hydraulic conductivity field with local transport parameters to investigate the role of heterogeneity on the rate of mass loss by biodegradation and the overall advection and dispersion of the plume. Sudicky & MacQuarrie (1989) concluded that a biodegradable solute plume will evolve differently to a conservative solute plume if the porous media is heterogeneous.

MacQuarrie *et al.* (1990) further developed the earlier model of Sudicky & MacQuarrie (1989) and the numerical results were compared to the results of a laboratory column experiment. The model equations adequately describe the behaviour of toluene, dissolved oxygen and the bacterial population without considering solute

Table 3. *The characteristic time for advective transport of ammonium in two column experiments*

Case	Equation	Reference	L	V	Characteristic time (days)
Min. for ammonium	(10)	Bouwer & Cobb (1987)	0.003	0.25	0.012
Max. for ammonium	(10)	Bouwer & Cobb (1987)	0.16	0.25	0.64
Min. for ammonium	(10)	Zysset *et al.* (194)	0.004	4.7	8.5×10^{-4}
Max. for ammonium	(10)	Zysset *et al.* (1994)	0.1	4.7	0.02

diffusion through stagnant fluid layers or biofilms (MacQuarrie *et al.* 1990). The model was further tested in a field setting to examine plume migration in a shallow aerobic aquifer. MacQuarrie & Sudicky (1990) used the model to assess the behaviour of a contaminant plume in uniform and random hydraulic conductivity fields. Figure 2 shows the distribution of oxygen and dissolved organic carbon in a random hydraulic conductivity field. In uniform groundwater flow a plume originating from a high concentration source will experience more spreading and slower normalized mass loss when compared to a plume from a lower initial source concentration because dissolved oxygen is more quickly depleted (MacQuarrie *et al.* 1990). Large groundwater velocities were predicted to result in increases in the rate of organic solute mass loss, attributed to the increased mechanical mixing of the contaminant plume with the oxygenated water. For substances which are easily degraded the mass loss was found to be only loosely dependent on the kinetic parameters; the degree of mixing of the dissolved organic and oxygen will control the rate of biodegradation under these circumstances.

Frind *et al.* (1989) used the earlier work of Sudicky & MacQuarrie (1989) to create a three-dimensional model to describe the coupled transport of an organic solute and an electron acceptor, both of which were assumed to be interacting with a stationary microbial population. Frind *et al.* (1989) conclude that three dimensions are important for simulating the plume development because of the dispersion issue. The rate at which mass of organic substrate can be reduced is dependent on the availability of an electron acceptor and it is commonly accepted that the main input of electron acceptor to a plume is controlled by dispersion. As dispersion is a three-dimensional process, Frind *et al.* (1989) argue that it should be considered as such so that biodegradation is not underestimated. No field or laboratory validation is provided for the model so its predictive capabilities are unknown, however it does provide an insight into the possible effects of neglecting the third dimension.

Molz & Widdowson (1988) also emphasized the potential for error introduced by vertically averaged models. The concern was raised from evidence obtained from field data from several locations around the world, which all pointed to consistently large vertical concentration gradients in aquifers and, by implication, the existence of very small vertical dispersivities (Molz & Widdowson 1988). Vertically averaged concentrations are inappropriate for the detailed analysis of a groundwater contaminant plume as they may lead to the assumption that aerobic zones are in existence where in reality they are anaerobic. It was also concluded that

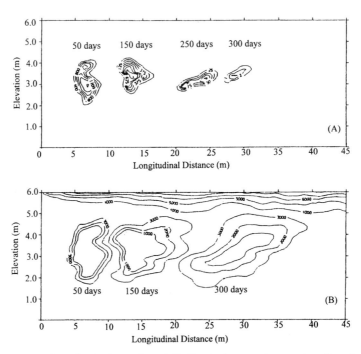

Fig. 2. The distribution of (**a**) dissolved organic and (**b**) dissolved oxygen in a random flow simulation. Concentration isolines are in micrograms per litre. Dissolved oxygen concentrations near the water table are for 300 days. After MacQuarrie & Sudicky (1990).

even within three-dimensional models care should be taken to reproduce the concentration gradient accurately. The simulation of an aerobic zone instead of an anaerobic one is of fundamental importance when trying to quantify the potential rates of degradation of a contaminant.

Alvarez *et al.* (1991) used the Lawrence & McCarty (1970) version of the Monod equation to represent biodegradation. They linearized the equation and assessed, using modelling and experimental data, whether the Monod equation is suitable for describing the fate of high concentrations of contaminants without incorporating an additional substrate inhibition term. As Monod's equation does not incorporate substrate toxicity effects it overestimates biodegradation rates at substrate concentrations sufficiently high to hinder microbial activity.

Chen *et al.* (1992) presented a two electron acceptor, microcolony biofilm model with Monod kinetics simulating the biological reactions. As the model was used for laboratory comparisons, it was considered that a kinetic approach was necessary even though the microbial degradation of BTX compounds is relatively fast. The appropriateness of the kinetic biofilm approach to modelling biodegradation was tested using data obtained from laboratory column experiments. Neither first-order nor instantaneous reaction models could accurately predict column behaviour. The kinetic biofilm approach could predict the one-dimensional transport of toluene and benzene provided the electron acceptor was not limiting (Chen *et al.* 1992). When the electron acceptor was limiting, acceptable calibrations could not be obtained. A number of explanations were suggested, including that the kinetic constants were inappropriate under the particular conditions of the laboratory experiments.

Michaelis–Menton kinetics

Kindred & Celia (1989) presented a model which simulates the transport of subsurface contaminants with biodegradation including simultaneous simulation of aerobic and anaerobic processes. To describe the process of nutrient uptake, Kindred & Celia (1989) used Michaelis–Menton expressions. These processes included multiple electron acceptors, enzyme inhibition, biomass limitation of uptake, fermentative consortia, and interactions between multiple substrates (Kindred & Celia 1989).

Srinivasan & Mercer (1988) also used Michaelis–Menton equations in their simulation of biodegradation in groundwater. To simulate the aerobic stage of biodegradation the Monod kinetics were used but for the anaerobic stage Michaelis–Menton kinetics were applied.

Instantaneous reactions

Borden & Bedient (1986; Borden *et al.* 1986) developed a model to simulate the process of biodegradation in a creosote and pentachlorophenol plume emanating from a creosoting plant into a shallow aquifer. Sensitivity analyses and model verification showed that the distribution of contaminant and oxygen were relatively insensitive to the microbial parameters used in the Monod kinetics approach. An instantaneous reaction model was more suitable to simulate this field situation. The model was found to represent the plume characteristics well except in the area in the immediate vicinity of the source. Here the kinetic model provided a better solution. The calibrated model was used to predict the consequences of a variety of remedial technologies at the site.

Bioplume II is possibly the most widely recognized model which incorporates the process of biodegradation. Bioplume II uses the theory developed by Borden & Bedient (1986; Borden *et al.* 1986) and uses their logic to support the use of an instantaneous rather than a kinetic model.

In Bioplume II, biodegradation is simulated by two independent sets of particles, oxygen tracer particles and hydrocarbon tracer particles. The oxygen and hydrocarbon tracer particles are moved independently and the resulting two plumes are combined after every particle move to simulate the reaction between oxygen and hydrocarbon (Rifai *et al.* 1987). Two very simple formulae are used to simulate the superimposition of the two resultant plumes:

$$S(t+1) = S(t) - \frac{O(t)}{F} \quad \text{where} \quad S(t) > \frac{O(t)}{F} \quad (11a)$$

$$O(t+1) = O(T) - S(t)F \quad \text{where} \quad O(t) > S(t)F \quad (11b)$$

where F is the ratio of oxygen to contaminant consumed, S is the substrate concentration and O is the oxygen concentration. Rifai & Bedient (1990) undertook a series of tests to compare the applicability of Monod and instantaneous models. They demonstrated that the instantaneous reaction was adequate for aquifers and contaminants that resulted in a large Damkohler number. The Damkohler number is the ratio of the rate of the reaction to the velocity of the groundwater (Rifai *et al.* 1995).

Rifai & Bedient (1990) highlight a number of difficulties experienced during comparisons of kinetic and instantaneous models:

- evaluations must be carried out both spatially and temporally;
- different deviations between the two model concepts may be experienced for chemicals with differing biodegradation rates;
- differences due to numerical errors must be separated from differences caused by conceptual errors.

A model involving instantaneous reactions has two main advantages:

- Only a limited amount of input data is required concerning the microbial population which should be available from a preliminary site investigation. Therefore, no unwarranted assumptions regarding the nature of the microbial population are made.
- The models are computationally efficient and relatively simple.

The instantaneous modelling approach would appear to have one major limitation; it is unable to simulate slowly degrading chemicals in a situation with a low Damkohler number.

Kinetic versus instantaneous calculations

A set of calculations can be used to indicate whether an aquifer should be simulated with instantaneous reactions or a kinetic description.

The Damkohler number (Equation (12)) is used to compare a rate of reaction with the groundwater velocity. The Damkohler number (D_{ai}) is effectively the ratio between two characteristic times, the first for reaction and the second for groundwater transport.

$$D_{ai} = \frac{RL}{V} \qquad (12)$$

where R is the reaction rate, L is a characteristic length and V is the velocity.

It is generally considered that if the Damkohler number is greater than 100 then the reaction can be conceptualized as instantaneous (Appelo & Postma 1993).

The same field site will be used as we looked at earlier with the biofilm, non-biofilm calculations. The calculations were undertaken with the aim to find values for the Damkohler number at three points in the plume: the source area, the centre and the periphery.

The rate of reaction was taken as k which was introduced in Equation (4) and is the maximum specific substrate utilization rate (mass$_{substrate}$/mass$_{microbes}$/time). k is calculated by dividing the maximum growth rate by the yield. The maximum growth rate μ_{max} was calculated using data from a column experiment conducted by Ardakani et al. (1975), where they compared the number of Nitrosomonas bacteria with time as a flux of ammonium is passed through the column. Nitrosomonas are bacteria which mediate the reaction where ammonium is oxidized to nitrite. The yield figure was obtained from a value published in Tchobanoglous & Burton (1991).

Table 4. *Results from kinetic versus instantaneous reaction calculations*

	Distance	Damkohler number
Source (BH17)	20 m	274
Plume (BH20)	75 m	1026
Periphery (BH18)	130 m	1779

In Table 4 the Damkohler number is greater than 100 at all three points in the plume. So, if the cut-off value of 100 is trusted then the reactions are suitably fast to be described with instantaneous reactions. One paper has been published which disagrees with the value of 100 and proposes a value nearer 3000 (Rifai et al. 1990). Further work is needed to establish a reliable cut-off point.

First-order decay

A first-order reaction is one in which the rate of reaction is proportional to the concentration of a single reactant (Walker 1991). An example of a well documented first-order reaction is radioactive decay (Equation (13)). If the concentration of a reactant, which follows a first-order decay rate, is doubled the rate also doubles (Appelo & Postma 1993).

$$\frac{dC}{dt} = -\lambda C \qquad (13)$$

where C is the solute concentration and λ is the reaction rate coefficient.

First-order decay has been used only in models which intend to simplify the process of biodegradation and which do not aim to fully represent the complexities. Zheng (1992) treats biodegradation in the same way as radioactive decay, but suggests that an alternative formulation for simulating biodegradation should be added to MT3D in the future.

Monod kinetics can be simplified to a first-order relationship for certain limiting values of the Monod parameters and the substrate concentration (MacQuarrie & Sudicky 1990; MacQuarrie et al. 1990). Monod kinetics simplify to either first-order or zero-order rate terms. In order to simplify Monod kinetics to first-order decay, constant microbial and electron acceptor concentrations must be maintained and K_s must be much larger than S and K_A must be much smaller than A in Equation (5). The first-order decay constant with respect to the organic substrate concentration is given by

$$\lambda^1 \approx \frac{M_t k'}{K_S} \qquad (14)$$

where λ^1 is the first-order decay rate (MacQuarrie et al. 1990), M_t is the total active microbial biomass concentration, $k' = k/R_s$, k is the maximum rate of substrate utilization, K_S is the primary substrate concentration at which the utilization rate is half its maximum (mg l^{-1}) and R_s is the retardation factor.

Bioplume III

Rifai et al. (1995) have developed a model which can simulate biodegradation using multiple electron acceptors – Bioplume III. The model uses the principle of sequential utilization of electron acceptors beginning with oxygen. As oxygen falls below a user defined concentration, nitrate, iron, sulphate and carbon dioxide are used respectively. Bioplume III enables the user to define initial concentrations of each of the electron acceptors and the contaminant. To increase the flexibility of the model, reactions within each electron acceptor band can be instantaneous, follow first-order decay or follow Monod kinetics. To date, no publications have reported any results from this model.

Summary

Many situations arise when solute transport modelling may require a biodegradation component to provide an adequate description of a contaminant plume. Over the past decade various techniques have been developed for modelling biodegradation of contaminants in a groundwater environment. A two-tier classification system was proposed to describe the various techniques available for modelling biodegradation; the first tier addresses the microbial setting and whether a biofilm is considered, while the second assesses the reaction type and whether a kinetic or instantaneous approach is used. Two sets of calculations have been described which provide a decision making tool to assess which techniques are the most applicable for modelling biodegradation in a particular situation. The calculations compare characteristic times to ascertain which process is limiting.

To summarize the methods available for modelling biodegradation in groundwater, four scenarios will be described and the appropriate method for modelling proposed.

- Scenario 1: An initial site investigation into a contamination event.
- Scenario 2: A column experiment to assess the transport of a slowly degrading compound.
- Scenario 3: A MTBE plume in a fast flowing aquifer.
- Scenario 4: An ammonium plume in a relatively slow flowing aquifer which may pose a risk to abstractions.

A flow chart is presented in Fig. 3 to show how the biodegradation modelling techniques were assessed for each of the scenarios.

The initial decision is whether modelling biodegradation is necessary. In the case of scenario 1 the answer is likely to be no, as during an initial investigation the data available are often not enough for simple flow and transport modelling and the introduction of biodegradation would be unwarranted. The next three scenarios are all assumed to have sufficient data to warrant a biodegradation model.

Scenario 2 is a column experiment to investigate the transport of a slowly degrading compound. From calculations using Equations (8)–(10), it can be shown

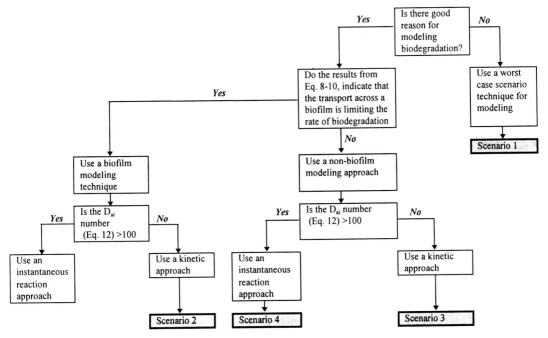

Fig. 3. Flow chart to illustrate a method for establishing the most appropriate technique for modelling biodegradation.

that transport across a biofilm could limit the rate of biodegradation, and consequently a biofilm approach should be used in the modelling. To ascertain what type of reaction is most suitable, Equation (12) is solved to find a value for the Damkohler number. If the Damkohler number is greater than 100 an instantaneous reaction model is usually sufficient, while for Damkohler numbers less than 100 a kinetic approach is sometimes required. This compound degrades slowly relative to the rate of groundwater transport through the column, resulting in a Damkohler number of less than 100 and a kinetic approach is recommended to describe the biodegradation reactions.

For scenario 3, diffusion across the biofilm has been calculated to be non-limiting, as is usually the case for field examples. Consequently the non-biofilm modelling type will be employed to describe this scenario. In the case of scenario 3 the Damkohler number is less than 100 as MTBE is a slowly degrading compound and the groundwater velocity is relatively high so a kinetic description is needed.

Scenario 4 has been used as an example for all the calculations throughout the paper. The example describes the modelling techniques for an ammonium plume that is degrading fast relative to the velocity of the groundwater. The results from the calculations presented in the paper indicate that the scenario should be modelled using a non-biofilm, instantaneous reaction approach.

It is therefore clear that no one model is suitable for modelling biodegradation in an aquifer environment but that a series of decisions are required for each individual scenario to assess the most applicable technique.

An important issue that was raised during the discussions in the paper was that of scale. At the column scale, diffusion across a biofilm has the potential to limit the rate of biodegradation, whereas at a field scale the process of mixing with oxygenated groundwater (dispersion) is the limiting process. Two important points can be derived from this. First, different types of model are required to simulate biodegradation in a column experiment and the field. Second, a different process is limiting the rate of biodegradation at the column scale relative to the field, leading to uncertainty in scale-ups of laboratory experiments.

Acknowledgements. This research is sponsored by the EU as part of the project, 'Processes underlying the remediation of creosote contaminated groundwater in fractured sandstone'. I would like to thank P. Bardos, J. Barker and W. Burgess for their useful comments.

References

ALVAREZ, P. J. J., ANID, P. J. & VOGEL, T. M. 1991. Kinetics of biodegradation of benzene and toluene in sandy aquifer material. *Biodegradation*, **2**, 43–51.

APPELO, C. A. J. & POSTMA, D. 1993. Geochemistry, groundwater and pollution. Balkema, Rotterdam.

ARDAKANI, M. S., VOLZ, M. G. & MCLAREN A. D. 1975. Consecutive steady state reactions of urea, ammonia and nitrate nitrogen in soil. *Canadian Journal of Soil Science*, **55**(2).

BARKER, J. A. 1985. Modelling the effects of matrix diffusion on the transport in densely fissured media. *In: Hydrogeology in the Service of Man, Memoirs of the 18th Congress of the IAH*. Cambridge, pp. 250–269.

BAVEYE, P. & VALOCCHI, A. 1989. An evaluation of mathematical models of the transport of biologically reacting solutes in saturated soils and aquifers. *Water Resources Research*, **25**(6), 1413–1421.

BORDEN, R. C. & BEDIENT, P. B. 1986. Transport of dissolved hydrocarbons influenced by oxygen limited biodegradation. 1. Theoretical development. *Water Resources Research*, **22**(13) 1973–1982.

——, ——, LEE, M. D., WARD, C. H. & WILSON, J. T. 1986. Transport of dissolved hydrocarbons influenced by oxygen limited biodegradation. 2. Field Application. *Water Resources Research*, **22**(13), 1983–1990.

BOUWER, E. J. & COBB, G. D. 1987. Modeling biological processes in the subsurface. *Water Science Technology*, **1**, 769–779.

BROHOLM, M. M., JONES, I., TORTENSSON, D. & ARVIN, E. 1998. Groundwater contamination from a coal carbonization plant. *This volume*.

CHAPELLE, F. H. 1993. *Groundwater Microbiology and Geochemistry*. Wiley, Chichester.

CHARACKLIS, W. G. & WILDERER, P. A. 1989. *Structure and Function of Biofilms*. Wiley Interscience, New York.

CHEN, Y. M., ABRIOLA, L. M., ALVAREZ, P. J. J., ANID, P. J. & VOGEL, T. M. 1992. Modeling transport and biodegradation of benzene and toluene in sandy aquifer material. Comparisons with experimental measurements. *Water Resources Research*, **28**(7), 1833–1847.

DOMENICO, P. A. & SCHWARTZ, F. W. 1990. *Physical and Chemical Hydrogeology*. Wiley, Chichester.

FRIND, E. O., SUDICKY, E. A. & MOLSON, J. W. 1989. Three-dimensional simulation of organic transport with aerobic biodegradation. *Groundwater Contamination*, IAHS Publication No. 185, pp. 89–96.

KINDRED, J. S. & CELIA, M. A. 1989. Contaminant transport and biodegradation, 2. Conceptual model and test simulations. *Water Resources Research*, **25**(6), 1149–1159.

KINZELBACH, W., SCHAFER, W. & HERZER, J. 1991. Numerical modeling of natural and enhanced denitrification processes in aquifers. *Water Resources Research*, **27**(6), 1123–1135.

KISSEL, J. C. 1986. Modeling mass transfer in biological waste water treatment processes. *Water Science and Technology*, **18**(6), 35–45.

LAWRENCE, A. L. & MCCARTY, P. L. 1970. A unified basis for biological treatment design and operation. *Journal of the Sanitary Engineering Division, Proceedings of the American Society of Civil Engineers*, **96**, 757–778.

LENSING, H. J., VOGT, M., & WERLING, B. 1994. Modeling of biologically mediated redox processes in the subsurface. *Journal of Hydrology*, **159**(1–4), 125–143.

MACQUARRIE, K. T. B. & SUDICKY, E. A. 1990. Simulation of biodegradable organic contaminants in groundwater. 2. Plume behaviour in uniform and random flow fields. *Water Resources Research*, **26**(2) 223–239.

——, —— & FRIND, E. O. 1990. Simulation of biodegradable organic contaminants in groundwater. 1. Numerical formulation and model calibration. *Water Resources Research*, **26**(2), 207–222.

MOLZ, F. J. & WIDDOWSON, M. A. 1988. Internal inconsistencies in dispersion-dominated models that incorporate chemical and microbial kinetics. *Water Resources Research*, **24**(4) 615–619.

——, —— & BENEFIELD, L. D. 1986. Simulation of microbial growth dynamics coupled to nutrient and oxygen transport in porous media. *Water Resources Research*, **22**(8), 1207–1216.

MONOD, J. 1949. Growth of bacterial cultures. *Annual Reviews of Microbiology*, **3**, 371–394.

RIFAI, H. S. & BEDIENT, P. B. 1990. Comparison of biodegradation kinetics with an instantaneous reaction model for groundwater. *Water Resources Research*, **26**(4) 637–645.

——, ——, BORDEN, R. C. & HAASBEEK, J. F. 1987. *Bioplume II, Computer model of two dimensional contaminant transport under the influence of oxygen limited biodegradation in groundwater. Users Manual Version 1.0*. Rice University, Houston, Texas.

——, NEWELL, C. J., MILLER, R. N., TAFFINDER, S. & ROUNSAVILLE, M. 1995. Simulation of natural attenuation with multiple electron acceptors 53–58. *In*: HINCHEE, R. E., WILSON, J. T. & DOWNEY, D. C. (eds) *Intrinsic Bioremediation*. Battelle.

RITTMANN, B. E. & MCCARTY, P. L. 1980. Model of steady state biofilm kinetics. *Biotechnology and Bioengineering*, **22**, 2343–2357.

SCHWARZENBACH, R. P., GSCHWEND, P. M. & IMBODEN, D. M. 1993. *Environmental Organic Chemistry*. Wiley, Chichester.

SRINIVASAN, P. & MERCER, J. W. 1988. Simulation of biodegradation and sorption processes in groundwater. *Groundwater*, **26**(4), 475–487.

SUDICKY, E. A. & MACQUARRIE, K. T. B. 1989. Behaviour of biodegradable organic contaminants in random stationary hydraulic conductivity fields. *In*: KOBUS, H. E. & KINZELBACH, W. (eds) *Contaminant Transport in Groundwater, Symposium*. Stuttgart, 4–6 April 1989.

TCHOBANOGLOUS, G. & BURTON, F. L. 1991. *Wastewater Engineering* (3rd edition). McGraw-Hill.

WALKER, P. M. B. 1991. *Chambers Science and Technology Dictionary*. Chambers.

WIDDOWSON, M. A., MOLZ, F. J. & BENEFIELD, L. D. 1988. A numerical transport model for oxygen and nitrate based respiration linked to substrate and nutrient availability in porous media. *Water Resources Research*, **24**(9), 1553–1565.

ZHENG, C. 1992. *MT3D, a modular three-dimensional transport model*, vs1.5, Documentation and Users guide, S. S. Papadopulos.

ZYSSET, A., STAUFFER, F. & DRACUS, T. 1994a. Modeling of reactive groundwater transport governed by biodegradation. *Water Resources Research*, **30**(8), 2423–2434.

——, —— & ——1994b. Modeling of chemically reactive groundwater transport. *Water Resources Research*, **30**(7), 2217–2228.

Contamination of sediments in the Forth Estuary, Scotland

P. Lindsay,[1] F. G. Bell[1] & N. Hytiris[2]

[1] Department of Geology and Applied Geology, University of Natal, Durban 4041, South Africa
[2] Department of Energy and Environmental Technology, Caledonian University, Glasgow, UK

Abstract. This paper considers the contamination of sediments in the Forth Estuary. When trace metals are released into the water column they can be transferred rapidly to the sediment phase by adsorption onto suspended particulate matter, to be followed by sedimentation. Intertidal flats may be considered as important trace metal sinks since they accumulate large amounts of suspended matter. Hence, in polluted estuaries the deposition of suspended particles on intertidal flats may thus cause severe contamination. The Forth Estuary has unique contamination for British estuaries: it is experiencing significant Hg pollution. In addition, due to the presence of a nuclear submarine base in the Forth Estuary, Co^{60} is detectable in the intertidal sediments. Temporal and spatial contamination patterns were analysed in relation to historical and present pollution point sources.

Introduction

The Forth is a turbid industrialised estuary and therefore an understanding of the movement of particle-bound contaminants is essential for its environmental management. The possibility that particle-bound contaminants in estuarine sink zones may be resuspended in overlying waters by tidal flow or dredging, and be desorbed into the water column, creates the need to quantify suspension periods of estuarine bed sediments. For example, Stanners & Aston (1982) calculated that caesium nuclides can be desorbed up to 30% of their initial activity after 10 days in suspension. In addition, recent toxic algal blooms and other environmental problems in the shallow coastal shelf zones have been speculatively related to nutrient inputs from estuaries (Balls 1992). Hence, research has concentrated on the seasonal and temporal aspects of various physicochemical fluxes at the mouths of estuaries.

The main fluvial input to the Forth Estuary is from the rivers Forth, Teith and Allan which contribute to a long-term mean of 41 m³ s⁻¹ reintroduced above Stirling (Fig. 1). Mean winter and summer fluvial inputs to the estuary are 63 and 12 m³ s⁻¹ respectively (Webb &

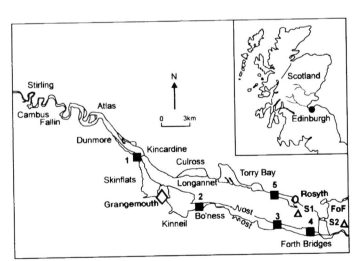

Fig. 1. Forth Estuary, eastern Scotland. This paper is concerned with the lower reaches from Kincardine to the Forth Bridges. Distances from tidal limit: Kincardine 32 km, Forth Bridges 56 km (■ = intertidal core sites 1–5; △ = suspended particulate matter flux measurement sites; ◇ = Grangemouth petrochemical complex; ○ = Rosyth Naval Dockyard; FoF = Firth of Forth; lwost = low water of spring tide; hwost = high water of spring tide).

LINDSAY, P., BELL, F. G. & HYTIRIS, N. 1998. Contamination of sediments in the Forth Estuary, Scotland. *In*: LERNER, D. N. & WALTON, N. R. G. (eds) 1998. *Contaminated Land and Groundwater: Future Directions.* Geological Society, London, Engineering Geology Special Publications, **14**, 179–187.

Metcalfe 1987). Mean water depths in the lower estuary (Forth Bridges to Kincardine) range from 10–15 m at Rosyth to 5–7 m at Kincardine and less than 2.5 m in the upper estuary between Kincardine and Stirling (Fig. 1). Mean spring and neap tidal ranges measured at Rosyth are 5.0 m and 2.5 m respectively.

Many authors have demonstrated a relationship between pollutant contamination and finer grain size. According to Bonnet *et al.* (1988), concentrations of Cs^{137}, in surface sediments of the Ribble Estuary, were six times greater in the <2 μm size range than for the >62.5 μm size range. Due to the importance of fine particulate matter in suspension adsorbing heavy metals and other pollutants involved in chemical spillages, it was important to understand and quantify the particle size of suspended particulate matter (SPM) in the lower Forth Estuary. The particulate matter sampled along a typical longitudinal estuarine profile often differs with respect to its degree of pollutant accumulation. Therefore, to understand the changes in pollutant concentrations in estuaries or to detect the transport of contaminated particles into different sinks, it is necessary to obtain information about the origin and transport of the sediment and pollution in the estuary in relation to contamination of intertidal sediments.

In the upper estuary there are two major sewage discharges, one at Stirling (0.4 tons BOD day^{-1} and another at Alloa (1.3 tons BOD day^{-1}) (Fig. 1). The introduction of full biological treatments at these plants in the last decade has substantially reduced the organic discharge from these sources. The estuary also receives waste from two brewery discharges, at Cambus 1.6 tons BOD day^{-1} enter the estuary via the River Devon, and at Alloa where 26.4 tons BOD day^{-1} of organic discharge enters the upper estuary (Fig. 1). The lower estuary receives substantial waste streams from a variety of domestic and industrial sources, including the chlorinated thermal effluent from a large direct-cooled power station at Longannet, petrochemical refinery wastes from Grangemouth, sewage at Bo'ness, Kinneil and Rosyth, and a variety of inputs from the Rosyth dockyards (Fig. 1).

Lindsay *et al.* (1996) noted that the long-term flux of contaminants and suspended particulate matter in the

Firth of Forth was landwards into the estuary, hence long-term contaminant trends will include the contaminants entering the Firth from Edinburgh (Fig. 1) and from marine-derived contaminants entering the North Sea from the Atlantic Ocean.

Case history

The sediment dynamics in the estuary have been quantified by Lindsay *et al.* (1996). In essence a strong turbidity maximum is maintained within the upper estuary between Stirling and Kincardine, and this turbidity maximum migrates up to 15 km downstream under high fluvial flow conditions which are normally related to wet winter conditions. Spring and neap tides also influence the location and magnitude of the turbidity maximum, with spring tides leading to suspended particulate matter concentrations (SPMc) of >6 g l^{-1} and neap tides resulting in SPMc of <0.5 g l^{-1} Table 1 summarizes the results of a study carried out in 1989/90 which measured long-term fluxes of SPMc at the mouth of the lower estuary and the inner Firth of Forth. The results imply a strong bottom movement of SPMc at sites S1 and S2 (Figs 2 & 3) during spring tide periods, and a dominant overall landward flux of SPMc, reinforcing the general concept that estuaries are geologically ephemeral features that are continually being infilled with sediment.

Cores were collected from five sample sites in the intertidal zone of the estuary (Fig. 1). In addition, ten random surface samples were collected in the vicinity of each core sample site to obtain results for normalisation. Core samples and SPM particle size results were obtained using a Malvern laser particle size analyser. Heavy metal concentration in the core sediment samples (Sites 1–4) were obtained using a technique involving bombardment of the particles in the sample by heavier charged particles leading to electron removal and subsequent higher energy level electron replacement. During this process, X-rays are emitted which are characteristic of the element and hence lead to element identification. This technique is termed proton-induced X-ray emission (PIXE). Normalization of the heavy metal data for grain

Table 1. *Suspended particulate matter flux variations between neap and spring periods, Forth Estuary*

Site S1 26/7/89–5/9/89	Bed + 5 m SPM flux $gm^2 s^{-1}$	Bed + 10 m SPM flux $gm^2 s^{-1}$	Site S2 12/9/89–24/10/89	Bed + 5 m SPM flux $gm^2 s^{-1}$	Bed + 10 m SPM flux $gm^2 s^{-1}$
Neap	−0.14	0.36	Spring	−3/9	1.72
Spring	−0.66	0.90	Neap	0.08	0.04
Neap	−0.12	0.02	Spring	−0.37	2.00
Spring	−4.40	−1.44	Neap	0.28	0.69
Neap	−0.78	−0.03	Spring	−6.93	1.70
Spring	−0.96	0.62	Neap	−1.74	1.21

The values are tidally averaged residual SPM fluxes (negative values = landwards; spring and neap periods = tidal cycles).

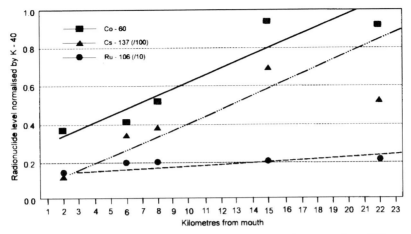

Fig. 2. Radionuclide activity levels, surface sediments. Forth Estuary, June 1990.

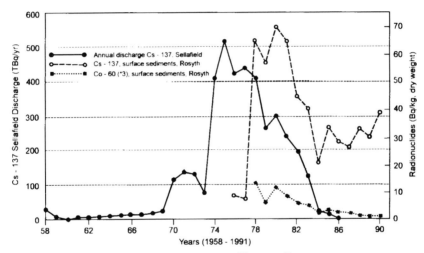

Fig. 3. Cs^{137} discharge from Sellafield and Cs^{137} and Cs^{60} levels at Rosyth.

sized variations used the linear relationship between heavy metal content and the fraction $<16\,\mu m$ in diameter (de Groot *et al.* 1971) in samples analysed at each intertidal site.

The total mercury content in the core samples was quantified using the cold vapour atomic adsorption system (CVAAS). Digestion of the sediment samples was performed in closed Teflon vessels using a $HNO_3\backslash HCl$ acid mixture, heated at $60°C$ during $12\,h$. Total Hg was then measured by CVAAS after preconcentration on a gold trap (Baeyans & Leermakers 1989), using $SnCl_2$ as a reductor. The sample was first oxidized with BrCl before the reduction step (Bloom & Crecelius 1983).

Radionuclide analysis was carried out with a Ge(Li) semiconductor detector by gamma spectrometry. The counting times ranged between 12 and 48 h. The emitted

signal data were calculated using the software program Canberra Spektran-F/PC. Radiocarbon dating was undertaken using standard procedures at the Scottish Universities Radioisotope Research Centre, East Kilbride.

Radiocarbon dating of a layer in the core (Site 1, Fig. 1) at depth 38.5–40 cm revealed an age of 1610 ± 80 years BP. The pre-industrial revolution age for the core base sample is confirmed by the heavy metal results in Tables 2–5. For example, the levels of Cu, Pb and Zn (at the 38.5–40 cm level), three of the major anthropogenic inputs, are factors of 16–23, 12–45 and 3–11 times less concentrated respectively in the Site 1 basal core sample as opposed to the polluted Bo'Ness (Site 2) and Port Edgar (Site 4) cores. The surface sample in the Site 1 core has higher concentrations of As, Cr, Cu, Pb, Zn,

Table 2. *Normalized element concentrations in sediment core samples (mg kg^{-1} dry weight or dry weight %), Kincardine, Site 1, lower Forth Estuary*

Element	Surface −2 cm to −3.5 cm	Surface −13.5 cm to −15 cm	Surface −21.5 cm to −23 cm	Surface −38.5 cm to −40 cm
Cr	150 ± 30	71 ± 30	74 ± 20	42 ± 20
Mn	450 ± 30	480 ± 40	370 ± 30	430 ± 40
Fe	3.3 ± 0.2%	4.1 ± 0.2%	2.7 ± 0.1%	2.8 ± 0.1%
Cu	16 ± 4	8 ± 3	9 ± 3	8 ± 3
Zn	75 ± 6	71 ± 4	43 ± 5	38 ± 4
Ga	15 ± 3	16 ± 2	16 ± 3	11 ± 2
Pb	34 ± 5	14 ± 4	12 ± 4	9 ± 3
As	18 ± 3	14 ± 2	16 ± 2	5 ± 2
Br	195 ± 6	53 ± 4	41 ± 3	35 ± 4
Cd	1 ± 0.05	0.89 ± 0.04	0.74 ± 0.04	0.17 ± 0.02
Sr	230 ± 10	202 ± 10	198 ± 10	168 ± 10
Y	44 ± 5	36 ± 5	37 ± 5	25 ± 6
Zr	640 ± 30	511 ± 20	458 ± 30	472 ± 20
Si	26 ± 1%	26 ± 1%	29 ± 2%	30 ± 2%
S	2000 ± 300	1900 ± 300	3200 ± 200	3000 ± 400
Cl	0.91 ± 0.04%	0.71 ± 0.04%	0.73 ± 0.04%	0.94 ± 0.04%
K	2.40 ± 0.1%	2.16 ± 0.1%	2.14 ± 0.1%	2.14 ± 0.1%
Ti	5700 ± 300	3500 ± 200	3900 ± 200	4700 ± 200
Hg	0.4	0.06	0.07	0.04
Rb	521	498	510	517

Table 3. *Normalized element concentrations in sediment core samples (mg kg^{-1} dry weight or dry weight %), Bo'Ness, Site 2, lower Forth Estuary*

Element	Surface −2 cm to −3.5 cm	Surface −13.5 cm to −15 cm	Surface −21.5 cm to −23 cm	Surface −38.5 cm to −40 cm
Cr	262 ± 40	170 ± 20	173 ± 30	121 ± 20
Mn	500 ± 80	551 ± 40	436 ± 30	412 ± 30
Fe	4.8 ± 0.2%	3.9 ± 0.2%	5.1 ± 0.2%	4.3 ± 0.2%
Cu	77 ± 5	61 ± 4	93 ± 4	124 ± 7
Zn	199 ± 5	142 ± 3	228 ± 6	128 ± 6
Ga	16 ± 3	15 ± 3	21 ± 2	18 ± 3
Pb	85 ± 9	74 ± 9	112 ± 7	163 ± 10
As	26 ± 4	17 ± 3	17 ± 3	32 ± 4
Br	210 ± 10	123 ± 7	121 ± 4	90 ± 5
Cd	1.43 ± 0.07	0.97 ± 0.03	2.11 ± 0.06	1.71 ± 0.04
Sr	189 ± 10	158 ± 9	187 ± 9	260 ± 10
Y	29 ± 6	19 ± 6	36 ± 5	28 ± 6
Zr	178 ± 10	181 ± 10	310 ± 20	220 ± 10
Si	26 ± 2%	22 ± 1%	28 ± 1%	23 ± 2%
S	7600 ± 400	6900 ± 300	7000 ± 400	11 200 ± 600
Cl	2.40 ± 0.1%	1.60 ± 0.06%	1.11 ± 0.04%	1.06 ± 0.09%
K	2.40 ± 0.1%	2.01 ± 0.06%	1.43 ± 0.07%	2.31 ± 0.09%
Ti	6900 ± 400	3600 ± 200	4300 ± 200	3200 ± 300
Hg	0.6	0.7	0.7	0.5
Rb	467	346	487	471

Cd and Ti than the deeper samples indicating that the surface layer at Site 1 is either a more recent mobile mud deposit and hence has the characteristics of polluted sediment, or else the pollution in the water column has infiltrated into the top layers of the sediment increasing the heavy metal content. The pattern of Fe concentration suggests Fe has managed to infiltrate to a depth of 15 cm in the sediment column.

The Br and Cl concentrations in the surface sediments at Kincardine and Bo'Ness are both significant, indicating that sedimentation is dependent on both marine and freshwater influences and mixing in these areas. Br is

Table 4. *Normalized element concentrations in sediment core samples (mg kg^{-1} dry weight or dry weight %), Society Point, Site 3, lower Forth Estuary*

Element	Surface −2 cm to −3.5 cm	Surface −13.5 cm to −15 cm	Surface −21.5 cm to −23 cm	Surface −38.5 cm to −40 cm
Cr	193 ± 30	211 ± 30	170 ± 20	134 ± 20
Mn	520 ± 30	590 ± 40	672 ± 30	583 ± 40
Fe	3.3 ± 0.2%	4.1 ± 0.2%	2.7 ± 0.1%	2.8 ± 0.1%
Cu	121 ± 4	144 ± 3	149 ± 3	128 ± 3
Zn	104 ± 7	85 ± 3	67 ± 3	91 ± 3
Ga	11 ± 3	17 ± 2	11 ± 3	23 ± 3
Pb	73 ± 6	29 ± 4	34 ± 4	29 ± 3
As	32 ± 3	29 ± 2	24 ± 2	26 ± 2
Br	178 ± 6	61 ± 4	57 ± 3	49 ± 2
Cd	1.40 ± 0.06	1.87 ± 0.04	1.90 ± 0.04	0.84 ± 0.04
Sr	308 ± 10	367 ± 10	286 ± 10	288 ± 10
Y	115 ± 7	52 ± 2	16 ± 3	44 ± 4
Zr	−	−	−	−
Si	27 ± 2%	35 ± 2%	23 ± 2%	24 ± 2%
S	7900 ± 300	10 300 ± 300	10 800 ± 200	11 300 ± 400
Cl	1.62 ± 0.06%	0.78 ± 0.04%	0.71 ± 0.04%	0.76 ± 0.04%
K	1.62 ± 0.1%	1.93 ± 0.09%	1.87 ± 0.08%	2.11 ± 0.06%
Ti	4200 ± 300	2500 ± 200	2900 ± 200	3200 ± 200
Hg	0.5	0.2	0.3	0.1
Rb	426	399	441	457

Table 5. *Normalized element concentrations in sediment core samples (mg kg^{-1} dry weight or dry weight %), Port Edgar, Site 4, lower Forth Estuary*

Element	Surface −2 cm to −3.5 cm	Surface −13.5 cm to −15 cm	Surface −21.5 cm to −23 cm	Surface −38.5 cm to −40 cm
Cr	100 ± 30	140 ± 20	234 ± 30	17 ± 30
Mn	1290 ± 60	560 ± 50	640 ± 50	490 ± 50
Fe	4.4 ± 0.2%	4.5 ± 0.2%	5.2 ± 0.2%	6.1 ± 0.2%
Cu	60 ± 6	77 ± 7	120 ± 5	185 ± 7
Zn	147 ± 10	211 ± 9	250 ± 9	333 ± 12
Ga	16 ± 3	16 ± 3	17 ± 4	25 ± 3
Pb	110 ± 9	120 ± 10	208 ± 10	308 ± 20
As	21 ± 4	25 ± 4	13 ± 4	20 ± 5
Br	162 ± 6	137 ± 7	124 ± 6	108 ± 5
Cd	1.48 ± 0.06	1.40 ± 0.06	2.31 ± 0.08	3.10 ± 0.09
Sr	200 ± 10	170 ± 10	312 ± 10	330 ± 20
Y	22 ± 1	30 ± 5	28 ± 1	62 ± 7
Zr	−	−	−	−
Si	22 ± 1%	22 ± 1%	21 ± 3%	20 ± 1%
S	8200 ± 400	17 000 ± 1000	12 500 ± 600	11 600 ± 700
Cl	2.02 ± 0.08%	2.19 ± 0.08%	2.04 ± 0.08%	2.31 ± 0.06%
K	2.30 ± 0.1%	2.53 ± 0.1%	2.48 ± 0.1%	3.31 ± 0.1%
Ti	6000 ± 200	5800 ± 200	6100 ± 200	4600 ± 200
Hg	0.6	0.6	0.3	0.2
Rb	521	486	472	447

associated with a riverine source which explains the lowest Br surface concentration being recorded at the most seaward site (Site 4, Table 5). The S content in sediment is a good indicator of marine water influence and Tables 3–6 indicate in the surface sediment that the S content decreases in a landward direction from 8200 mg kg^{-1} at Site 4 to 2000 mg kg^{-1} at Site 1.

It is recognized that some heavy metals have a particular affinity to particulates whereas other heavy metals will preferentially stay in solution in the water column.

Table 6. *Radionuclide activities ($Bq\,kg^{-1}$ dry weight), lower Forth Estuary, 12 June 1990, surface sediments*

Radionuclide	Kincardine Bridge	Bo'Ness	Society Point	Port Edgar
Ac^{228}	20.2 ± 0.2	16.7 ± 0.2	10.1 ± 0.2	19.1 ± 0.2
Pb^{212}	16.8 ± 0.4	12.6 ± 0.3	6.1 ± 0.1	14.2 ± 0.3
Bi^{212}	35 ± 1	28 ± 1	16 ± 1	13 ± 1
Th^{234}	36 ± 5	19 ± 3	35 ± 2	26 ± 4
Pb^{214}	16.2 ± 0.2	13.0 ± 0.1	8.0 ± 0.1	14.0 ± 0.2
Bi^{214}	22.0 ± 0.2	17.1 ± 0.2	11.1 ± 0.2	18.5 ± 0.3
Ra^{226}	–	–	10.5 ± 0.6	–
K^{40}	531 ± 3	388 ± 3	247 ± 2	498 ± 4
Cs^{134}	0.92 ± 0.05	1.10 ± 0.05	0.25 ± 0.03	0.23 ± 0.04
Cs^{137}	53.2 ± 0.3	51.3 ± 0.3	16 ± 1	13 ± 1
Co^{60}	0.82 ± 0.07	0.69 ± 0.05	0.19 ± 0.04	0.35 ± 0.06
Ru^{106}	2.11 ± 0.6	1.5 ± 0.04	0.9 ± 0.3	1.3 ± 0.5

For example, Pb has a strong affinity to particulates in that approximately 80% of Pb released will attach onto particulates. However, Zn has no particular affinity to particulates and prefers to stay in solution. Hence, at Bo'ness, Society Point and Kincardine, where large concentrations of Zn released from the petrochemical complex at Grangemouth are evident in particulate form in the core samples, it must be assumed that even greater amounts may be in solution in the water column in the estuary. Accordingly, partition coefficients need to be calculated for chemicals in the estuary in order to create an effective predictive pollution pathway model.

Recent deposition of this sediment may explain why Cu, Pb, As and Sr decrease in the top 15 cm of the core since in 1979 major changes were introduced to effluent dispersal from the petrochemical complex at Grangemouth (McLusky 1982). Forth River Purification Board requests led to the refinery effluents being removed from the River Avon, and being amalgamated so that the combined effluent of 15.4 to 18.2 million litres day^{-1} of ballast water, boiler and cooler tower blowdown and process water is now discharged onto the main Kinneil intertidal area (Fig. 1). Whether this directly led to a reduction in Cu, Pb, As or Sr is unclear since the concentration of these elements in the effluent is not known. However, related synoptic improvements to the sewage works at Bo'Ness and Kinneil led to levels of untreated domestic effluent being reduced, which would explain the reduction in Pb, Cu and As levels in the upper core samples. This general improvement in controlling chemical waste input to the estuary from the Grangemouth petrochemical complex was observed by Davies (1987). He noted that the total Hg input to the estuary decreased from 3.4 kg day^{-1} (1979) to 0.93 kg day^{-1} (1986).

Site 2 core (Table 4) shows the highest Zn concentration in the surface sample of the four sites surveyed (Tables 2–5). This may be related to a seasonal dissolved manganese peak reported in the upper part of the lower Forth Estuary by Laslett & Balls (1990). The manganese peak they discovered is associated with the dissolved oxygen minimum which is most pronounced at times of low river discharge. The dissolved manganese originates from particles under reducing conditions, either in the water column or in sediments. The magnitude of the peak was examined on the basis of the water residence time in the upper part of the estuary. Ni and Zn show mid-estuarine peaks in the Forth which coincide with that of dissolved manganese. These two elements are remobilized, as manganese is released from particles.

At Society Point (Site 3, Table 4) the surface sample indicates fairly similar levels of pollution in the heavy metal results as in surface Sites 2 and 4 core samples. However, the samples at depth in the core show much lower heavy metal concentrations than Sites 2 and 4, e.g. a factor of three times less for Cu, Zn and Pb concentrations. An explanation could be that the Site 3 layer is the only sample site that is exposed to wave and storm erosion. From the shear vane and particle size results (Lindsay 1993) it is suggested that Site 3 core is probably reworked coarser material apart from the top muddy mobile layer which is 2–3 cm thick. Thus, due to reworking, Site 3 is not showing a continuous pollution history pattern as is presumed to be observed at Sites 2 and 4. The heavy metal concentrations at Port Edgar (Site 4) show maximum pollution at the level of sample 4 at the bottom of the core (38.5 to 40 cm). During the Second World War the marina was used by the Royal Navy, hence these peak values may be the result of antecedent boat materials. Today, the marina is used by fibreglass yachts which may explain the less contaminated surface sample.

Comparison with the most recent environmental standard limits for the most toxic Annex I and II heavy metals based on recent British (ICRCL 1987) and ANZECC and NHMRC (1992) guidelines, indicate that in the surface sediments Cr, Cu and Zn just exceed the special care lower limits in all four sites. However, at depths greater than 20 cm in the cores at Port Edgar and Bo'Ness the Cr, Cu, Pb, Ni and Zn levels indicate levels close to the upper special care boundary and action levels.

Similarly surface levels of the toxic Annex 1 metal Cd are below the action levels requirement, but at depths of >20 cm in the cores the Cd levels rise into the lower action levels (>1.5 mg kg^{-1}) at Sites 2 and 4. It would appear that Hg pollution is still a problem within the estuary since levels of 0.7 mg kg^{-1} are recorded in core samples which are above the action level of 0.5 mg kg^{-1}. Whether these Hg levels are due to increased levels of Hg pollution from the petrochemical complex at Grangemouth since 1986 is uncertain since Hg occurs in many complex forms and remobilization and movement of Hg through sediment cores is very difficult to predict.

The results in Fig. 2 indicate levels of Cs^{137}, Ru^{106} and Co^{60} (normalized by K^{40} to account for particle size differences) in surface sediments in the lower Forth Estuary in June 1990. The dominant source of the first two radionuclides is Sellafield, Cumbria, and the source of Co^{60} is Rosyth Dockyard near the mouth of the Forth Estuary. Hence, these results indicate that radionuclides have entered the estuary at the seaward end and have become adsorbed onto suspended solids which have been transported to sediment sinks further upstream in the estuary. This appears to indicate that the long-term residual transport of suspended solids in the Forth Estuary is landwards (as implied in Table 1). In the long term, this involves persistent marine-derived contaminants becoming highly concentrated in the turbidity maxima zone of the estuary.

The ratio of Cs^{134}:Cs^{137} at Port Edgar in the surface samples is 0.017 ± 0.001 similar to the ratio before Chernobyl in 1985, which indicates that Chernobyl activity in the Forth has dispersed. The dominant source of Cs must therefore have resorted back to Sellafield. Further evidence that the Kincardine deposit is a glacial deposit is the complete absence of Cs^{134}, Cs^{137} and C^{60} throughout the three lower Kincardine core samples. The C^{60} introduced at Rosyth shows minimal amounts of activity are present at Bo'ness and Port Edgar.

The residual currents in the Irish Sea are northward, and a similar northward drift has been detected for radioisotopes from Sellafield, with C^{137}, for example, being traced around the north of Scotland and down to the Channel coast of Europe (Murray et al. 1978). Stanners & Aston (1982) have calculated transit times of approximately a year for Cs^{137} from Sellafield to be detected in intertidal sediment in the Solway Firth. Assuming similar dilution rates for the Cs^{137} plume each year as it is transported around Scotland, McKinley et al. (1981) calculated water movement involving Cs^{137} taking eight months to travel from Sellafield to the Clyde sea area and travelling with an advective velocity of approximately 1.6 km day^{-1} (McKinley et al. (1981) calculated that the transport northwards through the Hebridean Sea of the radiocaesium plume from Sellafield in 1976 had an advective velocity of 5 km day^{-1}.

The surface levels of Ru^{106} the Forth cores (Table 6) were lower than that of Cs^{137} even though the Sellafield discharges of the former are higher than those of the latter. This is probably due to the fact that the half-life of Ru^{106} is only one year whilst that of Cs^{137} is 30 years. The radionuclide results (Table 6) indicate low Cs^{134}:Cs^{137} levels of the order of 0.02 and low Ru^{106}:Cs^{137} levels of the order of 0.03, which suggests a fairly long travel time (lag time) from the discharge of the effluent radionuclides at Sellafield to their deposition in the Forth surface sediments.

Figure 3 indicates that the annual discharge of Cs^{137} from Sellafield peaked in 1975 and has gradually decreased since. Data collated from the Ministry of Agriculture, Food and Fisheries surveys (Hunt 1990) for Cs^{137} in surface sediments at Rosyth indicate a peak in Cs^{137} levels between 1978 and 1980 of the order of 70 Bq kg^{-1} (dry weight). Assuming that this peak is related to the Sellafield 1975 Cs^{137} output peak, then transit times of approximately 3 to 5 years from Sellafield to Rosyth are implied. This lag time fits in well with the literature mentioned above. The shoulder in the Cs^{137} levels in surface sediments at Rosyth from 1986 to 1990 (Fig. 3) could be due to Chernobyl fall-out from the 1986 incident or it may be due to varying Cs discharge from Dounreay Nuclear Power Station (northern Scotland) which normally discharges at a rate of approximately 10% of the Sellafield discharge. Figure 3 also indicates Cs^{60} at Site 5 and at Rosyth Naval Dockyard from 1975 to 1991. A reduction in the discharge limits of cooling water from nuclear submarines has led to a three-fold reduction in surface sediment Cs^{60} levels in the vicinity of Rosyth since 1975.

Samples from sediment cores taken from Sites 2, 4 and 5 have been analysed for Cs^{137}. These results are displayed in Fig. 4. The Cs^{137} results for the Site 5 core (Fig. 4) suggest a peak of Cs^{137} between 10 and 15 cm deep in the sediment, which if related to the Rosyth surface sediment peak level (1978–1980) suggests a deposition rate at Limekilns of approximately 1 cm ya^{-1}. Using this method, deposition rates of 1.5 and 2.1 cm ya^{-1} were derived for the Sites 2 and 4 intertidal areas respectively.

Conclusions

The heavy metal concentrations found in lower core samples taken from two sites in the Forth Estuary indicate that the lower Forth Estuary has been affected by substantial industrial pollution in the recent past. However, lower heavy metal concentrations in the surface core samples reflect the fact that in recent years some industrial discharges have been reduced due to pollution control legislation. In the less consolidated surface samples, Cu, Pb and Zn levels are 50–300% lower than concentrations in the more consolidated basal core samples. Results of radionuclide concentrations in subsurface sediments in the estuarine intertidal

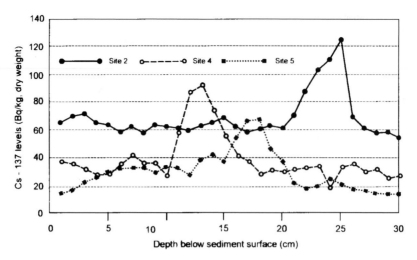

Fig. 4. Vertical zonation of Cs[137] levels in Forth Estuary sediment cores.

zones indicate that radionuclides derived from the seaward end are adsorbed onto SPM in the water column and these contaminated SPM demonstrate a long-term upstream pattern which means that more contaminated sediment is settling out in sediment sinks towards the turbidity maxima.

Heavy metal patterns do not follow the pattern of decrease from river to sea due to chemical desorption or physical mixing. This is because contaminants in this estuary enter from various sources from the land and seaward ends leading to contamination being site-specific. Recent surface sediments indicate no heavy metal layers towards the top end of the special care/action levels. However, older more contaminated sediments in the cores at Sites 2 and 4 indicate five Annex II heavy metals (Cr, Cu, Pb, Zn and As) having levels in the special care range. Contaminant levels in the surface and basal core samples at Site 1 indicate that since the Industrial Revolution, anthropogenic pollution has increased the contaminant level in surface sediments by two- to four-fold in Cr, Cu, Pb, Zn and As and by six-fold and twelve-fold in Cd and Hg levels, respectively.

References

ANZECC AND NHMRC 1992. *Australian and New Zealand guidelines for the assessment and management of contaminated sites.* Australian and New Zealand Environment and Conservation Council and National Health and Medical Research Councils.

BAEYANS, W. & LEERMAKERS, M. 1989. Determination of metallic mercury and some organomercury compounds using atomic adsorption spectrometry after amalgamation on a gold column. *Journal Atomic Absorption Spectrometry,* **4**, 635–640.

BALLS, P. W. 1992. Nutrient behaviour in two contrasting Scottish estuaries, the Forth and Tay. *Oceanology Acta,* **8**, 1–16.

BLOOM, N. & CRECELIUS, E. 1983. Determination of Hg in seawater at sub nanogram per liter levels. *Marine Chemistry,* **14**, 454–458.

BONNET, P. J. P., APPLEBY, P. G. & OLDFIELD, F. 1988. Radionuclides in coastal and estuarine sediments from Wirral and Lancashire. *The Science of the Total Environment,* **70**, 215–236.

DAVIES, I. M. 1987. Trace metals and organohalogen compounds in the Forth, Scotland. *Proceedings Royal Society Edinburgh,* **93B**, 315–326.

DE GROOT, A. J., DE GOEY, G. J. J. & ZEGERS, C. 1971. Contents and behaviour of mercury as compared with other heavy metals in sediments from the rivers Rhine and Ems. *Geologie Mijnbonw,* **50**, 393–398.

HUNT, G. J. 1990. *Radioactivity in Surface and Coastal Waters of the British Isles, 1985–1991.* Aquatic Environment Monitoring Report 14, Lowestoft. Ministry of Agriculture, Fisheries and Food, London.

ICRCL 1987. *Guidance Note 59/83, Guidelines on the Assessment and Redevelopment of Contaminated Land.* Interdepartmental Committee on the Redevelopment of Contaminated Land (2nd Edition), Department of the Environment, HMSO, London.

LASLETT, R. E. & BALLS, P. W. 1990. *Trace Metal Chemistry of the Firths and Estuaries of Forth and Tay (Scotland).* Paper presented at UK Oceanography 90 Conference, 10/9/90, Plymouth Polytechnic.

LINDSAY, P. *Some Aspects of Solute and Sediment Transport, Lower Forth Estuary, Scotland.* PhD thesis, University of Birmingham, UK

———, BALLS, P. W. & WEST, J. R. 1996. Influence of tidal range and river discharge on suspended particulate matter fluxes in the Forth Estuary (Scotland). *Estuarine Coastal and Shelf Science,* **42**, 63–82.

McKINLEY, I. G., BAXTER, M., ELLET, D. J. & JACK, W. 1981. Tracer applications of radiocaesium in the Sea of Hebrides. *Estuarine Coastal and Shelf Science,* **13**, 69–82.

McLUSKY, D. S. 1982. The impact of petrochemical effluent on the fauna of an intertidal estuarine mudflat. *Estuarine Coastal and Shelf Science*, **14**, 489–500.

MURRAY, C. N., KAUTSKY, H., HOPPENHEIT, M. & DOMIAN, M. 1978. Actinide activities in water entering the North Sea. *Nature*, **276**, 225–230.

STANNERS, D. A. & ASTON, S. R. 1982. Desorption of Ru-106, Cs-134, Cs-137, Ce-144 and Am-241 from intertidalsediment contaminated by nuclear fuel reprocessing effluents. *Estuarine Coastal and Shelf Science*, **14**, 687–691.

WEBB, A. J. & METCALFE, A. P. 1987. Physical aspects, water movements and modelling studies of the Forth estuary, Scotland. *Proc. Roy. Soc. Edinburgh*, **93B**, 251–272.

Characterization of extensive hydrocarbon contamination of an alluvial aquifer, Ploiesti, Romania

Stephen Wallace,[1] William Burgess,[1] Jane Dottridge,[1] Alexander Kim,[1] Daniela Zamfirescu[2] & Florian Zamfirescu[2]

[1] Hydrogeology Group, Department of Geological Sciences, University College London, London WC1E 6BT, UK
[2] University of Bucharest, Faculty of Geology and Geophysics, Bucharest, Romania

Abstract. The alluvial aquifer in Ploiesti, Romania, is severely contaminated with hydrocarbons. Petroleum products from four major refineries and 30 km of pipeline affect an area of 37 km^2, occurring as free product floating on the shallow water table, dissolved hydrocarbon in the groundwater, and residual hydrocarbon in the unsaturated zone. Surveys performed between 1975 and 1995 defined the extent, nature and rapid movement of the contamination at rates up to 100 m a^{-1}. Analysis of free product and soil samples showed a complex mixture of crude and refined hydrocarbons, with advanced biodegradation in both phases. Concentrations of non-volatile hydrocarbons in groundwater from the zone surrounding the free product plume were high, averaging 25 mg l^{-1}, with dissolved contaminants as far as 6 km down-gradient of the industrial area. Organic and inorganic analyses indicate that biodegradation is occurring. Remediation requires the prevention of further spillages and application of economical and innovative technology. The highly permeable aquifer favours the use of *in situ* remediation, but remedial action is currently limited to a few skimming wells to remove free product.

Introduction

The extensive contamination of the unconfined alluvial aquifer in the petroleum refinery areas of Ploiesti, Romania, is one of the most severe cases of hydrocarbon contamination in Europe. Ploiesti, 80 km north of Bucharest, has been the major petroleum refining centre in Romania since the start of commercial oil production in 1857. The long history of hydrocarbon processing, combined with damage from earthquakes and bombing, has resulted in widespread contamination from multiple sources. There are four large oil refineries (Fig. 1), over 30 km of pipelines, storage tanks and transport facilities for both crude and refined hydrocarbons. Around the industrial area, free-phase oils float on the water table, forming a layer up to 7 m thick close to the sources. Outside the zone of free product, groundwater in the shallow, permeable, alluvial aquifer is severely contaminated over an area of more than 27 km^2. This has resulted in the pollution of two major wellfields used for domestic and industrial supply to the city, dug wells used for water supply to eight villages, and damage to greenhouse plants in an area where the shallow water table rises to the root zone.

Since groundwater contamination was first detected in village wells in 1974, repeated surveys and regular monitoring have illustrated the movement of hydrocarbon contamination (ISPIF 1991, 1993; ICPA 1994; Manescu *et al.* 1994). The most recent study up-dated information on the extent and characterized the nature of contamination, to allow consideration of appropriate control and remediation options (Wallace 1995; Zamfirescu 1995). Although local people have dug numerous wells and trenches to recover oil for sale, only Brazi refinery has implemented active remediation. This consists of nine skimming wells, which can remove up to 5000 tonnes of free product per month, and a clay barrier, 2.5 km long, constructed at the leading edge of the plume in 1992. Oil is now accumulating behind this barrier, but unfortunately the oil recovery wells and other off-site skimming wells have been vandalized.

The scale of subsurface contamination by hydrocarbons at Ploiesti is significantly greater than is commonly encountered elsewhere. Containment and eventual clean-up of the contamination, using a technically feasible and cost-effective approach, present a challenge to the ingenuity of the environmental engineers and to the politicians to gain funding and public acceptance for remedial measures. Continued monitoring at Ploiesti provides a unique case study of contamination on an extremely large scale, with minimal intervention to clean up the aquifer. These data can provide valuable insights into the ability of natural mechanisms to attenuate and ultimately to remediate subsurface contamination, which will be useful in assessing the effectiveness of 'natural remediation', an approach which is gaining wide support.

WALLACE, S., BURGESS, W., DOTTRIDGE, J., KIM, A., ZAMFIRESCU, D. & ZAMFIRESCU, F. 1998. Characterization of extensive hydrocarbon contamination of an alluvial aquifer, Ploiesti, Romania. *In*: LERNER, D. N. & WALTON, N. R. G. (eds) 1998. *Contaminated Land and Groundwater: Future Directions.* Geological Society, London, Engineering Geology Special Publications, **14**, 189–193.

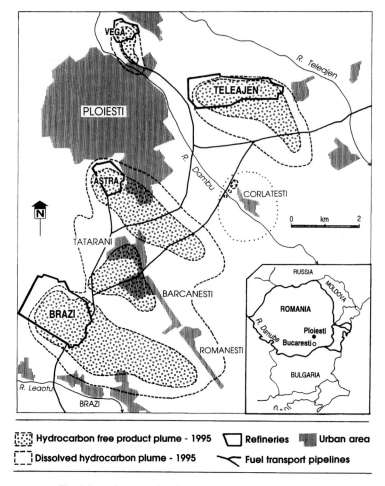

Hydrocarbon free product plume - 1995   **Refineries**   **Urban area**

Dissolved hydrocarbon plume - 1995   **Fuel transport pipelines**

Fig. 1. Location map showing extent of contamination in 1995.

Geology and hydrogeology of the Ploiesti region

The sands and gravels of the Prahova–Teleajen alluvial fan in the Ploiesti region are typical of the Quaternary deposits of the Romanian Plain, which overlie several thousand metres of Tertiary sediments accumulated during uplift of the Carpathian Mountains. The Prahova–Teleajen sands and gravels are 10–30 m thick, with a clay or silt matrix, and capped by a thin silty clay. A marl formation separates the unconfined alluvium from the deeper sands and gravels of the confined Cindesti aquifer, which provides the principal groundwater supply for the city of Ploiesti. The groundwater system drains to the River Danube and its tributaries, which traverse the Ploiesti region from northwest to southeast, parallel to the regional groundwater flow.

The alluvial aquifer is extremely vulnerable to contamination due to its high permeability and shallow water table, at a maximum depth of 15 m in the north, but only 2 m deep in the south. The permeability of the phreatic aquifer averages $100 \, m \, day^{-1}$, giving transmissivities between 200 and $4000 \, m^2 \, day^{-1}$, with the highest values in the north. The porosity of the unconsolidated alluvium is high, between 20% and 40%. Based on these values, the mean calculated velocity of groundwater flow is $130 \, m \, a^{-1}$, from northwest to southeast.

Sources of hydrocarbon contamination

The largest sources of continuous contamination are the four major refineries: Astra, Brazi, Teleajen and Vega (Fig. 1). Although the volume of hydrocarbons released into the groundwater is enormous from an environmental viewpoint, the losses are negligible compared with the huge scale of refining operations, which reached a peak capacity of 15 million tonnes per year in the 1970s. There is a legacy of past contamination from the long history of the petroleum industry in Ploiesti and heavy bombing during the Second World War. Leakage rates remain high due to deterioration and lack of investment in facilities, damage by a major earthquake in 1977, and working practices which lead to occasional explosions.

Railway depots and transmission pipelines provide other sources of hydrocarbon spills. The most frequent cause of contamination is deliberate rupturing of sections of 30 km of shallow, buried pipeline. The oil is rarely gathered directly from a pipeline break, but more commonly allowed to infiltrate and subsequently recovered through shallow trenches dug to the water table. These oil recovery trenches operate as a basic form of remediation, as floating oil is scooped off the surface in buckets and removed for sale, but carelessness results in frequent spills which provide a secondary source of contamination.

Occurrence and migration of contaminants

Floating free phase contamination

A plume of floating product is associated with each refinery and with ruptured pipelines at Tatarani (Fig. 1 and Table 1), but it is likely that several sources contribute to each plume resulting in a complex mixture of crude and refined hydrocarbons. The thickness of free product follows a classic pattern, thinning from source to toe of the plume, with some rapid local variations close to the sources. Repeated surveys over a 20-year period and the widespread distribution of oil recovery trenches provide data on the areal extent and movement of the free phase, at rates between 50 and 100 m a^{-1} (Table 1).

Residual contamination

Many exposed sections of the alluvium in trenches and banks of streams show evidence of hydrocarbon contamination immediately above the water table, beneath a clean unsaturated zone. This indicates that the contamination originates as a residue of the floating product, deposited through fluctuations in levels of oil and water. Although some soil samples from these exposures were analysed, it proved impossible to hand-auger through the alluvium (Wallace 1995), for collection of fresher samples.

Dissolved contaminants in the phreatic aquifer

A zone of contaminated groundwater containing high levels of dissolved hydrocarbons surrounds each of the free product plumes (Fig. 1). To the south of Ploiesti, three zones of contamination have coalesced to form an extensive area of contaminated groundwater covering over 30 km^2. Definition of the extent and rate of movement of contaminated groundwater is hindered by the lack of sampling points, as many of the monitoring boreholes have been blocked, although samples were obtained from domestic wells, some still in use for drinking water.

Analyses of 31 groundwater samples taken in 1995 provided the only set of data on concentrations of dissolved hydrocarbons in the shallow groundwater (Wallace 1995). Most of the earlier data relied on taste and odour to define the limits of contamination. The results showed an average concentration of non-volatile dissolved hydrocarbon of 25 mg l^{-1} in the zone of contamination, compared with background levels of

Table 1. *Extent of hydrocarbon contamination in the Ploiesti area*

Source	Free product area (km^2)	Maximum thickness of free product (m)	Free product migration rate (m a^{-1})	Dissolved contaminant area (km^2)
Astra refinery	3.5 (1977) 6.5 (1995)	4.0	100	7 (1990)
Brazi refinery	5.5 (1976) 8.5 (1995)	6.7	70	11 (1981)
Teleajen refinery	2 (1981) 4 (1992)	0.8	90	6 (1992)
Vega refinery	1 (1980) 1.5 (1989)	0.5	50	2 (1989)
Tatarani (ruptured pipelines)	3 (1990)	0.1	50	?

$1-3\,\mathrm{mg\,l}^{-1}$. The maximum concentration of $74\,\mathrm{mg\,l}^{-1}$ was recorded close to the site of a past pipeline rupture, with a clear trend of declining values down-gradient from this location.

Comparison of results from different dates show that the velocity of the contaminated groundwater is similar to that of the free product plume, from about $50\,\mathrm{m\,a}^{-1}$ at Brazi (1983–1995) to $130\,\mathrm{m\,a}^{-1}$ at Astra (1990–1995). These velocities are only slightly slower than the calculated groundwater flow rates of $70–160\,\mathrm{m\,a}^{-1}$, which suggests that there is little retardation.

Contaminant chemistry

GC and GC-MS analyses show that the free phase hydrocarbons are all characterized by low $n\text{-}C_{17}$: pristane and $n\text{-}C_{18}$: phytane ratios, which decrease down-gradient from the contaminant source, from 1.5 to less than 0.3. Straight chain and branched alkanes (C_{10}–C_{26}) dominate, and there is some indication on the chromatograms of an unresolved complex mixture (UCM). This suggests that the free product has undergone some biodegradation which increases down-gradient.

Analyses of contaminated groundwater and sediment showed that the composition of most samples is very complex and therefore difficult to 'fingerprint' and establish a point source. This is to be expected, as there are multiple contaminant sources each containing a different mixture of petroleum products. However, the absence of low molecular weight compounds (C_4–C_{12}) indicates loss of volatiles. Despite careful precautions, it cannot be discounted that this loss of volatiles may be partly due to the sampling and storage, but it could also result from weathering and/or sorption in the soil zone.

Sandy sediments contained a mean concentration of $26\,\mathrm{mg\,g}^{-1}$ (maximum $40\,\mathrm{mg\,g}^{-1}$) non-volatile hydrocarbon, whereas clay sediments contained background concentrations (below $1.2\,\mathrm{mg\,g}^{-1}$), which may reflect the influence of pore structure on permeability and pore entry pressure of the clay, or poor extraction efficiencies. In comparison with the free product samples, the hydrocarbons in the sandy sediments show the following characteristics:

- dominance of branched alkanes (C_{12}–C_{26}) over their corresponding straight chain n-alkane;
- increased proportion of the UCM;
- a more pronounced decrease down-gradient of $n\text{-}C_{17}$: pristane and $n\text{-}C_{18}$: phytane ratios (0.7–0.5 to less than 0.2).

All of these factors indicate that biodegradation is important in the free product plume and the zone of residual saturation, but loss of volatiles may be due to physical weathering.

GC analysis of the groundwater revealed substantial variation of the $n\text{-}C_{17}$: pristane and $n\text{-}C_{18}$: phytane ratios, and n-alkane distributions along the flow paths, which makes evaluation of degradation trends difficult. These apparently varying states of degradation are due to different ages and types of contaminants in close proximity. In an appreciable number of the groundwaters, the dominant feature is the UCM, which indicates an advanced state of biodegradation, except at the Astra plume where no UCM was observed.

The inorganic analyses supply supporting evidence of degradation of the hydrocarbons and the trends are similar to those from a study in the US (Baedecker *et al.* 1993). In comparison with background values, the samples of groundwater taken from beneath the free product plumes at Brazi and Teleajen show elevated concentrations of divalent iron and manganese, low nitrate, high ammonium and an increase in bicarbonate (Fig. 2). The available data can be ascribed to a series of reactions coupled with the oxidation of hydrocarbons, through microbial action under anaerobic conditions, but the relative importance of specific processes remains uncertain as the existing data on redox-sensitive parameters are incomplete.

Environmental management

The widespread hydrocarbon contamination around Ploiesti presents a serious threat to water resources and agriculture in the areas of shallow water table, affecting an area of $37\,\mathrm{km}^2$ in 1993, but spreading rapidly in the permeable alluvial aquifer. Monitoring data suggest that there is very little retardation, with both the free product and contaminated groundwater moving rapidly, at rates close to the predicted groundwater velocities. However, the composition of free and dissolved hydrocarbons both suggest that significant biodegradation occurs, and is more effective than physical weathering. These processes remove more of the lighter hydrocarbons, leaving a residue of heavier fractions in the sediments and groundwater.

The essential first step of any systematic remediation strategy should be to locate and stop all sources of contamination. Immobilization and removal of the free product plume is also necessary as it provides a continuous source of dissolved contaminants to the groundwater. Previous experience suggests that remediation is most effective at the refinery sites, where the thickness of free product is greatest, physical barriers can be installed to reduce off-site migration and installations are secure from vandalism. Elsewhere, the high permeability favours *in situ* remediation, but innovative methods will be needed to cope with the large scale of the contamination.

Acknowledgements. Many thanks to the British Council who funded this project under grant number BUC/980/4; the University of Bucharest, Petrostar and Prospectiuni for assistance with equipment and fieldwork; Astra Romana SA, ICPA,

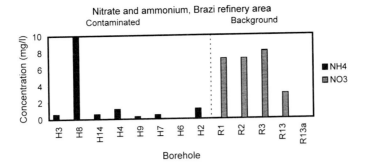

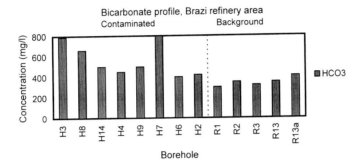

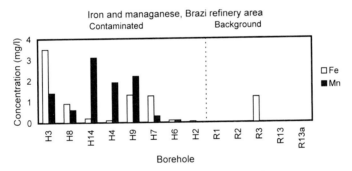

Fig. 2. Geochemical profiles for the Brazi refinery area.

INMH, Petrobrazi SA and Petrotel SA for data and site access; and the Departments of Biochemical Engineering and Archaeology at UCL and Department of Chemistry, King's College for laboratory facilities.

References

BAEDECKER, M. J., COZZARELLI, M., EGANHOUSE, R. P., SIEGEL, D. I. & BENNET, P. C. 1993. Crude oil in a shallow sand and gravel aquifer – III. Biogeochemical reactions and mass balance modeling in anoxic groundwater. *Applied Geochemistry*, **8**, 569–584.

ICPA 1994. *Implamentarea si urmarirea unui sistem de monitoring in zona solurilor poluate cu petrul si stabilirea influentelor ficcarei surse de poluare.* Report for Petrobrazi, Ploiesti.

ISPIF 1991. *Studiul hidrogeologic de sinteza privind poluarea petroliera a apelor freatice din zona unor rafinarii si objective anexa.* Report for Contract 8147/1.

——1993. *Studiul hidrogeologic privind reatunlizarea studilor anterloare si urimarirea evolutici gradului de poluare petroliera a apa freatice in zona Petrotel Ploiesti.* Report for Contract 9563/St.

MANESCU, M., BICA, I. & STAN, I. 1994. La pollution d'eau souterraine avec des produits petroliers dans la zone de Ploiesti. *Proceedings of the International Hydrogeological Symposium on Impact of Industrial Activities on Groundwater*, Constantza, Romania, 23–24 May, 356–368.

WALLACE, S. R. 1995. *Characterisation of Extensive Hydro-carbon Contamination of an Alluvial Aquifer, Ploiesti, Romania.* MSc Thesis, University of London.

ZAMFIRESCU, D. 1995. *Remediation Methodologies for Hydro-carbon Contaminated Groundwater.* Report on visit to UK, 9 October–9 November 1995.

SECTION 5

RESEARCH ON POLLUTANT BEHAVIOUR

Transport of dissolved creosote compounds through fractured clay: column and field experiments

K. Broholm,[1] P. J. Jørgensen,[2] A. B. Hansen,[3] B. Nilsson,[4] R. C. Sidle,[4] E. Arvin[1] & J. Fredericia[4]

[1] Institute of Environmental Science and Engineering, Technical University of Denmark, Building 115, DK-2800 Lyngby, Denmark
[2] Danish Geotechnical Institute, Maglebjergvej 1 DK-2800 Lyngby, Denmark
[3] National Environmental Research Institute, Frederiksborgvej 399, Postbox 358, DK-4000 Roskilde, Denmark
[4] Danish and Greenland Geological Survey, Thoravej 8 DK-2400 Copenhagen NV, Denmark

Abstract. Transport of selected creosote compounds and tracers in two column experiments and a field study in fractured clayey till are presented. Twenty-five organic compounds were used in the column experiments and 12 in the field experiment. This paper focuses on three organic compounds: phenol, naphthalene and dibenzofuran. One column was biologically inactive, and the other was biologically active with denitrifying conditions in the beginning and aerobic/denitrifying conditions later on in the experiment. The infiltration water at the field site was aerobic in the beginning and anaerobic (no oxygen, very little nitrate, and some sulphate) later. The results showed very rapid transport through clayey till of the tracers and the organic compounds. Despite the rapid transport through fractures, biodegradation may be an important process in fractured media at least for the easily degradable organic compounds.

Introduction

Clayey till has often been considered to be an efficient protecting layer for underlying aquifers due to its low permeability. However, within the last decade it has been recognized that fractures occur in clayey tills at different locations. In Denmark, excavations have revealed visible fractures in tills to depths of 4–6 m (Fredericia 1990; Jørgensen & Fredericia 1992; Klint & Fredericia 1995). A pump test has indicated hydraulically active fractures to depths of 18 m (Keller *et al.* 1986). Furthermore, there are indications from other pump tests that relatively extensive clay layers have been penetrated by hydraulically conductive fractures (D'Astous *et al.* 1989; Thomson 1990; Rudolph *et al.* 1991; Ruland *et al.* 1991). Fractures are created by desication, freezing/thawing events, or glacial tectonics. Other macropores, such as worm holes and decayed root channels, may persist in the upper portion of tills.

Previous experiments have revealed that the transport of different tracers (e.g. bromide and chloride), bacteriophages, some pesticides, and some creosote compounds is enhanced significantly due to the presence of fractures (Jørgensen & Spliid 1992; McKay *et al.* 1993*a,b*; Jørgensen & Foged 1994; Broholm *et al.* 1995; Hinsby *et al.* 1996). Despite this rapid transport in the fractures, an experiment has demonstrated that biodegradation may be an important process, at least for easily degradable organic compounds (Broholm *et al.* 1995).

The present study concentrates on selected dissolved creosote compounds. Creosote consists of hundreds of organic compounds, of which only a minor portion have been identified. Usually, polyaromatic hydrocarbons (PAHs) constitute about 85% of the organic compounds in the free phase of creosote, phenolic compounds 10%, monoaromatic hydrocarbons (BTEX) less than 1%, and heterocyclic compounds containing oxygen, nitrogen or sulphur (NSO-compounds) about 5%. In water in equilibrium with free phase creosote, NSO-compounds constitute about 35–40% and the phenolic compounds about 45% in the aqueous phase, whereas PAHs constitute only about 15–20%. This is due to the relatively large aqueous solubilities of the NSO-compounds and the phenolic compounds compared to the low solubilities of the PAHs (see Table 1). Thus, the phenolic and NSO-compounds pose a greater risk for groundwater contamination from creosote contaminated sites than the PAHs, even though they are present as a smaller fraction in creosote.

The purpose of the experiments reported here was to study the fate of 25 organic compounds in two intact clay columns and the transport of 12 organic compounds at a field location. The results presented here are preliminary and the final results will be reported later.

BROHOLM, K., JØRGENSEN, P. J., HANSEN, A. B., NILSSON, B., SIDLE, R. C., ARVIN, E. & FREDERICIA, J. 1998. Transport of dissolved creosote compounds through fractured clay: column and field experiments. *In*: LERNER, D. N. & WALTON, N. R. G. (eds) 1998. *Contaminated Land and Groundwater: Future Directions*. Geological Society, London, Engineering Geology Special

Table 1. *Relevant physical/chemical properties and the average influent concentrations of the organic compounds used in this study*

Compound	S	$log(K_{ow})$	Column 1	Column 2		Field
				Days 0–40	Days 40–	
	$(mg\,l^{-1})$	(–)	$(mg\,l^{-1})$	$(mg\,l^{-1})$	$(mg\,l^{-1})$	$(mg\,l^{-1})$
Benzene	1 780[1]	2.13[1]	2.75	2.81	0.45	–
Toluene	515[1]	2.69[1]	4.13	4.15	0.69	0.26
Ethylbenzene	152[1]	3.13[1]	4.72	5.05	0.95	–
p-Xylene	215[1]	3.18[1]	4.75	4.88	0.89	–
o-Xylene	220[1]	3.15[1]	5.11	5.24	0.96	–
Phenol	88 360[2]	1.46[2]	3.23	3.35	0.47	0.69
o-Cresol	26 000[2]	1.98[2]	4.42	4.23	0.65	0.42
2,4-Dimethylphenol	8 795[2]	2.35[2]	3.63	–	–	–
2,6-Dimethylphenol	6 230[2]	2.36[2]	–	–	–	0.31
3,5-Dimethylphenol	5 500[2]	2.35[2]	3.39	–	–	0.66
Naphthalene	31[3]	3.37[3]	2.47	2.52	0.49	0.36
1-Methylnaphthalene	28[3]	3.87[3]	1.95	2.08	0.45	0.44
Phenanthrene	1.1[3]	4.57[3]	0.28	0.88	0.15	–
Fluorene	1.9[3]	4.18[3]	0.36	1.17	0.15	–
Quinoline	6 330[4]	2.03[5]	3.77	5.19	1.26	0.79
2-Methylquinoline	–	2.59[5]	1.93	1.77	0.30	–
Acridine	46.6[4]	3.40[5]	0.33	0.38	0.04	0.26
Carbazole	1.2[4]	3.72[5]	0.24	0.63	0.10	–
Indole	1 875[4]	2.00[5]	2.31	2.72	0.55	0.25
Pyrrole	58 800[6]	0.75[5]	3.41	1.69	0.41	–
1-Methylpyrrole	–	–	2.57	2.89	0.36	–
Benzothiophene	130[4]	3.12[5]	3.51	3.39	0.57	0.27
Dibenzothiophene	1[4]	4.38[7]	0.19	1.00	0.14	–
Furan	28 600[6]	1.34[5]	–	–	–	–
Benzofuran	–	2.67[5]	2.53	3.35	0.47	–
Dibenzofuran	4.75[3]	4.31[3]	1.32	2.36	0.36	0.39

S is the aqueous solubility and K_{ow} is the octanol–water distribution coefficient.
[1] Mackay *et al.* (1992*a*). [2] Shiu *et al.* (1994). [3] Mackay *et al.* (1992*b*). [4] Pearlman *et al.* (1984). [5] Hansch & Leo (1979). [6] Katritzky (1963). [7] Hassett *et al.* (1980).

Materials and methods

Field site

The field site is located in Ringe, Island of Fyn, Denmark. Between 10 and 15 m of clayey till overlies an unconfined sandy aquifer. The clayey till contains some sand lenses with significant extention. The geology and fracture/macropore structure at the site have been described by Klint & Fredericia (1995). The upper approximately 2 m of till is dominated by root holes, and the till itself is relatively soft. From approximately 2 m to 5 m depth the till is more dense and dominated by numerous fracture systems. The upper till is dominated by quartz, feldspar and 9% clay. From approximately 2 m to 5 m depth the till is dominated by quartz, calcite, feldspar and 7% clay.

Column experiments

Two cylindrical samples of undisturbed fractured clay (0.5 m in height and 0.5 m in diameter) were obtained

from depths of 1–1.5 m and 2.5–3 m at an excavation in Ringe. The techniques for obtaining a clay column in the field and installing it in the laboratory have been described by Jørgensen & Foged (1994). This technique ensures that the columns are intact with respect to the fractures, and that the temperature and confining pressure are the same in the laboratory as in the field. Figure 1 shows an outline of the column set-up. The flow through the columns was controlled by a peristaltic pump. The average flow rate for Column 1 was 220 ml day^{-1} from Day 0 to Day 24, and 1350 ml day^{-1} from Day 24 to Day 139. The reason for increasing the flow rate was that by continuing at 220 ml day^{-1}, breakthrough of the compounds would have taken too long a time. For Column 2 the average flow rate was 1570 ml day^{-1}. The temperature for the two columns varied between 11°C and 13°C and the confining pressure was about 0.3 Bar (30 kPa) which corresponds to 3.1 m of water or 1.1 m of water-saturated clay.

The influent water for both columns was tap water. The water for Column 1 was supplied with 2 g l^{-1} of sodium azide (NaN$_3$) to kill the bacteria in the clay,

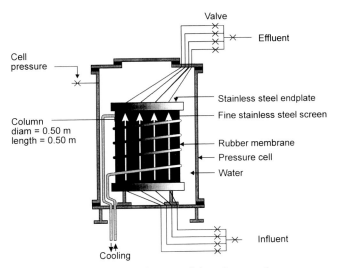

Fig. 1. Experimental set-up of the column study.

$200\,\text{mg}\,l^{-1}$ of sodium sulphite (Na_2SO_3) to remove oxygen from the water, $100\,\text{mg}\,l^{-1}$ of lithium bromide (LiBr) as a tracer, and some organics (see Table 1). The added Na_2SO_3 was sufficient to reduce $25.4\,\text{mg}\,O_2\,l^{-1}$ and hence there was enough Na_2SO_3 also to remove any oxygen that may diffuse into the bag containing the influent water. The column was infiltrated with water containing only NaN_3 and Na_2SO_3 prior to the infiltration of organics and the tracer started in order to acclimatize the clay before the actual experiment started.

The water for Column 2 contained $2.62\,\text{g}\,l^{-1}$ of sodium nitrate ($NaNO_3$) instead of the NaN_3 in order to produce denitrifying conditions in the column. The concentration of $NaNO_3$ was adjusted so that the influent water to Column 2 had the same ionic strength as the influent water for Column 1. The average nitrate concentration was $450\,\text{mg}\,N\,l^{-1}$. The standard deviation of the nitrate concentration was 6%. From Day 92 to Day 137 the influent water contained an average oxygen concentration of $9.0\,\text{mg}\,l^{-1}$ instead of Na_2SO_3. The standard deviation of the oxygen concentration was 11%. The influent water was prepared in a 5 l glass bottle filled with 5 l of tap water. The inorganic compounds were added to the water, whereafter 0.5 ml or 5 ml (depending on the actual stock solution) of the organic stock solution was added. In the period with oxygen addition the tap water was aerated before the addition of inorganic compounds. The bottle was then sealed with a stopper, and shaken vigorously until the different organic and inorganic compounds were dissolved completely in the water. The water was then transferred from the bottle and into a Tedlar bag through a tube. Eventually, the bag was connected to the pump through a Teflon tube and placed in a cooler at about $1\,°C$ to suppress any degradation in the bag.

Field experiment

The experimental set-up and the location of the sampling points at the field site is shown in Fig. 2. Water infiltrated over a cross-section of $16\,m^2$ in a basin created a vertical flow field in the clayey till. The average flow rate was $8.6\,m^3\,day^{-1}$, corresponding to $0.5\,m^3\,m^{-2}\,day^{-1}$, which was much higher than for the column experiments. The reason for this high flow rate in the field was that a sand lens was located at a depth of 4.5 m below ground surface. The sand lens drained the upper till so in order to maintain saturated conditions in the upper till the relative high flow rate was necessary. The influent water was prepared in an open tank ($4\,m^3$) whereafter it was pumped to a similar tank which was in hydraulic contact with the infiltration basin. Of course this design affected the in-fluent concentrations because some of the added organic compounds are volatile and may evaporate. However, the experiment was carried out in a period

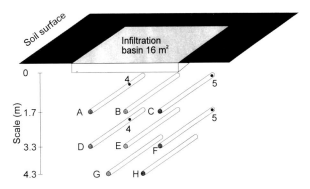

Fig. 2. Schematic of the field sampling scheme.

with air temperature around freezing which partly eliminated the problem. The influent concentrations of the compounds were measured in the infiltration basin, so they represent the infiltrated water. The organic compounds (see Table 1) were added together with chloride for a period of 7 days. The average concentrations of the organic compounds are listed in Table 1 and the average concentration of chloride was $497 \, mg \, l^{-1}$. Sodium sulphite was also added to the influent water to remove any oxygen present. However, for the first 4 days the added amount of sodium sulphite was not sufficient to remove the oxygen, so after 4 days the procedure was changed. Thus, during the first 4 days the influent water contained approximately $12 \, mg \, O_2 \, l^{-1}$, but after changing the procedure the oxygen influent concentration was approximately $0 \, mg \, O_2 \, l^{-1}$.

Based on the results from a previous tracer test, six sampling points were selected for intensive monitoring (about 50 samples at each sampling point over a period of 8 days) of the concentrations of organic compounds and chloride. Additionally, 14 sampling points were sampled daily for organic compounds and chloride. Furthermore, water samples were obtained daily for oxygen measurements and every fourth day for nitrate and nitrite. Twice a day samples were obtained from the influent for measuring organic compounds and chloride, daily for measuring oxygen, and every fourth day for nitrite and nitrate analysis.

Results and discussion

This paper will focus on the fate of three organic compounds: phenol, naphthalene, and dibenzofuran. They represent three different groups of compounds

with a wide range of physical and chemical properties (see Table 1).

Column 1: the abiotic column

Figure 3 shows the relative concentrations of the three organic compounds and bromide for Column 1. Azide was infiltrated to this column so the fate of the organic compounds should not be influenced by biodegradation. During the period of low flow rate (Days 0–24) the relative bromide concentration increased only very slowly, so it was decided to increase the flow rate at Day 24. As a result, bromide broke through much faster. After about 60 days the relative bromide concentration approached 1. At Day 106, bromide was removed from the influent water and bromide was leached from the column. The relative bromide concentration decreased within a day from about 1 to 0.25, after which a long leaching tail was observed. The initial breakthrough and flushing curves are quite different. The decrease in bromide concentration (flushing curve) appears to represent tracer transport in fractured media, but the increase in the bromide concentration does not look like a breakthrough curve for fractured media. However, during this period from Day 24 and the following 10 days the flow was not constant due to occasional pump malfunctions, and in a fractured system at this scale the behaviour of compounds (inorganic as well as organic compounds) is very sensitive to variations in flow rate.

Among the organic compounds, the breakthrough of phenol and naphthalene were delayed slightly compared to bromide, whereas dibenzofuran was delayed significantly and only reached a relative concentration of less than 0.2 after 107 days.

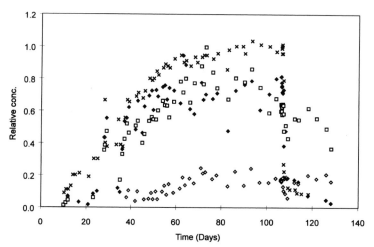

Fig. 3. The relative concentrtions of bromide (×), phenol (◆), naphthalene (□) and dibenzofuran (◇) for Column 1.

Column 2: the denitrifying/aerobic column

The relative concentration of the three organics and bromide is shown in Fig. 4 for Column 2. Before the injection of organics started, the column was infiltrated with water containing only nitrate for 82 days. During this period significant nitrate removal and nitrite concentrations were observed in the effluent from the column, indicating that significant denitrification occurred in the till. The only organic carbon in the system was the dissolved organic carbon in the tap water and the natural organic matter in the till. After initiation of the infiltration of organic compounds the nitrite and nitrate concentrations in the effluent did not reveal any degradation of the organics. Thus, at Day 40 the influent concentrations were decreased to about 20% of the initial influent concentrations. This change in influent concentrations did not seem to stimulate the degradation significantly based on the nitrite/nitrate concentrations, and at Day 92 oxygen was added to the influent water.

Among the organic compounds shown in Fig. 4 phenol and naphthalene broke through almost as fast as bromide, whereas dibenzofuran was attenuated significantly. There were no indications of degradation of the various organic compounds. At Day 40 where the influent concentrations were decreased, the relative concentration of phenol responded very fast compared to dibenzofuran, which seemed to behave like the organic compounds in the beginning of the experiment. However, the concentration of phenol continued to decrease and reached a relative concentration of approximately 0.05 at Day 90, whereas both naphthalene and dibenzofuran reached relative concentrations of approximately

0.2 which corresponded to the influent at this time. It seems that phenol is degraded under the denitrifying conditions in the column.

Oxygen was added at Day 92. The oxygen concentration in the effluent never exceeded $2\,mg\,l^{-1}$ during the following 35 days so oxygen was used for either biological or abiotic processes in the column. The relative concentration of naphthalene and dibenzofuran decreased significantly during this period indicating that they were both degraded under aerobic conditions in the column.

Field experiment

Figure 5 shows the relative concentrations of chloride, the three organic compounds, and the oxygen concentration for four selected sampling points, A4, C5, D4 and F5. Sampling point A4 is located directly above sampling point D4, and sampling point C5 is located directly above sampling point F5.

In general, the relative concentrations of chloride approached one for all the sampling points shown in less than three days. The breakthrough curves for chloride for sampling points A4 and C5 are identical, whereas the breakthrough is delayed slightly for sampling point D4 and more for sampling point F5. Assuming that the fractures are vertical and continuous, the water influencing sampling point A4 will also influence sampling point D4, and the water influencing sampling point C5 will also influence sampling point F5. Therefore the breakthrough of chloride should be delayed in sampling point D4 relative to sampling point A4, and the breakthrough should be delayed in sampling point F5 relative to sampling point C5, which also was observed.

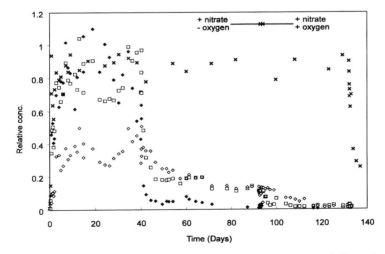

Fig. 4. The relative concentrations of bromide ($\times$), phenol ($\blacklozenge$), naphthalene ($\square$) and dibenzofuran ($\lozenge$) for Column 2.

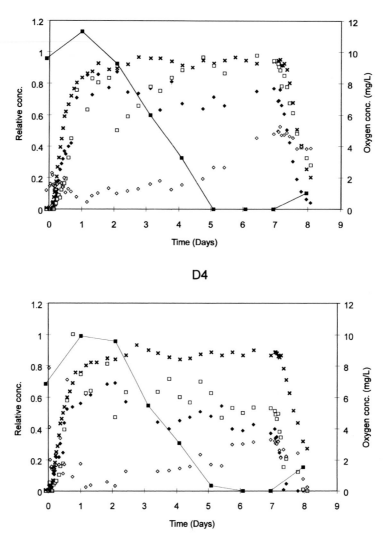

Fig. 5. The relative concentrations of chloride (×), phenol (◆), naphthalene (□), dibenzofuran (◇) and oxygen (■) for sampling points A4, C5, D4, and F5.

Among the organic compounds studied, the breakthrough of phenol and naphthalene was only slightly delayed relative to chloride in sampling points A4 and D4. However, the relative concentrations of both phenol and naphthalene were lower in sampling point D4 than in A4 which indicates that the compounds are degraded slightly during the transport from A4 to D4. Dibenzofuran was delayed significantly relative to chloride, which is expected due the high K_{ow} of dibenzofuran. Also by comparing sampling point C5 and F5 it seems

that at least some of the phenol and naphthalene are degraded. For sampling point F5, all the organic compounds were delayed compared to chloride, but biodegradation may also cause this delay. Based on the chloride breakthrough data, the transport time is greater from C5 to F5 than from A4 to D4 so the organics have more time to be degraded. However, it is difficult to interpret the results of the field experiment due to the changing redox conditions in the influent water, but it appears that the compounds are attenuated significantly.

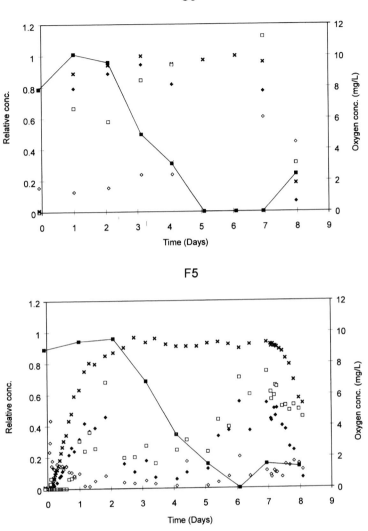

Fig. 5. (*continued*).

The attenuation is likely to be a combination of sorption/diffusion and biodegradation. Modelling of contaminant transport may eluciate the attenuation mechanisms.

Conclusion

All of the experiments carried out with creosote compounds and conservative tracers indicate that transport is very rapid through clayey tills. Additionally, some compounds like phenol and naphthalene are retarded only slightly relative to the tracers, whereas compounds like dibenzofuran are significantly retarded. In one column with denitrifying conditions phenol was degraded, whereas naphthalene and dibenzofuran were degraded when oxygen was added to the biological active column. Although transport is very rapid in fractured media, biodegradation may be an important process, at least for easily degradable organic compounds. In general, the experiments showed that fractured media do not protect the groundwater to any significant degree.

Acknowledgement. This study was financed by the Danish Environmental Research Programme.

References

BROHOLM, K., ARVIN, E., HANSEN, A. B., JØRGENSEN, P. R. & HINSBY, K. 1995. The fate of dissolved creosote compounds in an intact fractured clay column. *Proceedings of the International Conference on Groundwater Quality: Remediation and Protection (GQ95)*, Prague, 15–18 May.

D'ASTOUS, A. Y., RULAND, W. W., BRUCE, J. R. G., CHERRY, J. A. & GILLHAM, R. W. 1989. Fracture effects in the shallow groundwater zone in weathered Sarnia area clay. *Canadian Geotechnical Journal*, **26**, 43–56.

FREDERICIA, J. 1990. Saturated hydraulic conductivity of clayey tills and the role of fractures. *Nordic Hydrology*, **21**, 119–132.

HANSCH, C. & LEO, A. 1979. *Substituent Constants for Correlation Analysis in Chemistry and Biology*. Wiley, New York.

HASSETT, J. J., MEANS, J. C., BANWART, W. L., WOOD, S. G., ALI, S. & KHAN, A. 1980. Sorption of dibenzothiophene by soils and sediments. *Journal of Environmental Quality*, **9**, 184–186.

HINSBY, K., MCKAY, L. D., JORGENSEN, P. R., LENCZEWSKI, M. & GERBA, C. P. 1996. Fracture aperture measurements and migration of solutes, viruses, and immiscible creosote in a column of clay-rich till. *Ground Water*, **34**, 1065–1075.

JØRGENSEN, P. R. & FOGED, N. 1994. Pesticide leaching in intact blocks of clayey till. *Proceedings of the XIII ICSMFE*, New Delhi.

—— & FREDERICIA, J. 1992. Migration of nutrients, pesticides, and heavy metals in clayey till. *Geotechnique*, **42**, 67–77.

—— & SPLIID, N. H. 1992. Mechanisms and rates of pesticide leaching in shallow clayey till. *Proceedings of the European Conference on Integrated Research for Soil and Sediment Protection and Remediation*. MECC, Maastricht, 6–12 September.

KATRITZKY, A. R. (ed.) 1963. *Physical Methods in Heterocyclic Chemistry, Vol 1: Nonspectroscopic Methods*. Academic, New York.

KELLER, C. K., VAN DER KAMP, G. & CHERRY, J. A. 1986. Fracture permeability and groundwater flow in clayey till near Saskatoon, Saskatchewan. *Canadian Geotechnical Journal*, **23**, 229–240.

KLINT, K. E. S. & FREDERICIA, J. 1995. Fracture parameters in fractured clayey till. *Vand og Jord*, **2**, 208–214 [in Danish].

MACKAY, D., SHIU, W. Y. & MA, K. C. 1992a. *Handbook of Physical-chemical Properties and Environmental Fate for Organic Chemicals, Volume 1 Monoaromatic Hydrocarbons, Chlorobenzenes, and PCBs*. Lewis, London.

——, —— & ——1992b. *Handbook of Physical-chemical Properties and Environmental Fate for Organic Chemicals, Volume 2, Polynuclear Aromatic Hydrocarbons, Polychlorinated Dioxines, and Dibenzofurans*. Lewis, London.

MCKAY, L. D., CHERRY, J. A., BALES, R. C., YAHYA, M. T. & GERBA, C. P. 1993a. A field example of bacteriophage as tracers of fracture flow. *Environmental Science Technology*, **27**, 1075–1079.

—— & GILLHAM, R. W. 1993b. Field experiments in a fractured clay till. 2. Solute and colloid transport. *Water Resources Research*, **29**, 3879–3890.

PEARLMAN, R. S., YALKOWSKY, S. H. & BANERJEE, S. 1984. Water solubilities of polynuclear aromatic and heteroaromatic compounds. *Journal of Physical Chemical Reference Data*, **13**, 555–562.

RUDOLPH, D. L., CHERRY, J. A. & FARVOLDEN, R. N. 1991. Groundwater flow and solute transport in fractured lacustrine clay near Mexico City. *Water Resources Research*, **27**, 2187–2201.

RULAND, W. W., CHERRY, J. A. & FEENSTRA, S. 1991. The depth of fractures and active groundwater flow in a clayey till plain in southwestern Ontario. *Ground Water*, **29**, 405–417.

SHIU, W. Y., MA, K. C., VARHANÍČKOVÁ, D. & MACKAY, D. 1994. Chlorophenols and alkylphenols: A review and correlation of environmentally relevant properties and fate in an evaluative environment. *Chemosphere*, **29**, 1155–1224.

THOMSON, D. 1990. *Indentification of Open Wisconsinan Age Fractures in a Deep Clayey Till*. MSc. Thesis, Department of Earth Science, University of Waterloo, Waterloo, Ontario, Canada.

Sorption of three heterocyclic compounds and their hydrocarbon analogue from coal-tar contaminated water in a natural clayey till

Mette M. Broholm, Kim Broholm & Erik Arvin

Department of Environmental Science and Engineering, Technical University of Denmark, Building 115, DK-2800 Lyngby, Denmark

Abstract. The natural attenuation of contaminants in fractured media is controlled by biodegradation and by diffusion into the matrix. The effective rate of diffusion and the mass of contaminants thereby removed from the aqueous phase in the fracture depends on the sorption of the contaminants. The sorption of three heterocyclic compounds and their hydrocarbon analogue from an aqueous solution of a complex mixture of 25 organic coal-tar compounds including all major groups of organic coal-tar compounds in clayey till was studied in batch experiments for a large range of concentrations including concentrations approaching the effective solubility of the mixture and for two different solid:liquid (s:l) ratios. For the high s:l ratio sorption experiment the isotherms were close to linear and best fitted by Freundlich isotherms. Sorption of the four compounds was correlated with K_{ow}, but an order of magnitude greater than predicted from a K_{oc}–K_{ow} relationship for aquifer materials. Sorption was primarily dominated by hydrophobic sorption. However, at high surface density carbazole sorption appeared to be influenced by dipole–dipole attraction. For the low s:l ratio experiment at higher concentrations a dramatic increase in sorption was observed for all four compounds. The dramatic increase is likely a result of multi-layer formation/condensation of organic compounds on mineral surfaces at high surface density of organic compounds possibly induced by the complexity of solutes. The steepness of the increase and sensitivity to total compound surface density appears to be related to compound hydrophobicity. The impact of these four compounds on groundwater quality from sources of coal-tar in fractured clayey till overburden may be significantly lower than predicted from general sorption relationships.

Introduction

Coal-tar contamination in the subsurface is a widespread problem. Heterocyclic organic compounds constitute a significant part of the dissolved coal-tar components in water in contact with coal-tar. In clayey till deposits, hydraulically active fractures provide a pathway for dissolved organic compounds to reach the underlying groundwater reservoirs. The natural attenuation of contaminants in fractured media is controlled by biodegradation and by diffusion into the matrix. The effective rate of diffusion and the mass of contaminants thereby removed from the aqueous phase in the fracture depends on the sorption of the contaminants.

If free phase coal-tar is present in a fracture the aqueous phase will contain a complex mixture of dissolved organic compounds in concentrations approximating the effective aqueous solubilities of the individual compounds in the immediate vicinity of the free phase coal-tar. The complex mixture will include basic N-heterocyclic compounds and acidic phenolic compounds as well as neutral compounds including other N-heterocyclic, and S- and O-heterocyclic compounds (NSO), mono-aromatic hydrocarbons (BTEX), naphthalenes, and poly-aromatic hydrocarbons (PAH). For the majority of these compounds the sorption of the individual compounds in single solute systems in a variety of sediments and soils has been studied. The effect of multiple solutes on the sorption of the individual compounds has gained little interest and is mostly restricted to two or three solute systems, which do not reflect the complexity of solutes from coal-tar contamination.

In this presentation we will concentrate on the sorption of three heterocyclic compounds: carbazole, dibenzofuran and dibenzothiophene, and their hydrocarbon analogue, fluorene, in clayey till from a complex coal-tar mixture (25 compounds) in aqueous solution. The four compounds have very similar molecular structures, differing only by substitution of a carbon-atom by a heteroatom (N, O and S) in the heterocyclic compounds (see Fig. 1). Results for some of the other compounds studied are presented and the effects of the complexity of solutes on the sorption of individual compounds is discussed in more detail by Broholm *et al.* (1997*a*,*b*).

BROHOLM, M. M., BROHOLM, K. & ARVIN, E. 1998. Sorption of three heterocyclic compounds and their hydrocarbon analogue from coal-tar contaminated water in a natural clayey till. *In:* LERNER, D. N. & WALTON, N. R. G. (eds) 1998. *Contaminated Land and Groundwater: Future Directions.* Geological Society, London, Engineering Geology Special Publications, **14**, 205–212.

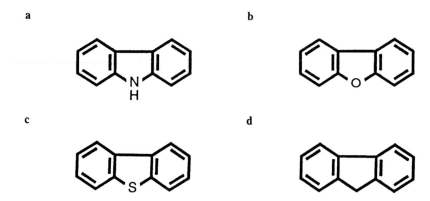

Fig. 1. Molecular structures of (**a**) carbazole, (**b**) dibenzofuran, (**c**) dibenzothiophene and (**d**) fluorene.

Sorption theory

As partitioning between phases is a linear function, the sorption of contaminants to soil organic matter has often been described with linear isotherms:

$$q_e = K_d \times C_e \tag{1}$$

where q_e is the amount sorbed (mmol kg^{-1} dry soil), C_e is the equilibrium aqueous concentration (mmol l^{-1}) and K_d is the linear partitioning coefficient (l kg^{-1}).

However, for subsurface soils, there is mounting evidence of isotherm non-linearity. For surface adsorption phenomena over large concentration ranges non-linearity should be expected. Non-linearity may also be exhibited for absorption into organic matrices if interactions between sorbed solute molecules increase or decrease their affinity for those matrices.

The most frequently used non-linear model is the Freundlich model which is empirical:

$$q_e = K_f \times C_e^{1/n} \tag{2}$$

where K_f is the Freundlich partitioning coefficient and $1/n$ is a measure of the non-linearity of the isotherm.

If hydrophobic sorption dominates, then normalizing the linear sorption coefficients with the fraction of organic carbon in the soil (f_{oc}) results in unique constants (K_{oc}) for the individual compounds (e.g. Karickhoff et al. 1979):

$$K_{oc} = \frac{K_d}{f_{oc}} \tag{3}$$

K_{oc} can be predicted from the octanol–water partitioning coefficient (K_{ow}). Abdul et al. (1987) found the following relationship for hydrophobic compounds based on five aquifer materials:

$$\log K_{oc} = 1.04 \times \log K_{ow} - 0.84 \tag{4}$$

Numerous relationships have been reported by other authors. Most of these, including the relationship by Karickhoff et al. (1979), are based primarily on young river sediments and top-soils of relatively high f_{oc}, whereas the relationship by Abdul et al. (1987) is based on older aquifer materials of low f_{oc}. With respect to depositional age and f_{oc}, the clayey till resembles the aquifer materials, hence the relationship by Abdul et al. was expected to be more representative of the sorption to the clayey till.

Non-hydrophobic interactions may contribute to or dominate sorption. This tends to occur for compounds with highly polar or ionizable functional groups conductive to significant site-specific bonding with polar groups or charged sites on sorbent surfaces, and for sorbents with low organic carbon content, especially if coincident with high clay content.

A critical fraction of organic carbon (f_{oc}^*) has been defined as the f_{oc}-value corresponding to equal amounts of a chemical being sorbed to the organic fraction and to the mineral fraction (McCarty et al. 1981). The critical content of organic carbon (f_{oc}^*) was estimated from the relationship by McCarty et al. (1981) after substitution of the coefficients based on a relationship by Karickhoff et al. (1979) with those from the Abdul et al. (1987) relationship:

$$f_{oc}^* = \frac{S}{46} \times \frac{1}{K_{ow}^{0.88}} \tag{5}$$

where S is the specific surface area (m^2 g^{-1}). As K_{ow} increases, the sorption to organic carbon increases, and eventually the amount sorbed to mineral surfaces relative to the amount sorbed to organic matter may be insignificant even for materials of low f_{oc}.

Materials and methods

Clayey till

The clayey till samples used in this study were collected from an uncontaminated section of a natural fractured, clayey till deposit in Ringe, Denmark, from a depth of 6.05 m below ground surface (bgs) in an open excavation.

The clayey till deposit in Ringe is 10–15 m thick and overlies a sand aquifer used for regional water supply. The deposit is highly fractured (Klint & Fredericia 1995). The clayey till is silty and sandy, with gravel and dispersed stones. The deposit is divided into an upper section (0.5–2 m bgs) of softer material with low or no chalk content and with multiple root-holes preferentially following the fracture surfaces; and a lower section of harder material rich in chalk and with increasing sand content with depth. A local sand lens was observed from 4.7 to 5.9 m bgs at the sampling location.

The collected sample of clayey till was carefully homogenized by hand after removal of stones and coarse gravel (>approximately 2 mm) shortly after collection. The sample was aired but not left to dry out. Sub-samples were placed in plastic bags and kept at 10°C. All further characterization and experiments were performed with homogenized samples.

The homogenized sample was dominated by quartz, calcite and feldspar and contained smaller amounts of clay. The fine clay fraction (<0.0002 mm) was dominated by smectite and also contained kaolinite, illite and a smaller amount of vermiculite. The coarse clay fraction (0.0002–0.002 mm) consisted of approximately even amounts of smectite, vermiculite, illite and kaolinite. Other clayey till parameters determined for the homogenized sample used in the experiments reported here are summarized in Table 1. The techniques used and the variability of the parameters with depth/location in the till deposit are described in Broholm et al. (1997a).

Coal-tar compound mixture

A mixture of 25 coal-tar compounds was prepared. The individual compounds and their concentration in the mixture were selected to represent a simplified composition of compounds representative of the composition of groups of compounds in dissolved phase contamination from free phase coal-tar. NSO-compounds were well represented in the mixture. The mixture consisted of (molefraction in brackets): benzene (0.087), toluene (0.067), ethylbenzene (0.063), o-xylene (0.056), p-xylene (0.057), naphthalene (0.016), 1-methylnaphthalene (0.013), phenol (0.057), o-cresol (0.041), 2,4-xylenol

Table 1. *Clayey till characterization*

Sample location		Ringe, DK
Sample depth (m bgs)		6.05
Water content (%)		12.2
pH_{CaCL_2} (1:2.5)		7.8
Organic carbon content (%)		0.02
Grain size distribution	Small stones (% bulk)	3.2
	Gravel (% bulk)	1.6
	Sand and coarse silt (%)	50
	Fine silt (%)	43
	Clay (%)	7
Exchangeable bases (meq/100 g)	CEC	6.56
	Ca + CaCO₃	8.57
	Mg	0.30
	Na	0.09
	K	0.2
Specific surface area (m² g⁻¹)		10

(0.037), 3,5-xylenol (0.035), fluorene (0.004), phenanthrene (0.003), furan (0.107), benzofuran (0.017), dibenzofuran (0.011), benzothiophene (0.023), dibenzothiophene (0.003), pyrrole (0.133), 1-methylpyrrole (0.073), indole (0.027), carbazole (0.003), quinoline (0.051), 2-methyl-quinoline (0.012), and acridine (0.003). The compounds all appeared to be completely dissolved in the resulting liquid at room temperature. The results of analysis of aliquots of the mixture dissolved in ether–pentane with internal standard could be repeated. The response on FID for the individual compounds agreed reasonably well with expectations based on previous calibrations.

For each experiment, a stock solution of the compound mixture was prepared by addition of an aliquot of the mixture to a specific volume of matrix water (defined below). Solutions of lower concentration were prepared from the stock solution by dilution with matrix water. At the pH of the solutions in this study the N-bases and phenols in solution were primarily present in their neutral form. Some loss of the most volatile compounds and of the least soluble compounds occurred during solution preparation by volatilization and sorption to glass surfaces. Therefore, solution concentrations were determined analytically.

The content in the coal-tar mixture and selected physical–chemical parameters of the four compounds of interest for this paper are presented in Table 2.

Experimental procedure

Sorption was studied in batch equilibrium experiments with clayey till in contact with an aqueous solution of

Table 2. *Compound content in coal-tar mixture and physical–chemical parameters*

Compound	Carbazole	Dibenzofuran	Dibenzothiophene	Fluorene
Content in mixture (mole/total moles of coal-tar compounds)	0.003	0.011	0.003	0.004
Molecular weight[1] (g/mole^{-1})	167.21	168.19	184.26	166.22
Melting point^{-1} (°C)	247	86	99	116
Solubility[2,3], 25°C (mmol l^{-1})	0.86	0.07	0.02	
	0.98	0.11	0.03	0.09[6]
	1.58	0.24[6]	0.04	
$\log(K_{ow})$[4]	3.72	4.12	4.38[7]	4.18[6]
		4.31[6]		
$\log(K_{oc})$[5]	3.03	3.44	3.72	3.51
f_{oc}^{*} (%)[5]	0.012	0.005	0.003	0.005

[1] Lide (1992).
[2] As supercooled liquid, calculated based on Mackay and Shiu (1981).
[3] Pearlman *et al.* (1984).
[4] Hanch & Leo (1979).
[5] Calculated values, Equation (4).
[6] Mackay *et al.* (1992).
[7] Hassett *et al.* (1980).

the coal-tar mixture. The experiments were conducted in centrifuge pyrex-glass tubes ('25 ml') with screw-caps sealed with Teflon-silicon disks.

Each batch contained approximately 6 or 15 g homogenized clayey till (corresponding to 5.3 and 13 g dry sample, respectively). A solution consisting of 0.01 M CaCl$_2$ in distilled water was pre-equilibrated with clayey till and centrifuged free of solids (2800 rpm for 1 h decanted and centrifugation repeated twice) to obtain comparable conditions in the controls and the clayey till batches with an ionic strength of the solutions resembling that of pore-water. The exchangeable bases (inorganic cations) of the clayey till are dominated by Ca^{2+}. This matrix solution was purged with nitrogen to remove oxygen prior to addition of the coal-tar compound mixture for preparation of the stock solution and dilutions. The controls and clayey till batches were filled to minimal head-space with solutions (approximately 30 ml per batch). Clayey till batches and controls were prepared in triplicate.

To prevent aerobic degradation of the compounds, Na$_2$SO$_3$ was added at a concentration of approximately 200 mg l^{-1} in batches with 6 g clayey till and in controls, and at a concentration of approximately 500 mg l^{-1} in batches with 15 g clayey till, as the latter contained more entrapped air. These concentrations were found to be sufficient to prevent degradation of toluene and quinoline, two of the most easily degradable coal-tar compounds, for a minimum of 8 days in batches with clayey till.

The batches were placed in a slowly rotating box (end over end) at room temperature (22°C) for 4 to 6 days for sorption to reach equilibrium. No measurable change in solution concentration was observed in a kinetic experiment with dibenzofuran after 3 to 4 days (Broholm *et al.* 1997*a*), and a 4-day-long kinetic experiment with the coal-tar mixture indicated that equilibrium was reached within the same time for all the compounds. Clayey till batches were centrifuged at 2800 rpm for a minimum of 40 min until clear, prior to sub-sampling for analysis. Subsequently, the pH of the remaining solution was measured by electrode. All chemicals used were of analytical grade.

Aqueous phase samples (10 ml) were extracted with an ether (85%)–pentane (15%) mixture (1 ml) with analytical-grade 1-bromonaphthalene as internal standard at a consistent temperature of approximately 20°C The extracts were analyzed on a Shimatzu gas chromatograph 14A equipped with a flame ionization detector (FID) and a 25 m Wcot fused silica 32 mm ID CP-sil 19CB Chrompack column. The GC was operated at 45°C for 2 min, 10°C min increase to 280°C, and held for 2 min. Data collection and peak integration were performed using MAXIMA. Internal standard calibration was used. Standards were prepared in extraction fluid by the addition of aliquots of the base standard-solution and subsequent equilibration with matrix-water under the same conditions as for sample extraction. The calibration curve was obtained by best-fit linear regression through the origin of six to eight calibration standard concentrations versus relative peak area. Standard deviations on nine separate equilibrations with matrix-water and analysis of a standard were (as a percentage of the average); fluorene 1.1% dibenzofuran 0.9% dibenzothiophene 2.8% and carbazole 3.7%. The method is described in more detail in Broholm *et al.* (1997*b*).

The mass sorbed was calculated from the measured aqueous concentration and corrected for sorption to septa and glass from the results of controls assuming linear sorption within the concentration range of equilibrium concentration of batches and controls of each set.

The linear and Freundlich isotherm coefficients for the individual compounds in the multi-solute experiments were determined by linear regression.

Physical and chemical parameters including estimated K_{oc} and f^*_{oc} values are given in Table 2. The estimations of K_{oc} and f^*_{oc} are based on the f_{oc} and S values measured for the homogenized clayey till sample used for the experiments reported here. As the f_{oc} is close to the method detection limit, accuracy is expected to be $\pm 50\%$. S values vary only a few per cent with depth/location in the clayey till deposit, whereas the f_{oc} values of all other samples were three to eight times higher than the f_{oc} measured for the homogenized clayey till sample used for the experiments reported in this paper (Broholm et al. 1997a).

this study) and/or consideration of f_{oc} variation in the clayey till deposit results in decreased f^*_{oc} values relative to f_{oc}. Hence, the four compounds (if neutral) are all expected primarily to sorb to the organic fraction of the clayey till.

For the low s:l ratio experiment the sorption at low concentrations correlate well with the results of the high ratio experiment for dibenzofuran, dibenzothiophene and fluorene, whereas the sorption of carbazole is greater.

At higher concentrations a dramatic increase in sorption is observed for all four compounds. The steepest increase is observed for dibenzothiophene followed by fluorene and dibenzofuran. The steepness of the dramatic increase in sorption appears to increase with increasing hydrophobicity. The scatter at high aqueous concentrations is a result of the large fraction of the total mass of the compound in the sorbed phase, as small variations in the mass sorbed (i.e. due to small variations in composition of the clayey till) result in a great relative variation in the amount dissolved.

Results

The isotherm data for carbazole, dibenzofuran, dibenzothiophene and fluorene from the high and low s:l ratio experiments are illustrated in Fig. 2.

The isotherms of the s:l ratio 0.5 experiment were close to linear and best fitted by Freundlich isotherms. The sorption coefficients for the best fit by linear and Freundlich isotherms and the f_{oc} normalized K_d values for the four compounds are given in Table 3.

The fluorene sorption isotherm is more linear than the isotherms for the heterocyclic compounds.

The lowest sorption is observed for carbazole. Within the concentration range studied, the sorption of dibenzofuran and fluorene are comparable, and the sorption of dibenzothiophene is greatest. Sorption increases with decreasing solubilities (supercooled liquid) and increasing hydrophobicity expressed by K_{ow}. This is consistent with hydrophobic theory.

The f_{oc} normalized K_d-values for all four compounds are about an order of magnitude greater than the estimated K_{oc} values (based on the same f_{oc} value). Considering the span in K_{oc}–K_{ow} relationships and the variation between the individual measurements these are based on, an order of magnitude difference is not inconsistent with hydrophobic theory.

The K_d/f_{oc} values are presented as a function of K_{ow} value and compared to the K_{oc}–K_{ow} relationship in Fig. 3. The log–log plot of K_d/f_{oc} versus K_{ow} appears linear and parallel to the K_{oc}–K_{ow} relationship. The critical f^*_{oc} value estimated for the four compounds are lower than the clayey till f_{oc} value. Use of other K_{oc}–K_{ow} relationships (including the one which may be derived from the data of

Discussion

The greater linearity of the fluorene isotherm relative to the heterocyclic compound isotherms may be an indication that sorption to mineral surfaces relative to partitioning to organic matter is of greater significance for the heterocyclic compounds than for fluorene.

The linear trend of the K_d/f_{oc} versus K_{ow} parallel to the K_{oc}–K_{ow} relationship indicates that sorption is dominated by hydrophobic sorption for all four compounds. This correlates well with the expectations for neutral compounds based on f^*_{oc} estimates. The effect of the complexity of solutes on the sorption of individual compounds is discussed in Broholm et al. (1997b).

Carbazole is sorbed less strongly than the other three compounds. This corresponds with the higher polarity of carbazole, also reflected in higher solubility and lower hydrophobicity (K_{ow}). Due to its relatively high polarity, carbazole may potentially be sorbed by dipole–dipole attraction to clay minerals. However, as carbazole does not deviate significantly from the linear trend, the sorption of carbazole like the three other compounds appears to be dominated by weak solute–solvent interaction rather than strong solute–sorbent interaction.

For the low concentration range of the low s:l ratio experiment, sorption isotherms and thereby f_{oc} normalized K_d values for fluorene, dibenzofuran and dibenzothiophene would correspond to those of the high s:l ratio experiment. But carbazole would deviate from the linear trend for the low concentration range as sorption

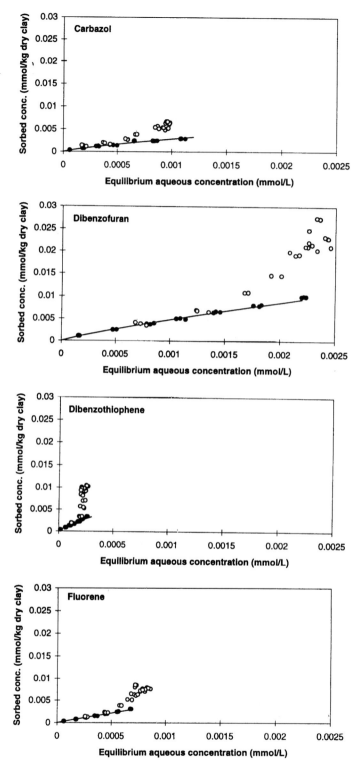

Fig. 2. Sorption isotherm data for carbazole, dibenzofuran, dibenzothiophene and fluorene for s:l ratio 0.5 (●) with best fit Freundlich isotherm (—) and for s:l ratio 0.2 (○).

Table 3. *Sorption coefficients for best fit linear and Freundlich isotherms (concentrations in mmol l^{-1} and mmol kg^{-1} for aqueous and sorbed phase, respectively)*

Compound	K_d	r^2	K_f	$1/n$	r^2	$log(K_d/f_{oc})$
Carbazole	2.92	0.92	0.71	0.80	0.99	4.16
Dibenzofuran	4.53	0.99	1.66	0.85	1.00	4.36
Dibenzothiophene	12.3	0.99	2.27	0.81	0.98	4.79
Fluorene	4.38	1.00	2.87	0.95	1.00	4.34

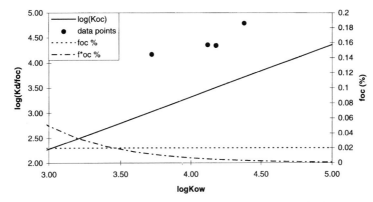

Fig. 3. K_d/f_{oc} as a function of K_{ow} compared to K_{oc}–K_{ow} relationship by Abdul *et al.* (1987), Equation 4 and the clayey till f_{oc} compared to the f_{oc}^* as a function of K_{ow}.

of carbazole in the low s:1 ratio experiment is stronger than in the high s:1 ratio experiment. Dipole–dipole attraction of carbazole to clay minerals seem to have a greater influence on its sorption at the low s:1 ratio. The stronger sorption of carbazole may be an indication that sorption by dipole–dipole attraction is enhanced in systems of higher surface density of compounds.

The trend of the isotherms (low s:1 ratio experiment) corresponds to BET type 2 gas sorption isotherms (Lindgren 1987; Weber 1972) for single-solute systems, where the effect is caused by multi-layer sorption or condensation on mineral surfaces. This suggests that multi-layer sorption or condensation of the compounds have occurred in this experiment, and that the density of total organic compounds sorbed is of significance. The BET model has been applied successfully to the data in Broholm *et al.* (1997*b*).

However, observations of a dramatic increase in sorption as observed in the low s:1 ratio experiment of this study have not previously been reported for multi-solute sorption or for sorption of non-polar compounds in single-solute systems. The different behaviour of the compounds in this experiment is possibly a result of the complexity of the solute mixture. Ainsworth *et al.* (1987) observed S-shaped isotherms for quinoline

sorption on Na-montmorillonite. At low concentrations quinoline was sorbed primarily as the cation even at solution pH significantly higher than the pK_a value. At higher concentrations multi-molecular layer adsorption occurred when the surface density of quinoline was high. Organo-clays are smectite clays where long-chain alkyl ammonium ions (organic cations) have been sorbed to the clay minerals by cation exchange, which greatly increases the sorptive capacity for hydrophobic organic contaminants (Brownawell *et al.* 1990; Nzengung *et al.* 1996). The findings by Ainsworth *et al.* (1987) suggest sorbate-assisted interactions on the clay surfaces similar to those found for organo-clays. This may suggest that the dramatic increase in the sorption of the four compounds in the low s:1 ratio experiment has been induced by the sorption of cationic N-heterocyclic compounds present in the coal-tar mixture, and that the surface density of the organic cationic species on clay minerals may be of significance. In that case, the presence of other sorbed compounds may well be important as they may increase the density for available sites of organic cations.

The steepness of the dramatic increase appears to increase with increasing compound hydrophobicity. If the sorption of individual compounds is viewed as a function of total compound mixture concentration (or of total surface density of compound mixture) then the concentration at which the dramatic increase in sorption occurs appears to decrease for increasing compound hydrophobicity. This indicates that the effect of total compound mixture concentration or cation concentration (or surface density) on the sorption of the individual compounds is related to their hydrophobicity.

Conclusions

The sorption of the four compounds in the clayey till is linearly correlated to compound hydrophobicity. It is an order of magnitude greater than predicted from the K_{oc}–K_{ow} relationship for aquifer materials, which however is considered to be within the expected variation of hydrophobic theory.

The sorption of the four compounds appears to be dominated by hydrophobic sorption. The sorption of carbazole may be influenced by dipole–dipole attraction in the experiment with a higher surface density of compounds (s : l ratio 0.2).

Sorption of all four compounds increases dramatically at higher concentrations in the low s : l ratio experiment. It appears likely that this increase is a result of multi-molecular layer sorption or condensation on surfaces in the clayey till at high surface density of organic compounds. The increase may have been induced by the presence of sorbed cation species of N-heterocyclic compounds.

The steepness of the dramatic increase and the effect of total compound or cation surface density on the sorption of the individual compounds may be related to compound hydrophobicity.

Implications

Sorption may increase dramatically if the surface density of a complex mixture of organic contaminants is high, resulting in significantly lower concentrations in the percolating water. The impact of these four compounds on groundwater quality may therefore be lower than expected when complex mixtures such as coal-tar are present in fractured clay.

Acknowledgements. The project was carried out as part of the Strategic Environmental Research Programme sponsored by the Danish Ministry of Environment. The analysis for characterization of the clayey till was carried out by the H. Lindgren, the Danish Geological Survey. His insight on clayey tills is greatly acknowledged by the authors.

References

ABDUL, A. S., GIBSON, T. L. & RAI, D. N. 1987. Statistical correlations for predicting the partition coefficient for nonpolar organic contaminants between aquifer organic carbon and water. *Hazardous Waste and Hazardous Materials*, **4**, 211–222.

AINSWORTH, C. C., ZACHARA, J. M. & SCHMIDT, R. L. 1987. Quinoline sorption on Na-montmorillonite: contributions of the protonated and neutral species. *Clays and Clay Minerals*, **35**, 121–128.

BROHOLM, M. M., BROHOLM, K. & ARVIN, E. 1997a. Sorption of heterocyclic compounds in natural clayey till. *Journal of Contaminant Hydrology*.

——, —— & ——1997b. Sorption of heterocyclic compounds from a complex mixture of coal-tar compounds in natural clayey till. *Journal of Contaminant Hydrology*.

BROWNAWELL, B. J., CHEN, H., COLLIER, J. M. & WESTALL, J. C. 1990. Adsorption of organic cations to Natural Materials. *Environmental Science and Technology*, **24**, 1234–1241.

HANCH, C. & LEO, A. 1979. *Substituent Constants for Correlation Analysis in Chemistry and Biology*. Wiley, New York.

HASSETT, J. J., MEANS, J. C., BANWART, W. L. & WOOD, S. G. 1980a. *Sorption Properties of Sediments and Energy-related Pollutants*. US Environmental Protection Agency, No. EPA-600/3–80-041.

KARICKHOFF, S. W., BROWN, D. S. & SCOTT, T. A. 1979. Sorption of hydrophobic pollutants on natural sediments. *Water Research*, **13**, 241–248.

KLINT, K. E. & FREDERICIA, J. 1995. Sprækkeparametre i moræneler. *Vand & Jord*, **5**, 208–214.

LIDE, D. R. (ed.) 1992. *CRC Handbook of Chemistry and Physics* (73rd edition). CRC, New York.

LINDGREN, H. 1987. Experiments on adsorption and molecular sieving and inferences on primary migration in Upper Jurassic claystone source rocks, North Sea. *AAPG Bulletin*, **71**(3), 308–321.

MCCARTY, P. L., REINHARD, M. & RITTMANN, B. E. 1981. Trace organics in groundwater. *Environmental Science and Technology*, **15**, 40–51.

MACKAY, D., & SHIU, W. Y. 1981. A critical review of Henry's law constants for chemicals of environmental interest. *Journal of Physical Chemical Reference Data*, **10**, 1175–1199.

——, —— & MA, K. C. 1992. *Illustrated Handbook of Physical–Chemical Properties and Environmental Fate for Organic Chemicals: Volume 2: Polynuclear Aromatic Hydrocarbons, Polychlorinated Dioxins and Dibenzofurans*. Lewis, Michigan.

NZENGUNG, V. A., VOUDRIAS, E. A., NKEDI-KIZZA, P., WAMPLER, J. M. & WEAVER, C. E. 1996. Organic cosolvent effects on sorption equilibrium of hydrophobic organic chemicals by organoclays. *Environmental Science and Technology*, **30**, 89–96.

PEARLMAN, R. S., YALKOWSKI, S. H. & BANERJEE, S. 1984. Water solubilities of polynuclear aromatic and heteroaromatic compounds. *Journal of Physical Chemical Reference Data*, **13**, 555–562.

WEBER, W. J. JR. 1972. *Physicochemical Processes for Water Quality Control*. Wiley Interscience, New York.

Estimation of solid phase activity coefficients for non-ideal cation exchange behaviour in laboratory samples of UK Triassic sandstones

H. El-Ghonemy

School of Earth Sciences, University of Birmingham, Edgbaston, Birmingham B15 2TT, UK

Abstract. A traditional laboratory method for measuring cation exchange parameters was applied to plugs of Triassic sandstone core. The objective of the study was to measure cation exchange capacities and selectivity coefficients in the Ca–Mg–Na–K system in intact rock samples, and to investigate the extent to which the system departs from ideality. The method involved the use of NH_4Cl as a high ionic strength exchange salt solution in column experiments. Non-ideal behaviour was observed, being most obvious for the K–Na, K–Mg and K–Ca exchange systems. Activity coefficients for the exchanger phase were estimated and a dependence on the composition of the exchanger was recognized. An equation for exchange equilibria is proposed where this dependence is accounted for in the form of a power function.

Introduction

The Permo-Triassic sandstone aquifer is a major source of groundwater in England. It is important to quantitatively describe ion exchange in order to understand present natural and pollutant solute distributions, to predict future distributions and to develop remedial action plans. The influence of ion exchange on groundwater chemistry has been recognized qualitatively in the aquifer but little quantitative work has been done. The purpose of the present research is to try to quantify major ion exchange reactions in laboratory samples of Triassic sandstones.

Equilibrium constant expressions for the ion exchange reaction in Equation (1) can be written as Equation (2), where (M^{m+}) and (MX) are dissolved and solid phase activities, respectively, m^+ is the valence and K is the exchange equilibrium constant.

$$M^{m+} + NX \rightarrow N^{n+} + MX \qquad (1)$$

$$K = \frac{(MX)(N^{n+})}{(NX)(M^{m+})} \qquad (2)$$

The main problem in using this equation is in the determination of the solid phase activities. The common approach is to assume solid phase activities to be equal to mole (Vanselow convention) or equivalent (Gaines–Thomas convention) fractions. This is valid for an ideal exchanger. For the more common case of a non-ideal exchanger, this is invalid and leads to apparent variation in the equilibrium 'constant' with exchange site composition. As a result, equilibrium constants are normally termed 'selectivity coefficients' in recognition of their role in expressing selectivity and in recognition of their behaviour as coefficients rather than as constants.

This is inconvenient in that the variation of each selectivity coefficient with exchange site occupancy needs to be determined in a given non-ideal system.

Recent research by Carlyle (1991) suggests that the Gaines–Thomas convention may not adequately describe the exchange characteristics of the sandstones. The importance of accurately describing ion exchange reactions through applying the appropriate exchange convention is illustrated by Appelo *et al.* (1990). Their experimental work produced a large range in selectivity coefficients for three sediments for the various cations. They claim that a better understanding of the factors which control the differences in selectivities among different sediments is needed before application to a field situation.

The results presented here are part of a research project designed to examine closely the ion exchange processes in the Triassic sandstones. The research includes the application of both traditional and revised methods. The preliminary results reported here are the product of applying the traditional methods. Although the work is still in progress, these results indicate the possibility of describing ion exchange quantitatively using a true equilibrium constant with empirically determined solid phase activity coefficients. If this is confirmed by later work, this result may be of considerable use in reactive solute transport modelling.

Materials and methods

The samples used are from the Permo-Triassic sandstone aquifer in the Lower Mersey Basin of northwest England. Two samples are from a core drilled out of the Speke Reservoir observation borehole (SP4 and

EL-GHONEMY, H. 1998. Estimation of solid phase activity coefficients for non-ideal cation exchange behaviour in laboratory samples of UK Triassic sandstones. *In:* LERNER, D. N. & WALTON, N. R. G. (eds) 1998. *Contaminated Land and Groundwater: Future Directions.* Geological Society, London, Engineering Geology Special Publications, **14**, 213–217.

SP12) and two are from the Breeze Hill observation borehole (BH12 and BH13). Two samples (plugs) were used from each core to observe the natural variability in the results. The samples are between 4 and 8 cm long, 3.5 cm in diameter and were drilled as cylindrical plugs parallel to the lamination. All samples are well cemented with both silica and calcite. X-ray diffraction work identified illite, chlorite, montmorillonite and orthoclase in the samples.

The experimental method is based on the technique used by Jensen & Babcock (1973), where the exchanger is saturated with a series of di-cationic solutions each consisting of different ratios of the two cations for the K–Na, K–Ca, K–Mg and Ca–Mg systems. The sample is leached until equilibrium is reached between exchanger and solution. The exchanger site occupation is then determined by flushing the sample with a concentrated solution of a third salt.

Experiments were done for both the homovalent (K–Na and Ca–Mg) as well as the heterovalent (K–Ca and K–Mg) systems. The solutions were prepared as chloride salts with varying cationic compositions of a cation pair but all with an ionic strength of 0.05. This ionic strength was chosen to represent natural groundwater in the sandstones. The pH values of the solutions were between 5.20 and 7.80. A laboratory column technique was used to allow solutions to flow through the core plug (Fig. 1). The samples were sealed in silicon sealant, PTFE tape and enclosed in heat-shrinking plastic. The samples were vacuum-saturated and attached to a pressurizable reservoir containing the solution that will flow through the core. The reservoir is attached to a N_2 gas cylinder fixed with a pressure regulator for controlling the flow rate. The sandstone was brought to equilibrium with the salt solutions by leaching the plug, and equilibrium was assumed when the composition of the solution exiting the sample was equal to that of the input solution.

A 0.5 M NH_4Cl solution was flushed through the core following each of the input solutions to determine the exchanger site occupation. For every cation pair, small samples were collected in a fraction collector for each pore volume in order to ensure that there were no exchangeable cations remaining on the exchange sites. Total exchangeable cations were measured by analysing the sample collected after the NH_4Cl flush and converting concentration to mass in milligram equivalents (meq). These results represent the exchange site population and are used to calculate the cation exchange capacity (CEC) as well as the selectivity coefficients. The dissociation of NH_4^+ to NH_3 and H^+ causes the dissolution of calcite in the sandstone samples, a source of error during the measurement of CEC. Similar results were reported by Reardon et al. (1983). This excess Ca^{2+} was estimated by measuring total alkalinity during the experiments.

Preliminary experiments on sample SP4 were done with six different solutions for both the K–Na and Ca–Mg exchange systems. Only three solutions were used for the K–Ca and K–Mg systems, and only three solutions were used for all four systems for the three other samples. All analyses were done using either an inductively coupled plasma spectrometer (Philips PU 7450) or an atomic absorption spectrophotometer (Perkin Elmer 460). All leaching was done initially in duplicate to test the reliability of the experimental

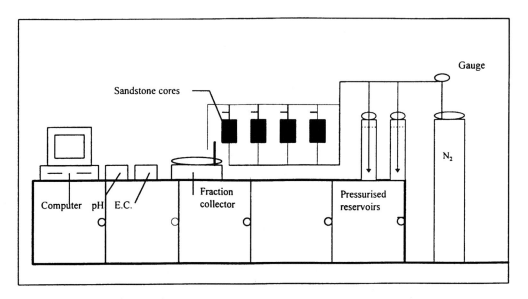

Fig. 1. Diagram of the laboratory apparatus used for the ion exchange experiments.

method. The error estimated for the selectivity coefficient calculations was approximately 10%. The error in calculating the cation exchange capacity values was estimated to be less than 10% in most cases, although the values from the Breeze Hill samples illustrated errors of up to 25%. Possible sources of error in the CEC measurements are incomplete replacement of the exchangeable cations by NH_4^+ and incomplete replacement of NH_4^+ by the aqueous cations in the subsequent experiment. The alkalinity measurements are another source of error in the experiments involving calcium ions. The measurement of CEC is the subject of continuing investigation. Full details of these experiments are reported in El-Ghonemy (1996).

Results and discussion

Cation exchange capacity

Mean values for cation exchange capacity were determined for three solutions from each of the four exchange systems described above (12 values in total for each sample). The mean values for cation exchange capacity for SP4 and SP12 were 1.60 and 2.10 meq per 100 g, with a standard deviation of 0.42 and 0.40, respectively. For BH12 and BH13, the mean CEC values were 4.15 and 5.08 meq per 100 g, with a standard deviation of 1.18 and 1.42, respectively. The mean CEC values are generally higher than those reported by other workers.

Selectivity coefficients and their dependence on exchange site occupancy

Selectivity coefficients were determined for the four different exchange systems using Equation (2). The solid phase activities were assumed to be equal to the mole

Table 1. *Data for* $K_{Ca/Mg}$ *for the four samples*

Equivalent fraction of Mg^{2+}	SP4	SP12	BH12	BH13
0.05	0.66	0.60	1.12	1.0
0.5	1.49	1.26	1.38	1.02
0.95	3.23	3.01	1.65	2.15

fraction on the exchanger according to the Vanselow convention (Vanselow 1932). Dissolved phase activity coefficients were calculated using the extended Debye–Huckel equation. The results for the homovalent K–Na experiments on all the samples are illustrated in Fig. 2, which shows decreasing selectivity for K^+ over Na^+ with increasing site occupation by K^+ Data for the Ca–Mg exchange system are shown in Table 1. The Ca–Mg exchange system shows selectivity coefficients closer to unity for the Speke samples, but nevertheless dependent on exchanger composition. This has been reported by other investigators for different exchangers (Jensen & Babcock 1973; Bolt et al. 1976; McBride 1994). Similar values for $K_{Ca/Mg}$ were reported by Carlyle (1991) and Ranasinghe (1988).

The K/Mg and K/Ca selectivity coefficients are within ranges of 1–7 and 2–6, respectively. The non-constancy of these values suggests that the exchange is non-ideal for all the samples examined. The non-ideal exchange of potassium has also been reported by Jensen & Babcock (1973) and Bjerg et al. (1993) and has been attributed to the selectivity of specific sites in the clay lattice for cations of a certain size and valence (Bolt & Bruggenwert 1976).

Solid phase activity coefficients

If an exchange surface behaves as an ideal solid the selectivity coefficient is a constant value equal to the thermodynamic equilibrium constant for all surface compositions. Few cation exchangers can be considered ideal if the constancy of the selectivity coefficient over a range of MX values is used as the criterion of ideality, and it is clear that the Triassic sandstones do not behave in an ideal way. Non-ideal behaviour is assumed to occur because the solid phase activity is not adequately described as a mole or equivalent fraction. This problem can be avoided by introducing activity coefficients (f) to correct the mole fractions (X_M):

$$(MX) = f_M X_M \qquad (3)$$

Application of the correction factors f to the selectivity coefficient will produce an equilibrium constant K where the non-ideality is expressed within the ratio of f values.

Adsorbed activity coefficients (f) were calculated from the selectivity coefficients for all the exchange

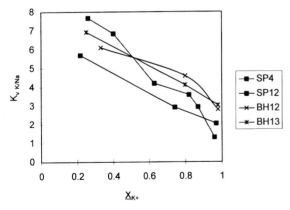

Fig. 2. Plot of the Vanselow selectivity coefficients K_v for K/Na exchange against the equivalent fraction of K^+ on the exchanger for four samples.

systems for the four samples with the relevant equations as originally described by Argersinger *et al.* (1950). A plot of the log *f* values for K$^+$ with increasing Na$^+$ on the exchange sites for all samples is shown in Fig. 3 suggesting similar behaviour for different samples. Figure 3 illustrates the dependence of the exchange-phase coefficients on the mole fraction. There appears to be a linear relationship between the *f* values and the exchanger composition. As mentioned above, the exchange reactions studied here represent non-ideal behaviour. This is common in ion exchange and the behaviour of the solid solution has been found to conform to that of a regular solution model when studied in detail (Barrer & Falconer 1956; Chenebeaux 1960; Barrer *et al.* 1969; Kielland 1935; Howery & Thomas 1965; Truesdell & Christ 1968). For the samples examined in the present research, non-ideal behaviour has been attributed to factors such as the interaction between ions on neighbouring sites which is directly related to competitive ion exchange. This interaction is expressed in terms of the constant *B* in the regular solution model. Thus, *B* denotes the energy of interaction between two ions at the exchanger surface. Implicit in the exponent *n* therefore, is a description of the variation of the solid phase activity coefficients with exchanger composition.

The regular solid solution is described by the following equation for ions M and N (Garrels & Christ 1965):

$$\log F_M = \frac{B}{2.303RT} X_N^2 \tag{4}$$

or

$$\log f_M = B' X_N^2 \tag{5}$$

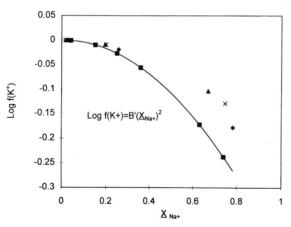

Fig. 3. Plot of the activity coefficients on the exchanger f(K$^+$) against the equivalent fraction of Na$^+$ on the exchanger for four samples. The solid line represents the function log $f_{K^+} = B'(X_{Na^+})$ for sample SP4 as in equation 3.

Table 2. *B values calculated for the four samples*

	K–Na	K–Mg	K–Ca	Ca–Mg
SP4	−0.59	−0.43	−0.51	−0.57
SP12	−0.40	−0.37	−0.21	−0.61
BH12	−0.32	−0.38	−0.38	−0.13
BH13	−0.32	−0.46	−0-.18	−0.26
Mean	−0.41	−0.41	−0.32	−0.39
SD	0.13	0.04	0.15	0.23

where $B' = B/2.303RT$, *R* is the gas constant (8.314 J mol^{-1} K^{-1}), *T* is the absolute temperature (K) and *B* is a constant (J mol^{-1}). The solid line in Fig. 3 expresses Equation (3) where $B' = -0.43$. Values for *B* were calculated for each exchange system and are shown in Table 2.

Implications for the quantitative prediction of ion exchange reactions. The application of the regular solid solution analogy described above is at an early stage. However, it would appear that this analogy can be used to describe the dependence of the solid-phase activity coefficients on exchanger site composition. Therefore, it may be possible to predict ion exchange behaviour using a 'true' equilibrium constant, with the solid phase activity coefficients calculated from the regular solid solution equation. This eliminates the need to alter the *K* values with exchange site occupancy. If the solid is treated as a regular solution (Garrels & Christ 1965), the equilibrium constant equation for cation exchange becomes

$$\frac{(M^+)}{(N^+)} = K_{N/M}\left(\frac{X_M}{X_N}\right) \tag{6}$$

where (A^+) and X_A are aqueous activity and solid-phase mole fraction, respectively. The exponent is:

$$n = 1 - \frac{B}{2RT} \tag{7}$$

The calculated values for *n* are 1.35, 1.35, 1.27 and 1.33 for the K–Na, K–Mg, K–Ca and Ca–Mg systems, respectively. The variation in B values is less than the variation in the K_v values for the four exchange systems. This approach provides a concise description of the variation of selectivity coefficients with exchanger composition. The ideal application of this approach is to correlate lithology with *B* (or *n*) values and use them to characterize specific zones of an aquifer in a field situation.

Conclusions

A column leaching technique was applied for measuring cation exchange parameters of samples of Triassic sandstones in the laboratory. Vanselow selectivity coefficients for four cation pairs were calculated at different exchanger compositions. For the systems involving K^+ the selectivity coefficients indicated a selectivity for K^+ over Na^+ Ca^{2+} and Mg^{2+}, which decreased with increasing occupation of the sites by K^+. This behaviour is interpreted as being non-ideal due to factors not yet identified. The Ca–Mg system also shows non-ideal behaviour but with a much smaller range of selectivity coefficients.

The regular solid solution analogy may provide a practical approach for accommodating the non-ideal behaviour recognized in the Triassic sandstones. Further work is continuing on many of the questions raised by these results, including closer examination of the theoretical implications, the practical applications and the range of validity. A particular study will be made of the relationship between the selectivity of the exchanger and the mineralogy. It is hoped that the latter will produce a correlation between the exponent (n) in the regular solution equation and specific characteristics of the Triassic sandstone lithologies.

References

APPELO, C. A. J., WILLEMSEN, A., BEEKMAN, H. E. & GRIFFOEN, J. 1990. Geochemical calculations and observations on salt water intrusions, II. Validation of a geochemical model with laboratory experiments. *Journal of Hydrology*, **120**, 225–250.

ARGERSINGER, W. J., DAVIDSON, A. W. & BONNER, O. D. 1950. Thermodynamics and ion exchange phenomena. *Trans. Kans. Acad. Sci.*, **53**, 404–410.

BARRER, R. M. & FALCONER, J. D. 1956. Ion exchange in feldspathoids as a solid-state reaction. *Royal Soc. (London) Proc.*, **A236**, 227–249.

——, DAVIES, J. A. & REES, L. V. C. 1969. Comparison of the ion exchange properties of zeolites X and Y. *Journal of Inorg. Nucl. Chem.*, **31**, 2599–2609.

BJERG, P. L., AMMENTORP, H. C. & CHRISTENSEN, T. H. 1993. Model simulations of a field experiment on cation exchange-affected multicomponent solute transport in a sandy aquifer. *Journal of Contaminant Hydrology*, **12**, 291–311.

BOLT, G. H. & BRUGGENWERT, M. G. M. 1976. *In*: BOLT, G. H. & BRUGGENWERT, M. G. M. (eds) *Soil Chemistry, A. Basic Elements* (2nd edition) Elsevier, Amsterdam, 43–53.

—— & KAMPHORST, A. 1976. *In*: BOLT, G. H. & BRUGGENWERT, M. G. M. (eds) *Soil Chemistry, A. Basic Elements* (2nd edition). Elsevier, Amsterdam, 43–53.

CARLYLE, H. F. 1991. *The Hydrochemical Recognition of Ion Exchange during Seawater Intrusion at Widnes, Merseyside, UK*. PhD Thesis, University of Birmingham.

CHENEBEAUX, M. J. 1960. Exchange reactions of alkali ions on granitic glasses. *Acad. Sci. (Paris). Comptes rendus*, **250**, 1046–1049.

EL-GHONEMY, H. M. R. 1996. *Laboratory Experiments for Quantifying and Describing Cation Exchange in UK Triassic Sandstones*. PhD Thesis, University of Birmingham.

GAINES, G. L. & THOMAS, H. C. 1953. Adsorption studies on clay minerals. II. A formulation of the thermodynamics of exchange adsorption. *Journal of Chemical Physics*, **21**, 714–718.

GAPON, E. N. 1933. Theory of exchange adsorption in soils. *J. Gen. Chem. (USSR)*, **3**(2), 144–152 (translated by A. Mazurak).

GARRELS, R. M. & CHRIST, C. L. 1965. *Solutions, Minerals, and Equilibria*. Freeman, Cooper & Co, San Fransisco.

HOWERY, D. G. & THOMAS, H. C. 1965. Ion exchange on the mineral clinoptilolite. *Journal of Physical Chemistry*, **69**(2), 531–537.

KIELLAND, J. 1935. Thermodynamics of base-exchange equilibria of some different kinds of clays. *Soc. Chem. Industry (London) J.*, **54**, 232T–234T.

McBRIDE, M. B. 1994. *Environmental Chemistry of Soils*. Oxford University Press, New York.

REARDON, E. J., DANCE, J. T. & LOLCAMA, J. L. 1983. Field determination of cation exchange properties for calcereous sand. *Ground Water*, **21**, 421–428.

TRUESDELL, A. H. & CHRIST, C. L. 1968. Cation exchange in clays interpreted by regular solution theory. *American Journal of Science*, **266**, 402–412.

VANSELOW, A. P. 1932. Equilibria of the base exchange reactions of bentonites, permutites, soil colloids and zeolites. *Soil Science*, **33**, 95–113.

Distribution of volatile organic compounds in porewater of the seasonally unsaturated Chalk aquifer

B. A. Fretwell,[1] **W. G. Burgess,**[1] **N. L. Jefferies**[2] **& J. Dottridge**[1]

[1] Jackson Environment Institute and Hydrogeology Group, University College London, 5 Gower Street, London WC1E 6HA, UK
[2] AEA Technology plc, Harwell, Didcot, Oxfordshire, OX11 0RA, UK

Abstract. The Chalk aquifer is contaminated at many sites at outcrop by volatile organic compounds (VOCs). Most studies of VOCs concentrate on the saturated zone, ignoring potentially significant accumulations of dissolved contaminants within porewaters of the unsaturated zone. Of particular interest in the Chalk is the large zone of the aquifer over which seasonal fluctuation of the water table occurs. VOCs accumulated in this zone (resulting from vertical migration and diffusion from contaminated ground water at seasonal high water levels) can form a reservoir of contaminants which will be released into the aquifer over a long period. Better understanding of the VOC behaviour in the seasonally unsaturated zone is needed to improve risk assessment and optimize remediation response.

Determination of VOC occurrence and concentration in the seasonally unsaturated zone at a contaminated site on the Chalk outcrop is described. Some 500 samples of chalk have been taken from cores drilled in the unsaturated zone over a depth interval of 20 m. Headspace analysis has been used to determine porewater chemistry for a range of VOCs. Vertical profiles of contaminant concentration are presented and interpreted in terms of VOC transport mechanisms. Hydrocarbon contamination at the site poses an additional element of complexity. The presence of chloride associated with VOC contamination provides a conservative comparison for the distribution behaviour of the VOCs.

Introduction

The Chalk outcrop is known to have been contaminated by volatile organic compounds (VOCs) at a number of locations in the UK (e.g. Longstaff *et al.* 1992, Lawrence *et al.* 1996). VOCs are of particular concern in groundwater due to their long life and resistance to degradation. They are also only sparingly soluble and so relatively small volumes of VOCs can contaminate large volumes of groundwater. Additionally, allowable concentrations in drinking water for many of these compounds are typically very low ($1–30\,\mu g\,l^{-1}$) and unlikely to be controlled by solubility considerations.

Chalk hydrogeology

Saturated zone. The Chalk is a dual porosity aquifer consisting of matrix blocks divided by a well developed, orthogonal fissure network. Within the matrix blocks porosity is high (20–45%) but characterized by small pore throat sizes of $0.01–1\,\mu m$. As a result, matrix hydraulic conductivity is low, in the range 10^{-7} to $10^{-9}\,m\,s^{-1}$ (Price *et al.* 1993). In the saturated zone the matrix porewater can be considered as virtually immobile where hydraulic gradients are low. Fissure porosity is typically less than

1% in the Chalk but can increase the hydraulic conductivity to 10^{-3} to $10^{-5}\,m\,s^{-1}$ (Price *et al.* 1993). Particularly important in the Chalk is the presence of solution-enhanced secondary fissures which have been found with very high individual transmissivities. The low fissure porosity gives a low specific yield and as a result seasonal water level fluctuations can exceed 30 m (Price *et al.* 1993). This seasonal fluctuation creates a zone of water table fluctuation (ZWTF) which is the focus of the work described here.

Unsaturated zone. The small pore throat sizes found in the matrix of the Chalk allow it to support a capillary zone of up to 30 m. Consequently the matrix remains saturated under most conditions outside the zone affected by plant roots. Therefore the permeability of the matrix in the unsaturated zone is only marginally less that in the saturated zone (Price *et al.* 1993) and is capable of accommodating much of the recharge flow. Due to their relatively larger apertures, fissures drain and remain unsaturated with the exception of periods of recharge where the infiltration rates exceed the permeability of the matrix.

Contaminant transport. Transport of aqueous phase contaminants in the Chalk can be considered to occur by

FRETWELL, B. A., BURGESS, W. G., JEFFERIES, N. L. & DOTTRIDGE, J. 1998. Distribution of volatile organic compounds in porewater of the seasonally unsaturated Chalk aquifer. *In*: LERNER, D. N. & WALTON, N. R. G. (eds) 1998. *Contaminated Land and Groundwater: Future Directions.* Geological Society, London, Engineering Geology Special Publications, **14**, 219–226.

two mechanisms: advection in fissures and lateral diffusion between fissures and matrix blocks. Dispersion also occurs at a field scale as a result of the discontinuous nature of fissures. Diffusion between fissures and matrix blocks is governed by Fick's Law, with diffusion rates proportional to concentration gradients.

In the ZWTF an additional complexity is the seasonal nature of fissure–matrix interactions. During periods of high water table, diffusive flux from fissures to matrix will occur as in the saturated zone. At other times the matrix is isolated from groundwater, although diffusion will continue within matrix blocks to promote equilibrium.

After the passing of a contaminant plume or following remediation of fissure water the direction of diffusive flux will be reversed. Diffusion from matrix blocks will control the rate at which contaminants are released to fissure water. In the ZWTF the intermittent contact with fissure water will lead to a considerable increase in the time required to flush out contaminants and hence to achieve clean-up. In effect the ZWTF will act as a reservoir of contaminants long after the original source has dissipated. Volatilization is an additional process which will influence contaminant concentration.

Geology and hydrogeology of the study site. The site of this study lies on the Lower Chalk. The Chalk at the site is some 70 m thick, underlain by the Gault Clay. A band of stronger rock, a hardground equivalent to the Totternhoe Stone, approximately 1 m thick, occurs at 3 m depth and forms the only laterally continuous marker horizon in the succession.

The Chalk beneath the site can be divided into three hydrogeological units: an upper aquifer, an intermediate aquitard and a lower aquifer. The upper unconfined unit is some 30 m thick. The water table in this aquifer unit occurs at depths which can fluctuate by up to 15 m between 8 and 23 m below ground level (m bgl). Seasonal water table fluctuations have been irregular in recent years, with almost no recharge occurring in dry years, whilst in other years full recharge has occurred in early winter.

The upper, unconfined unit is separated from the lower, confined aquifer by 5 m of low permeability Chalk marl which maintains a head difference of 3–4 m between the two units. The lower aquifer terminates in a low permeability Chalk marl. Hydraulic conductivities for the different units have been determined by short interval packer testing giving values of 10^{-4} to 10^{-5} m s^{-1} for the upper aquifer, approximately 10^{-6} m s^{-1} for the aquitard and approximately 10^{-4} m s^{-1} for the lower aquifer.

Investigation

Background

The site investigated by this study had been used for the disposal of chemical waste in shallow excavations

(approximately 3 m deep) within the Chalk. Waste disposal operations took place over many years before ceasing in the late 1970s. Available records indicate that approximately 20 tonnes of chlorinated hydrocarbons (CHCs) were deposited into the pits during the operational life of the waste disposal site. Detection of CHCs in a nearby public water supply borehole led to a series of investigations. These have revealed an extensive plume of contaminated groundwater extending 600 m downgradient from the source within the upper aquifer. Contamination is almost completely confined to the upper aquifer with only minor traces found within the lower unit.

Principal aqueous phase contaminants are CHCs although a range of other hydrocarbon contaminants have also been detected in groundwater at the site. A floating layer of hydrocarbon has been detected in a single monitoring well at the site and the presence of oil droplets on fissure surfaces was noted in previous core analysis. Analysis of these oil droplets has revealed percentage levels of CHCs and other contaminants.

A hydraulic containment scheme is currently in operation consisting of an arc of wells which abstract contaminated groundwater from the upper aquifer downgradient of the source. Abstracted water is passed through a treatment plant and then re-injected upgradient resulting in no overall abstraction of groundwater from the aquifer.

Present study

The investigation described here is based upon the detailed analysis of two cored boreholes (Borehole A and Borehole B) drilled close to the site of the disposal operation. The upper part of the cores were drilled using a hollow stemmed auger; however, the hard band at 3 m bgl meant that rotary coring with water flush had to be used to reach the completion depths of 30 and 20 m below ground level (m bgl), respectively. The locations of the disposal pits and boreholes are shown on Fig. 1.

Once at the surface, cores were rapidly logged and sampled on site to minimize losses due to volatilization. Samples were taken for headspace analysis of porewater for VOCs, and for analysis of physical properties. For headspace analysis, samples were obtained by breaking open the core and taking a 1–2 g piece of fresh Chalk, avoiding rock that had been in contact with drilling water. The sample was placed in a weighed vial and immersed beneath de-ionized water, leaving a known headspace volume, before being sealed with a PTFE-coated septum and re-weighed. Samples were transferred to a cold store and maintained at less than 4°C prior to analysis. Duplicate samples were taken at frequent intervals. The large number of samples taken made it difficult for all the headspace analyses to be undertaken within the short period of time usually recommended. Results from a subset of samples were obtained within

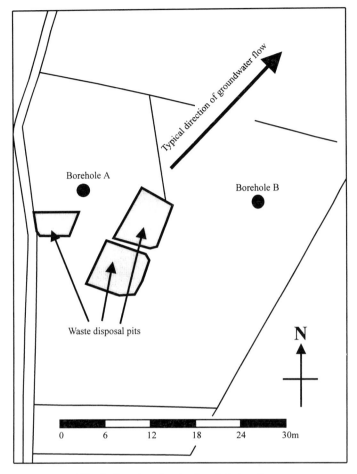

Fig. 1. Site plan showing borehole locations.

days of collection. Comparison of these results with those of the majority of samples tested some weeks after collection show only small differences relative to the variability within the profile indicating that storage did not lead to significant loss of volatiles.

Headspace analysis offers the advantage of minimizing sample handling and exposure whilst giving reproducible results.

Analysis of headspace samples was undertaken following a method described by Stuart (1991). This method establishes diffusive equilibrium between porewater and the added water and hence headspace is representative of the diluted porewater. The rate limiting step is the movement of solute from porewater to the added water. Equilibrium between porewater, added water and headspace is promoted by incubating the sample at 70°C. Following cooling to room temperature, samples of headspace vapour are injected directly onto a gas chromatography column using a gas-tight syringe.

Detection of CHCs was achieved using an electron capture detector.

Over 200 samples were taken for headspace analysis per borehole with an average vertical spacing of 0.1 m. Sampling was concentrated on zones of interest, particularly in the ZWTF.

Many of the samples were also analysed for chloride, known to be present at elevated concentrations within the plume of contaminated groundwater.

Porosity measurements have also been undertaken at a number of points within the profile using a helium porosimeter.

Results

Results of headspace analysis (Tables 1 and 2) have been used to construct vertical profiles of the concentration of CHCs in porewater, shown in Fig. 2. These

Table 1. *Total chlorinated hydrocarbon and chloride ion porewater concentrations: borehole A*

Sample depth (m bgl‡)	Porewater concentration‡ Total CHCs* (mg l⁻¹)	Chloride (mg l⁻¹)	Sample depth (m bgl‡)	Porewater concentration‡ Total CHCs* (mg l⁻¹)	Chloride (mg l⁻¹)	Sample depth (m bgl‡)	Porewater concentration‡ Total CHCs* (mg l⁻¹)	Chloride (mg l⁻¹)	Sample depth (m bgl‡)	Porewater concentration‡ Total CHCs* (mg l⁻¹)	Chloride (mg l⁻¹)
0.30	1	39	5.95	15	1520	11.20	5	113	15.60	16	501
0.50	6	–	6.00	12	687	11.30	20	–	15.80	37	634
0.70	1	134	6.10	11	508	11.35	5	404	15.90	57	532
0.80	10	–	6.30	8	897	11.40	56	303	15.95	46	452
0.90	6	52	6.35	7	1332	11.50	7	–	16.05	149	–
1.00	2	–	6.45	30	1227	11.70	10	–	16.10	0	513
1.10	1	–	6.50	10	–	11.75	3	602	16.15	114	526
1.30	2	–	6.70	0	–	11.95	30	–	16.20	33	452
1.40	5	43	6.80	8	1112	12.00	7	737	16.25	29	581
1.50	2	–	7.05	14	–	12.05	45	–	16.30	141	–
1.60	4	50	7.15	25	1121	12.15	8	788	16.35	201	462
1.70	28	66	7.25	3	1134	12.20	25	750	16.40	16	500
1.80	3	46	7.30	7	–	12.25	5	–	16.45	7	424
2.05	6	92	7.55	13	1584	12.30	10	821	16.60	6	–
2.15	7	–	7.60	37	1808	12.40	2	450	16.70	12	664
2.20	7	–	7.65	10	–	12.50	5	582	16.80	157	402
2.30	8	–	7.70	9	1358	12.55	40	–	17.00	3	144
2.40	9	–	7.90	5	877	12.60	17	–	17.40	9	83
2.50	5	40	8.00	11	527	12.70	19	–	17.45	5	137
2.60	11	–	8.30	24	348	12.80	94	533	17.55	38	178
2.70	4	58	8.50	17	806	12.95	34	243	17.60	10	93
2.80	11	52	8.70	7	–	13.05	6	535	17.70	4	166
2.90	6	44	8.90	17	774	13.13	1	326	17.75	6	141
2.95	6	–	9.00	9	592	13.16	13	–	17.80	15	142
3.10	6	157	9.10	1	695	13.20	5	448	18.00	41	–
3.30	9	61	9.20	1	1541	13.40	10	–	18.20	16	199
3.50	3	–	9.25	6	784	13.50	14	229	18.25	30	229
3.70	1	24	9.30	9	–	13.70	58	284	18.30	39	219
3.85	10	–	9.35	7	761	13.75	12	263	18.40	28	308
3.95	33	40	9.40	0	–	13.80	37	371	18.43	143	297
4.00	9	45	9.65	34	711	13.85	22	332	18.46	7	355
4.10	8	107	9.70	20	867	13.90	3	–	18.50	48	278
4.30	9	–	9.75	3	–	13.95	7	–	18.70	33	252
4.40	3	–	9.80	38	–	14.10	9	669	18.75	4	285
4.50	4	–	10.00	10	–	14.15	51	936	18.80	16	145
4.65	1	127	10.05	3	1644	14.30	61	999	18.95	49	160
4.70	3	133	10.10	12	867	14.50	63	904	19.00	57	243
4.80	11	211	10.15	1	785	14.70	204	949	19.10	>300	210
4.95	4	373	10.20	7	1013	14.80	66	518	19.30	169	391
5.00	5	173	10.40	10	–	14.90	97	–	19.35	11	336
5.10	1	–	10.60	3	964	14.95	34	297	19.40	18	203
5.15	10	–	10.65	6	1133	15.00	9	332	19.45	22	204
5.25	22	–	10.80	17	809	15.05	124	380	19.70	4	148
5.30	12	1314	10.95	11	–	15.10	10	347	19.80	73	157
5.40	19	1264	11.00	3	693	15.20	11	210	19.90	7	174
5.60	17	–	11.05	1	550	15.30	77	–			
5.80	7	794	11.10	23	–	15.40	24	–			
5.90	33	857	11.15	19	–	15.50	69	–			

*Sum of five chlorinated hydrocarbons (CHCs): TCA, TCE, PCE, carbon tetrachloride, chloroform.
† m bgl, metres below ground level.
‡ Porewater concentration obtained from sample concentration using the measured moisture content.

Table 2. *Total chlorinated hydrocarbons and chloride porewater concentrations: borehole B*

Sample depth	Porewater concentration‡		Sample depth	Porewater concentration‡		Sample depth	Porewater concentration‡	
	Total CHCs*	Chloride		Total CHCs*	Chloride		Total CHCs*	Chloride
(m bgl‡)	(mg l⁻¹)	(mg l⁻¹)	(m bgl‡)	(mg l⁻¹)	(mg l⁻¹)	(m bgl‡)	(mg l⁻¹)	(mg l⁻¹)
0.40	0	55	8.75	44	621	15.30	18	673
0.80	1	84	8.80	21	558	15.40	3	595
1.00	11	96	8.90	29	499	15.50	2	529
1.20	1	187	9.10	52	217	15.60	3	741
1.40	–	66	9.50	30	528	16.00	8	664
1.60	2	60	9.80	–	533	16.10	2	655
1.80	3	77	10.40	3	782	16.30	2	538
2.00	4	81	10.50	8	625	16.40	4	678
2.40	2	95	10.60	12	1440	16.50	9	558
2.60	4	91	10.70	8	131	16.55	4	624
2.80	3	72	10.80	21	1149	16.60	25	–
3.00	2	114	10.90	9	651	16.63	15	401
3.20	3	–	11.10	11	1661	16.70	3	393
3.30	1	48	11.20	11	838	16.75	3	–
3.40	3	99	11.30	19	2015	16.80	21	449
3.50	5	148	11.40	50	2335	16.85	8	530
3.55	–	184	11.50	22	1005	16.90	3	500
3.60	6	1064	11.60	5	938	17.00	17	544
3.65	3	112	11.70	2	461	17.05	4	556
3.70	–	741	11.75	2	979	17.10	11	403
3.80	–	190	11.80	3	1244	17.20	5	466
4.00	–	190	11.85	38	1374	17.30	4	503
4.20	6	–	11.90	5	1178	17.50	14	165
4.50	–	113	12.10	9	715	17.65	19	146
4.80	15	170	12.30	3	969	17.70	25	275
5.10	4	169	12.40	2	948	17.75	41	827
5.50	4	110	12.70	3	988	17.80	25	498
5.70	16	164	13.10	3	888	17.90	41	556
5.90	5	246	13.23	3	1030	18.00	46	347
6.05	12	124	13.30	5	–	18.10	5	112
6.10	3	153	13.40	4	1074	18.20	4	219
6.15	5	964	13.50	7	1203	18.45	24	–
6.20	2	107	13.70	5	881	18.50	17	238
6.30	6	289	13.90	4	820	18.60	21	231
6.60	16	151	14.00	4	982	18.70	12	271
6.65	8	72	14.20	7	941	18.80	16	295
6.75	5	90	14.30	1	894	18.90	35	310
6.90	4	194	14.40	2	850	18.95	45	274
7.30	2	120	14.45	1	636	19.10	23	198
7.90	2	169	14.60	4	475	19.20	30	291
8.10	14	179	14.65	7	–	19.40	4	456
8.30	–	141	14.75	13	445	19.50	7	–
8.50	3	356	14.80	10	488	19.60	–	822
8.65	1	604	14.85	20	433	19.70	18	675
8.70	19	571	15.10	35	478	19.90	7	378

* Sum of five chlorinated hydrocarbons (CHCs): TCA, TCE, PCE, carbon tetrachloride, chloroform.
† m bgl, metres below ground level.
‡ Porewater concentration obtained from sample concentration using the measured moisture content.

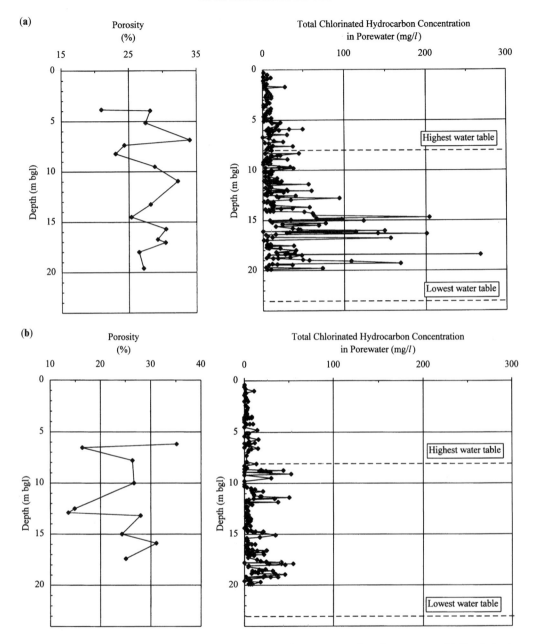

Fig. 2. Profiles of porosity and total chlorinated hydrocarbon concentrations in porewater (**a**) Borehole A, (**b**) Borehole B.

profiles show that concentrations are highly variable, in particular the profiles are 'noisy' with large changes in concentrations between adjacent samples. The main contaminants found in headspace analysis were trichloromethane (TCM) and tetrachloroethene (perchloroethene or PCE). Trichloroethane (TCA), trichloroethene (TCE)

and tetrachloromethane (carbon tetrachloride) were also found at significant concentrations.

The upper part of the profiles corresponding to the permanently unsaturated zone show only relatively low concentrations of CHCs. Higher concentrations are found within the ZWTF. The profile for borehole B shows a marked rise in CHC concentrations below the highest water table, reaching peaks at 9 m bgl, 12 m bgl and 18–20 m bgl. A zone of relatively low concentrations exists between 12 and 14 m bgl.

Concentrations found in borehole A are higher than in borehole B, reflecting its proximity to the source area. Here the profile shows a general increase in CHC concentrations with depth below 11 m bgl, although with much variation between adjoining samples. Two concentration peaks can be seen at 14–17 m bgl and 18–20 m bgl.

Oil droplets were noted on fissure surfaces in both boreholes at around 19 m bgl corresponding with the peaks in porewater CHC concentration. Analysis of this oil has revealed that it contains percentage concentrations of CHCs and, in addition, significant concentrations of other contaminants, notably PCBs.

Duplicate samples gave much variation, with differences of 30% between duplicates not being unusual. Porosity varies over the range 15 to 35% (Fig. 1).

Porewater CHC concentrations have been examined in terms of the proximity of fissures. Figure 3 distinguishes samples taken close to fissure surfaces or from within matrix blocks. No clear pattern emerges from this analysis, although it is clear that the highest concentrations occur within matrix blocks.

Profiles of chloride concentrations in porewater are shown in Fig. 4. The chloride distributions are very different from those of the CHCs in the respective boreholes. In borehole A chloride concentrations are generally low in the permanently unsaturated zone (less than 200 mg l^{-1}), start to rise at around 5 m bgl to a peak at around 8 m bgl and decline to approximately 200 mg l^{-1} at 20 m bgl. Borehole B shows a slightly different pattern; here chloride concentrations begin to rise at around 8 m bgl and reach a peak in excess of 1800 mg l^{-1} around 11 m bgl. Below this, concentrations show a general trend of decline. Whilst the two profiles have peaks at different depths, the asymmetric patterns are similar. In each profile the more gradual decline in concentration with depth below the peak suggests that they have developed in response to similar conditions.

Discussion and conclusions

The profiles of CHC concentration in porewater are 'noisy' when compared to the much smoother porewater profiles obtained from the saturated zone elsewhere (Lawrence *et al.* 1996). This may be an apparent difference due to the much more frequent sampling interval or may be associated with the differences between the ZWTF and the saturated zone. Nevertheless, reproducibility of duplicate samples of the volatile component suggests some caution in applying this argument.

Chloride is present as an inorganic contaminant from the disposal pits, but its original form – whether as an

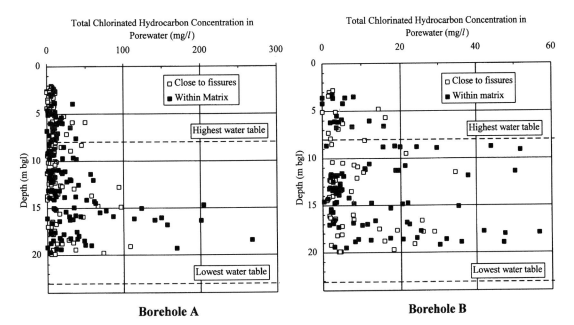

Fig. 3. Profiles of total chlorinated hydrocarbon concentrations in porewater showing variation between samples taken close to fissures and within matrix.

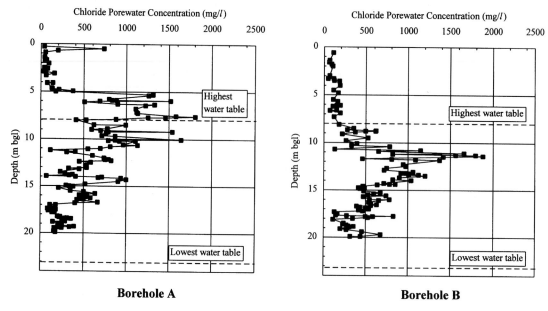

Fig. 4. Profiles of chloride concentration in porewater.

inorganic salt, hydrochloric acid or as a product of CHC degradation – is unknown. Nevertheless, chloride shows a distinct pattern of distribution in the ZWTF. The highest concentrations occur in the area of the profile which experiences the shortest contact time with fissure water. This suggests that the present chloride distribution is controlled by diffusion from matrix blocks. Groundwater in uncontaminated monitoring wells has a background concentration of $50 \, mg \, l^{-1}$ and within the contaminant plume groundwater has a chloride concentration of around $500 \, mg \, l^{-1}$. The difference between peak groundwater concentration and the higher peak porewater concentration may be a result of mixing within the water column in monitoring wells.

Differences in porewater profile shape between chloride and the chlorinated solvents may be attributed to differences in the mechanisms operative in each case. In particular, the major difference between CHCs and chloride is their ability to partition into the vapour phase. Volatile CHCs will partition into air-filled fissures from porewater and directly from the water table. This vapour will move by diffusion away from the source. As it moves it will no longer be in local equilibrium with porewater and some re-partitioning into the aqueous phase will occur. This might explain the presence of CHCs above the maximum recorded elevation of the water table. This effect will be more significant for those parts of the profile in contact with air for longest, i.e. within the upper part of the ZWTF. It is also possible that events prior to the installation of water level recorders exceeded the maximum water table shown on

Figs 2–4 permitting diffusion of CHCs at higher elevations.

The role that fissure spacing and distribution play in the distribution of contaminants in the ZWTF is not fully clear from the work presented here and additional work is currently under way in an attempt to address this issue.

Acknowledgements. The work described in this paper forms part of a PhD research programme funded by the Jackson Environment Institute with support from AEA Technology. Headspace analysis was undertaken at the Department of Civil Engineering, Imperial College, University of London.

References

LAWRENCE, A. R., STUART, M. E., BARKER, J. A. & TESTER, D. J. 1996. A case study of deep penetration by non-aqueous phase liquids. *Journal of the Institute of Water and Environmental Management*, **10**(4), 263–272.

LONGSTAFF, S. L., ALDOUS, P. J., CLARK, L., FLAVIN, R. J. & PARTINGTON, J. Contamination of the chalk aquifer by chlorinated solvents: a case study of the Luton and Dunstable area. *Journal of the Institution of Water and Environmental Management*, **6**(5), 541–550.

PRICE, M., DOWNING, R. A. & EDMUNDS, W. M. 1993. The Chalk as an aquifer. *In*: DOWNING, R. A., PRICE, M. & JONES, G. P. (eds) *The Hydrogeology of the Chalk of Northwest Europe*. Clarendon, Oxford, 35–58.

STUART, M. E. 1991. *Determination of Chlorinated Solvents in Aquifer Porewaters*. British Geological Survey, Technical Report WD/91/37.

An initial evaluation of Synperonic PE surfactants as soil washing agents

Iain F. Paterson,[1] Babur Z. Chowdhry[2] & Stephen A. Leharne[1]

[1] School of Environmental Sciences, University of Greenwich, Creek Road, Deptford, London SE8 3BW, UK
[2] School of Chemical and Life Sciences, University of Greenwich, Wellington Street, Woolwich, London SE18 6PF, UK

Abstract. The utility of the Synperonic PE range of block copolymeric nonionic surfactants in the decontamination of soil is systematically investigated. In the case of the solubilization of naphthalene in the absence of soil by the six Synperonic PE surfactants studied, the molar solubilization ratio (MSR), which is a measure of the solubilizing power of surfactants in their aggregated (i.e. micellar) form, broadly increases with an increase in the weight percentage content of the hydrophobic polypropylene oxide portion of the surfactant. Significantly, solubility enhancements are substantial even below the tensiometrically determined critical micelle concentration. The sorption of a number of these surfactants onto a soil of organic carbon content 0.6% is shown to be described by Freundlich isotherms, and is significant, adding considerably to the organic content of the soil. However, the surfactants substantially reduce the soil-water partition coefficient of naphthalene, phenanthrene and pyrene, indicating that they may potentially find applications in soil decontamination.

Introduction

Much concern is expressed about the environmental hazard posed by the presence of hydrophobic organic compounds (HOCs) in soil-water systems. Among the methods proposed for decontamination is treatment with surfactant solutions (Chambers 1991). Treatment may be carried out either *in situ*, in which case it is termed surfactant soil flushing, or *ex situ*, in which case it is termed surfactant soil washing. Surfactant soil flushing involves flooding the contaminated zone with surfactant solution which, via a number of mechanisms, mobilizes the contaminants, which are then brought to the surface by strategically placed extraction wells. Surfactant soil washing requires that the contaminated material be excavated prior to treatment. Surfactants are amphiphilic molecules, consisting of a hydrophilic moiety, commonly referred to as the head group, and a hydrophobic moiety, usually termed the tail group, which are distinguished from other amphiphiles by their high degree of surface activity (the word surfactant is a contraction of the term *surf*ace *act*ive age*nt*). The surfactants used in this investigation, Synperonic PE surfactants, are unusual in having two hydrophilic groups attached to a central hydrophobic group. Characteristically, surfactants self-assemble in aqueous solution into clusters called micelles, often roughly spherical in shape, in which the hydrophilic components are directed outward into the aqueous phase, and the hydrophobic portions form a nonpolar interior 'pseudophase' (a schematic diagram of Synperonic PE micellization is given in Fig. 1). The lowest concentration at which this self-assembly, or aggregation, takes place is termed the critical micelle concentration or CMC, and is in the range 0.1–10 mM for most surfactants (West & Harwell 1992). The micellar pseudophase provides a compartment into which hydrophobic solutes may favourably partition. This phenomenon, termed solubilization, accounts for the utility of surfactants in enhancing the apparent aqueous solubility of hydrophobic organic compounds and provides the main mechanism by which it is proposed surfactants could remove such compounds from contaminated soils. Operations in the field have yielded mixed results (Nash 1987, Sale *et al.* 1989), and the use of surfactants in this application remains at the developmental stage. In this context a study was initiated to evaluate systematically the potential utility of the Synperonic PE range of nonionic surfactants in the decontamination of soils. Synperonic PE surfactants, also known as Pluronics and Poloxamers, are ABA block copolymers of ethylene oxide (the A blocks) and propylene oxide (the B block), in which the central polypropylene oxide (PPO) segments form the hydrophobic portion of the molecule, and to which the hydrophilic end polyethylene oxide (PEO) blocks confer aqueous solubility. They find wide use in industry as rinse aids, emulsifiers and antifoams, are of low toxicity, and are commercially available as a series of products with a range of PPO and PEO block lengths. In common with other polyoxyethylenated surfactants, aqueous solutions of these polymers become turbid at a temperature known as the cloud point, which signals

PATERSON, I. F., CHOWDHRY, B. Z. & LEHARNE, S. A. 1998. An initial evaluation of Synperonic PE surfactants as soil washing agents. *In*: LERNER, D. N. & WALTON, N. R. G. (eds) 1998. *Contaminated Land and Groundwater: Future Directions*. Geological Society, London, Engineering Geology Special Publications, **14**, 227–233.

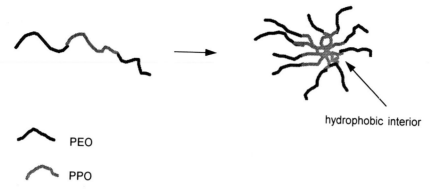

hydrophobic interior

⌒ PEO

⌒ PPO

Fig. 1. Schematic illustration of Synperonic PE micellisation.

the onset of separation of the solution into two phases. Key properties to be considered in evaluating a surfactant in this application are its sorption to the soil medium and its ability to disperse soil particles, lower surface and interfacial tensions, and solubilize the contaminants of interest. Soil sorption and solubilization properties are the focus of the present study. The extent to which six Synperonic PE surfactants spanning a range of compositions enhanced the aqueous solubility of a model hydrophobic contaminant (naphthalene) in the absence of soil was determined, and the sorption behaviour of several of these surfactants to a well characterized uncontaminated sandy soil examined. Experiments were also carried out to investigate the partitioning of naphthalene, phenanthrene and pyrene between soil and surfactant solutions at a number of concentrations.

Experimental

Synperonic PE surfactants, the chemical compositions of which are detailed in Table 1 were obtained as a gift from ICI Surfactants (Cleveland, UK). Key characteristics of the surfactants may be inferred from the system of nomenclature used: the initial letter denotes the physical state of the polymer (F = flake, P = paste,

Table 1. *Composition of the Synperonic PE surfactants studied*

	Molar mass	Molar mass of PPO	% of PEO
L92	3 450	2 750	20
P103	4 950	3 250	30
P84	4 200	2 250	40
P105	6 500	3 250	50
F127	12 000	4 000	70
F108	14 000	3 250	80

L = liquid), the last figure represents the w/w% content of polyethylene oxide and the remaining figures denote the mass of the polypropylene oxide block on an arbitrary scale. Naphthalene, phenanthrene and pyrene were obtained from Aldrich (Gillingham, Dorset), and used without further purification. A well characterized uncontaminated sandy soil of organic carbon content 0.6% was obtained from Agrisearch UK Ltd (Wilson, Derbyshire) and air-dried prior to use.

The solubilization experiments were carried out by preparing saturated solutions of naphthalene as follows: 2 ml ambered glass vials were filled with aqueous solutions of the surfactant in the range 0.1–8 w/v%. A single crystal of naphthalene was placed in each solution and the vials sealed with open-topped screw caps fitted with Teflon-backed septa. The vials were placed in a rotary shaker and shaken at 100 rev min^{-1} at 25°C for 24 h, and the saturated solution injected directly into a high performance liquid chromatograph (Phillips Pye Unicam PU4100) fitted with a UV detector (Phillips Pye Unicam 4020) and a Spherisorb ODS-5 column. Dilution of the naphthalene solution with methanol prior to injection was occasionally required to bring the naphthalene concentration to within the calibration range.

The soil sorption experiments were carried out as follows: 15 g soil was weighed into 14 100 ml Erlenmeyer flasks. Fifty grams of each of 14 solutions of surfactant prepared in the concentration range 3×10^{-3} to 6 w/v% was added to the flasks which were then sealed with Parafilm and placed in a rotary shaker at 100 rev min^{-1} for 24 h at 25°C. After a period of 60 h, during which the contents of the flasks were allowed to settle, the surface tension of the supernatant was measured using the ring method of DuNuoy with a digital tensiometer (White Electrical Instrument Co. Ltd., Model DB2ks). Comparison the surface tension of the surfactant solutions before and after equilibration with the soil enabled the amount of surfactant sorbed onto the soil to be calculated.

The partitioning of three polyaromatic hydrocarbons (PAHs) between soil and surfactant solutions were determined by weighing 2.23 g soil and 7.42 g of surfactant solution into Pyrex tissue culture tubes of approximate volume 8.9 ml. A stock solution (50 μl) of either naphthalene, phenanthrene or pyrene in acetonitrile was injected into the solution, and the tubes were sealed with Teflon lined screw caps, placed in a rotary shaker, and shaken at 100 rev min^{-1} at 25°C for 24 h. By reference to the solubilization data from this study and that of Hurter & Hatton (1992), and the work of Liu et al. (1991) on the estimation of the sorption capacity of soils for PAHs, it was ensured that the amount of PAH added did not exceed the combined capacity of the soil and surfactant for PAH (i.e. no separate phase PAH was present in the tubes). The solution phase was separated from the soil by centrifugation and filtering through a 0.45 μm PTFE syringe filter (Gelman Sciences), and analysed for solute using the HPLC method described for the solubilization experiments above.

Results and discussion

A plot of enhanced solubilization of naphthalene (the ratio of the solubility of naphthalene in the surfactant solution to its aqueous solubility) against surfactant concentration for three of the surfactants studied is given in Fig. 2. For each of the surfactants (including those not shown in Fig. 2) the plot may be divided into two regions. As the surfactant concentration increases beyond that at which surface tension measurements indicate the onset of micelle formation (usually between 0 and 1 w/v%, depending on the surfactant), a substantial linear increase in naphthalene solubility is observed. At lower concentrations, the increase in naphthalene solubility as a function of surfactant concentration is more modest, though still significant (a fivefold increase in aqueous solubility in the case of P103). This enhancement of solute solubility below the nominal critical micelle concentration has been observed for molecularly non-homogeneous alkyl ethoxylate and alkylphenol ethoxylate surfactants (Kile & Chiou 1989), and has been ascribed to successive micellization of the separate molecular components. Synperonic PE surfactants are polydisperse and contain PEO-PPO diblock impurities, and are thought to micellize in a similar manner (Alexandridis & Hatton 1995). In the context of soil remediation, it appears likely that they would be capable of mobilizing contaminants at sub-CMC concentrations. The data are in reasonable agreement with an earlier study of the solubilizing power of these polymers (Hurter & Hatton 1992). It is apparent from both studies that solubilization power increases as a function of decreasing weight percentage PEO content (i.e. increasing percentage PPO content) of the surfactant.

The increase in solute solubility with increasing surfactant concentration above the CMC may be expressed as the molar solubilization ratio (MSR) (Edwards et al. 1991), defined as the number of moles of solute solubilized per mole of surfactant in micelle form. MSR generally increases with weight percentage PPO content (Fig. 3), those surfactants having a central PPO block of molar mass 3250 (P103, P105 and F108) exhibiting a linear relationship. The deviation of F127 and P84 from linearity confirms the conclusion of Hurter and Hatton that solubilization also increases as a function of the molar mass of the central PPO hydrophobe (L92 was above its cloud point at the concentrations studied, and its unexpectedly high MSR is possibly accounted for by

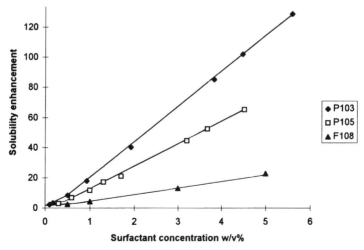

Fig. 2. Solubility enhancement of naphthalene by P103, P105 and F108.

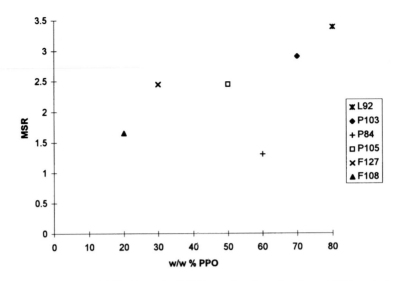

Fig. 3. Molar solubilisation ratio (MSR) as a function of surfactant PPO content.

the increase in micellar size which is thought to coincide with the clouding of polyoxyethylenated surfactants (Rosen 1978).

Sorption experiments using a soil/surfactant solution ratio of $0.3\,\mathrm{g\,g^{-1}}$ were performed on four of the surfactants (F108, F127, P103 and L92). Surface tension is plotted against the log of surfactant dose, defined as the concentration of surfactant in the solution prior to equilibration with soil. An example is given in Fig. 4 with data obtained in the absence of soil plotted on the same axes. The difference between surfactant concentrations interpolated at a given surface tension value from

each plot in Fig. 4 when multiplied by the ratio of the solution mass to the mass of soil, gives Q_g, the mass of surfactant sorbed per unit mass of soil. This may be plotted against the concentration of surfactant in the supernatant, C, to yield an adsorption isotherm. A linear plot are obtained if the data are plotted as a Freundlich isotherm of the form:

$$Q_g = KC^{1/n}$$

The parameters $\log K$ and n are given in Table 2 and examples of Freundlich isotherm plots in Fig. 5.

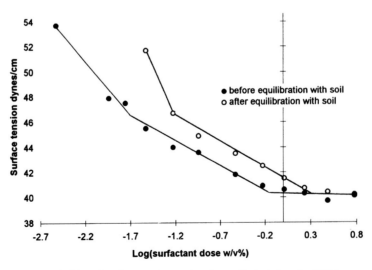

Fig. 4. Plot of surface tension against log surfactant dose for F108.

Table 2. *Experimental parameters obtained from surface tension measurements*

	cmc w/v%	n	log K	Q_{max} (g g^{-1})
L92	1.24	1.18	0.58	0.032
P103	0.41	1.68	−0.047	0.012
F127	0.53	1.17	1.14	0.017
F108	0.83	1.11	1.52	0.035

The values of n are all between 1 and 2 which is in accordance with values obtained by Liu *et al.* (1992) for the absorption of micelle-forming nonionic surfactants to soil of organic carbon content 0.96%. In the same study, it was found that micelles did not sorb onto soil, and thus that the maximum value of Q_g obtained from the surface tension data (at the point in the surface tension versus surfactant dose plots corresponding to the CMC at which the gradient changes sharply to zero) represented the maximum amount of surfactant sorbed onto the soil, denoted Q_{max}. If the system presently under investigation behaves similarly, the values of Q_g at the CMC for the four surfactants studied may be designated as Q_{max} values. With the caveat that such an assumption would require experimental verification, values of Q_{max} are given in Table 2. Since sorption of surfactant will cease once the surfactant concentration in the bulk solution phase has reached the point at which micelles will form, it might be expected that surfactants having low CMCs might also have low Q_{max} values. The rather limited data set in Table 2 would tend to confirm

this hypothesis. It is also apparent that the amounts of surfactant sorbed will represent a significant addition to the organic carbon content of the soil. The impact of this on soil decontamination would be largely dependent upon the effectiveness of the sorbed surfactant as a sorptive phase for hydrophobic contaminants. These data are not available at present, but could potentially be determined using the model of Sun *et al.* (1995).

P103, having exhibited good solubility enhancement and relatively low sorption to soil, was selected as potentially the most useful of the surfactants studied, and its effect on the partitioning of naphthalene between soil and water was determined. Data for P105 and F108 was also obtained. A plot of fraction of naphthalene against surfactant dose – the original concentration of the surfactant solution added to the system – is given in Fig. 6. It is evident that P103 provides the most favourable partitioning medium for naphthalene, and is also similarly effective in the case of phenanthrene and pyrene (Fig. 7). The data presented in Figs 6 and 7 appear to show qualitative agreement with models proposed to describe similar systems (Edwards *et al.* 1994; Sun *et al.* 1995).

Conclusion

P103, having the lowest CMC and amongst the highest MSRs of the surfactants studied, would appear to be potentially the most useful in respect of soil decontamination. Current work in the authors' laboratories

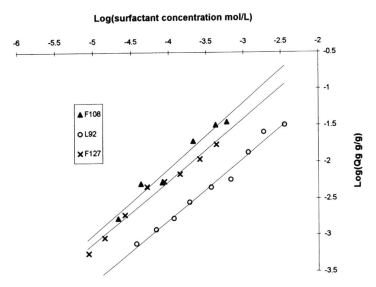

Fig. 5. Sub-CMC Freundlich isotherms.

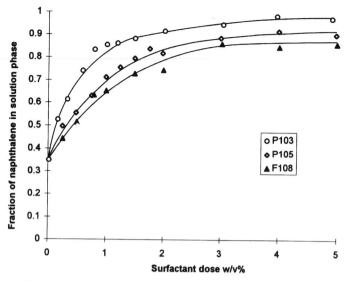

Fig. 6. Fraction of naphthalene in solution phase vs. surfactant dose.

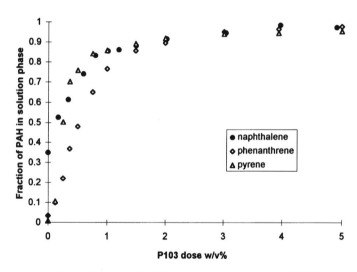

Fig. 7. Fraction of PAH in solution phase vs. dose of P103.

suggests that P103 is as effective in washing coal-tar contaminated soils as Triton X-100, an alkylphenol ethoxylate surfactant which has previously been identified as a potential soil washing agent (Yeom *et al.* 1995, 1996). Concern has been expressed as to the oestrogenic effects of alkylphenol ethoxylates and their breakdown products on fish and mammals (Soto *et al.* 1991; Jobling & Sumpter 1993); the low toxicity of P103 and the other Synperonic PE surfactants may thus prove advantageous in environmental applications.

References

ALEXANDRIDIS, P. & HATTON, T. A. 1995. *Colloids Surfaces, A: Physicochemical and Engineering Aspects*, **96**, 1.

CHAMBERS, D. (ed.) 1991. *In Situ Treatment of Hazardous Waste Contaminated Soils* (2nd edition). Noyes Data Corporation, New Jersey.

EDWARDS, D.A, LUTHY, R. G. & LIU, Z. 1991. *Environ. Sci. Technol.*, **25**, 127.

——, LIU, Z. & LUTHY, R. G. 1994. *J. Environ. Eng.*, **120**, 5.

HURTER, P. N. & HATTON, T. A. 1992. *Langmuir*, **8**, 1291.

KILE, D. E. & CHIOU, C. T. 1989. *Environ. Sci. Technol.*, **23**, 832.

JOBLING, S. & SUMPTER, J. P. 1993. *Aquatic Toxicology*, **27**, 361.

LIU, Z., LAHA, S. & LUTHY, R. G. 1991. *Wat. Sci. Tech.*, **23**, 475.

——, EDWARDS, D. A. & LUTHY, R. G. 1992. *Wat. Res.*, **26**, 1337.

NASH, J. H. 1987. *Field studies of* in situ *soil washing*. EPA/600/2–87/110, US Environmental Protection Agency, Edison, NJ.

ROSEN, M. J. 1978. *Surfactants and Interfacial Phenomena*. Wiley, New York.

SALE, T., PIONTEK, K. & PITTS, M. 1989. Chemically enhanced *in situ* soil washing. *In: Proc. Conf. on Petrol. hydrocarbons* and Organic Chem. in Ground Water. Water Well J. Pub. Co., Worthington, OH, 487–503.

SOTO, A. M., JUSTICIA, H., WRAY, J. W. & SONNENSCHEIN, C. 1991. *Environ. Health Perspect.*, **92**, 167.

SUN, S., INSKEEP, W. P. & BOYD, S. A. 1995. *Environ. Sci. and Technol.*, **29**, 903.

WEST, C. C. & HARWELL, J. H. 1992. *Environ. Sci. and Technol.*, **26**, 2324.

YEOM, I. T., GHOSH, M. M., COX, C. D. & ROBINSON, K. G. 1995. *Environ. Sci. Technol.*, **29**, 3015.

YEOM, I. T., GHOSH, M. M. & COX, C. D. 1996. *Environ. Sci. Technol.*, **30**, 1589.

The relevance of a DNAPL-tracer test conducted at Base Borden, Canada, to solvent groundwater contamination in the UK

Michael O. Rivett,[1] Stan Feenstra[2] & John A. Cherry[2]

[1] School of Earth Sciences, University of Birmingham, Edgbaston, Birmingham B15 2TT, UK
[2] Waterloo Centre for Groundwater Research, University of Waterloo, Waterloo, Ontario N2L 3G1, Canada

Abstract. The relevance of key conclusions obtained from a tracer test performed at the Base Borden research site in Canada to solvent contamination in the UK is indicated. The tracer test represented a world unique opportunity to study groundwater contamination arising from a known DNAPL source zone in a natural aquifer environment. The test involved the controlled emplacement of a source zone of residual solvent DNAPL (dense non-aqueous phase liquid) below the water table from which a dissolved plume of chlorinated solvents developed. Significant data were collected on DNAPL dissolution, plume transport and remediation. Conclusions from the test are shown to be relevant to the development, investigation and remediation of solvent contamination in UK aquifers.

Introduction

Groundwater contamination by chlorinated solvents has been reported in the UK (Rivett *et al.* 1990; Burston *et al.* 1993) and wider industrialized world. Contamination is attributed to widespread historical solvent use, deep penetration of DNAPL into aquifers and solvent persistency and mobility in most groundwater environments. Although some notable solvents research has been conducted in the UK (Lawrence *et al.* 1990; Lerner 1993), larger research programmes have been undertaken abroad, particularly in North America. The prompt introduction of groundwater legislation in the US has instigated much groundwater investigation and remediation, and driven associated programmes of research.

Key conclusions from a DNAPL-tracer test conducted at the Base Borden field research site in Canada are indicated and their relevance to UK solvent contamination discussed. Details of the test have been reported (Rivett *et al.* 1994; Rivett 1995) and are to be reported elsewhere (Rivett *et al.* in prep.). The experiment was conducted by the authors as part of the Waterloo Centre for Groundwater Research 'Solvents-in-Groundwater Research Program' that has been on-going since 1989. The programme is a multi-million dollar initiative funded by a consortium of North American industrial and government sponsors.

The tracer test was conducted in the shallow unconfined glaciolacustrine sand aquifer at Base Borden. The test involved the controlled emplacement of a block-shaped source zone of residual chlorinated solvent DNAPL below the water table. DNAPL within the 'emplaced source' (ES) comprised a mixture of the chlorinated solvents: TCM, TCE and PCE (trichloromethane [chloroform], trichoroethene and perchloroethene respectively). Groundwater flow through the source caused slow dissolution of its residual DNAPL and development of a continuous dissolved solvent plume down-gradient. Figure 1 indicates the principal phases of the 'ES test': the natural gradient tracer test; pump-and-treat remediation; and, passive source zone control remediation.

Over 2000 groundwater monitoring points enabled 3-D 'snapshots' of the dissolved plume to be produced during the 420-day natural groundwater gradient tracer test. Remediation of the resulting 60 m-long dissolved plume and control of the contamination continuing to dissolve from the DNAPL source was then attempted. Remediation was initially accomplished by pump-and-treat and later by a passive permeable reaction wall. Regular monitoring of the remediation and on-going DNAPL dissolution was continued until three years after the original source installation and terminated in late 1992.

Key conclusions from the ES test on DNAPL dissolution, dissolved plume transport and remediation are reviewed and their relevance to the UK indicated. Conclusions from the ES test are not necessarily original in all instances, but may conveniently provide corroborative field-scale evidence for similar conclusions derived from other research, or observations that have been made at real sites.

RIVETT, M. O., FEENSTRA, S. & CHERRY, J. A. 1998. The relevance of a DNAPL-tracer test conducted at Base Borden Canada to solvent groundwater contamination in the UK. *In:* LERNER, D. N. & WALTON, N. R. G. (eds) 1998. *Contaminated Land and Groundwater: Future Directions.* Geological Society, London, Engineering Geology Special Publications, **14**, 235–241.

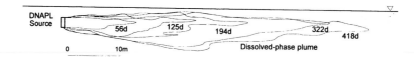

(a) DNAPL dissolution and dissolved plume natural gradient tracer test.

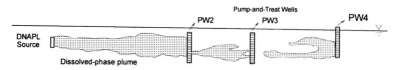

(b) Pump-and-treat remediation and continued DNAPL dissolution.

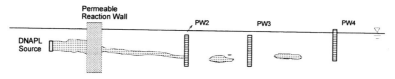

(c) Passive source zone control and continued pump-and-treat remediation.

Fig. 1. Overview of the Emplaced Source tracer test and remediation. Plumes depicted are based on data for TCM. Vertical exageration ×1.75.

Tracer test conclusions

DNAPL dissolution

Conclusions concerning DNAPL dissolution are illustrated in Fig. 2(a), which shows the expected dissolution of the DNAPL source extrapolated from three years of monitoring data, and Fig. 2(b) provides an example of dissolved concentrations 1 m down-gradient of the DNAPL source. Key DNAPL dissolution conclusions are as follows:

- Dissolution is a fundamental process controlling dissolved plume generation.
- Dissolution may occur at equilibrium (effective) solubiity concentrations.
- Macro-scale effects may inhibit dissolution and promote source longevity.
- Estimation of DNAPL source zone dissolution rates is difficult.

The rate of DNAPL dissolution exerts a fundamental control over the generation of dissolved solvent plumes. Although the volume of DNAPL originally in the source

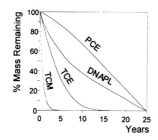

(a) Estimated source dissolution.

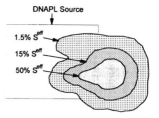

(b) Source dissolved concentrations.

Fig. 2. (a) Estimated long term dissolution of Emplaced Source DNAPL; and, (b) example of dissolved TCE concentrations observed in a fence of groundwater monitoring located 1 m down gradient of DNAPL source zone (contoured as % of TCE effective solubility).

was low (15 l, 8% of a drum), slow dissolution resulted in only 23% of the DNAPL being depleted after three years. The DNAPL was estimated to take 25 years to fully dissolve and cease plume generation.

Dissolved solvent concentrations in groundwater that is in equilibrium with a multi-component DNAPL are theoretically expected to follow a modification of Raoult's Law:

$$S_i^{eff} = X_i \times S_i \qquad (1)$$

Hence, for any individual solvent component of the DNAPL, its maximum equilibrium dissolved concentration 'effective solubility' (S_i^{eff}) is always expected to be less than its pure phase solubility (S_i) and will vary in relation to its mole fraction (X_i) remaining in the depleting DNAPL. Maximum dissolved concentrations monitored in the DNAPL source and 1 m downgradient were similar to the effective solubility values predicted by Raoult's Law. Solvent dissolution trends were also consistent with Raoult's Law, TCM being fully dissolved, TCE partially dissolved, and PCE little dissolved and largely responsible for the extended DNAPL lifetime. Dissolution research has suggested groundwater–DNAPL contact times on the order of an hour are usually sufficient for equilibrium solubility (single component DNAPL), or equilibrium effective solubility (multi-component DNAPL) concentrations to be achieved. Less than equilibrium concentrations would only occur in groundwater exiting DNAPL when the groundwater velocity is very high, DNAPL path length is short, or residual DNAPL saturations are low. Sufficient contact time would be expected with the ES DNAPL for equilibrium to occur.

Figure 2(b), however, indicates that the area of concentrations at or close to effective solubility 1 m down-gradient of the DNAPL was limited in comparison to the size of the DNAPL source suggesting effects that inhibit DNAPL dissolution and promote source longevity. These were thought to relate to macro-scale rather than pore-scale dissolution effects. The observations were primarily attributed to groundwater flow around the DNAPL source zone due its permeability to groundwater being approximately 0.3 of the mean permeability measured in the surrounding natural aquifer material. This arose from the incorporation of gypsum powder in the source to provide conservative sulphate tracer and to a lesser extent the presence of DNAPL residual. Additionally, cores from the source suggest that 'dissolution fingers' had developed, these being pathways through the source of preferential dissolution and hence depletion. Fingers were thought to be due to surrounding aquifer heterogeneity and minor spatial variability of DNAPL within the source. Concurrently, some parts of the source had received comparatively little dissolution and may cause long-term low levels of dissolved solvents to the aquifer (i.e. 'concentration tailing'), and even prolong the source lifetime beyond that estimated in Fig. 2(a).

The above illustrates that even for a relatively well characterized source zone, the estimation of DNAPL source zone dissolution rates and lifetimes is difficult. At real sites where the mass of DNAPL spilt and its distribution is almost always unknown, prediction of source dissolution rates and lifetimes is expected to be extremely onerous, if not impossible.

Plume dispersion

Conclusions concerning plume dispersion are illustrated in Fig. 3, which shows plan and longitudinal views of a narrow TCM plume that exhibited near-conservative transport behaviour. Key plume dispersion conclusions are as follows:

- longitudinal dispersion is comparable to other tracer tests of similar scale;
- transverse dispersion (vertical and horizontal) is very weak;

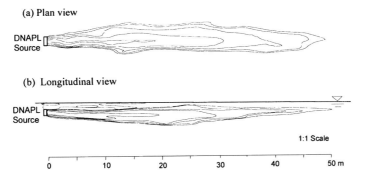

Fig. 3. TCM plume developed from the Emplaced Source DNAPL after 322 days. Contours shown at 0.01, 0.1, 1, 10 and 100 mg/l.

- groundwater flow field transience induced significant lateral plume movement;
- the above results in narrow, shifting plumes that are difficult to monitor.

The ES test yielded a longitudinal dispersivity on the order of 0.5 m and a transverse vertical dispersivity of about 1 mm, i.e. on the order of diffusion coefficients. These compare to previous Borden dispersion measurements (Rajaram & Gelhar 1991). The horizontal transverse dispersivity was also found to be very low at just 1.5 mm, much reduced from a previous Borden value of 5 cm obtained at a site located about 100 m away. The latter value did not explicitly account for the effects of groundwater flow field transience, whereas the former did. The dynamic groundwater flow regime (39° range at the ES site) produced limited lateral spreading of the ES plume, a dispersivity of 0.7 cm being required to fit the plume if groundwater flow transience is not explicitly modelled. The value is still much smaller than the previous Borden test and is attributed to the more dynamic flow regime that has since been measured at that site.

Transience in the groundwater flow regime also induced significant lateral ES plume movement. Movements tended to be gradual events exhibited over seasonal timescales. The combination of lateral plume shifts and weakness of transverse horizontal dispersion caused monitoring difficulties. The laterally shifting plume caused some monitored concentrations, that would have otherwise been expected to remain constant, to decline from elevated concentrations to near-detection limit. These observations indicate the fundamental control of the temporal groundwater flow regime on plume transport.

Plume retardation

Key conclusions from the ES test concerning plume retardation are as follows:

- Dissolved plumes were very mobile.
- Simple retardation calculations gave reasonable mobility estimates.
- Mobility was enhanced by competitive solute and non-linear sorption.
- Sorption is a complex process and elucidation of sorption aspects is difficult.

All solvent plumes were very mobile with retardation factors (R) measured after 322 days of TCM 1.03, TCE 1.1, and PCE 1.7. Plume appearances after 322 days transport were similar to those illustrated for TCM in Fig. 3 but with plume fronts at 33 m for PCE and 41 m for TCE, compared to 48 m for TCM. R values are consistent with the relative hydrophobicities of these compounds, the most hydrophobic compounds TCM and TCE exhibiting close to conservative behaviour.

Minimal retardation and longitudinal dispersion resulted in all plume fronts at 322 days travelling in advance of the mean groundwater transport distance of 27.2 m equivalent to a groundwater velocity of 8.4 cm day^{-1}.

Although sorption behaviour is recognized as being highly complex, application of the simple physiochemical based equations below predicted R values close to those measured on site:

$$R = \frac{\textit{Velocity of groundwater}}{\textit{Velocity of contaminant}} = 1 + \frac{\rho_b}{n} K_d;$$

$$K_d = f_{oc} \times K_{oc} \tag{2}$$

where ρ_b is dry bulk density; n is porosity; K_d is the sorbed-aqueous dissolved phase distribution coefficient; f_{oc} is organic carbon content; K_{oc} is organic carbon-water partition coefficient.

There are many reasons why such calculations should not apply to the Borden site, most notable being that the f_{oc} of 0.04% is well below the recognized level at which hydrophobic f_{oc} partitioning is dominant. Although sorption to mineral surfaces, both inter- and intra-granular, is thought dominant at Borden (Ball & Roberts 1991), the above equations gave reliable retardation estimates.

The R for PCE of 1.7 was much lower than previous Borden field estimates, which were found to be in the range 2.7 to 5.9 (Roberts et al. 1986). It is probable that orders of magnitude higher concentrations present in the ES test caused plume mobility enhancements due to the effects of sorption isotherm non-linearity and multi-solute competitive sorption (Rivett et al. in prep).

The ES test was not ideally suited to the investigation of the various nuances of sorption. In addition to the above effects, other sorption processes previously observed at Borden were expected to operate, including non-equilibrium sorption and spatial variability of sorption. Concurrent operation of many sorption processes means that the elucidation of individual processes is difficult and would be better addressed through experiments having less variables to consider.

Remediation

Conclusions concerning the pump-and-treat (P&T) and permeable reaction wall remediations are illustrated in Figs 1 and 4. Figs 1(b) and 1(c) depict areas of TCM contamination remaining after 100 and 400 days of P&T. Figure 4 indicates concentration variations at pumping well PW2 that is located closest to the DNAPL source. Key remediation conclusions are as follows:

- successful P&T removal of dissolved plume;
- several factors significantly inhibited P&T dissolved plume remediation;

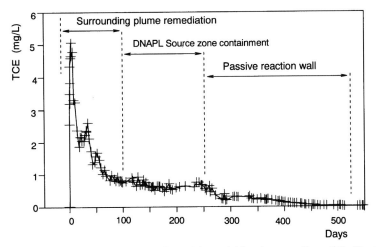

Fig. 4. Variation of TCE concentrations in P-&-T well PW2 located 25 m down gradient of the Emplaced Source DNAPL.

- successful P&T DNAPL source zone containment;
- successful demonstration of novel source zone containment technology.

P&T successfully remediated the dissolved plume located in the aquifer down-gradient of PW2. The total solvent mass extracted by the P&T in this zone was within 2% of the mass estimated to be present at the termination of the natural gradient tracer test. Figure 1(c) indicates that only localized zones of low concentration contamination remained in this zone following the P&T.

The P&T dissolved plume remediation was inhibited by factors such as (i) low groundwater flow through hydraulic stagnation zones created between pumping wells; (ii) increased sorption of more hydrophobic solvents, e.g. PCE; (iii) non-equilibrium desorption; and (iv) slow release of contaminants from low permeability horizons. These cause the gradual 'tailing' decline in PW2 concentrations observed between 0 and 150 days in Fig. 4 the irregular concentration distribution in Fig. 1(b) and persistent concentrations in Fig. 1(c). To achieve drinking water standards in groundwater abstracted at PW3 and PW4, a volume of water many times the original contaminated plume volume had to be abstracted. After 100 days, 20 plume volumes had been abstracted and drinking water standards still not attained.

PW2 concentrations plateau at levels two orders of magnitude greater than typical drinking water standards between 150 and 250 days. The plateau is attributed to PW2 functioning as a source zone containment well that successfully captured contamination continuing to dissolve from the DNAPL source. Since the P&T did not increase groundwater velocities through the DNAPL zone and hence dissolution rates, PW2 would have to be pumped for 13 years to contain TCE and 25 years for PCE in accordance with the estimated DNAPL dissolution profiles in Fig. 2.

The longevity of DNAPL sources emphasizes the need for more passive source zone containment technologies, or technologies that destroy or remove the DNAPL. Figure 1(c) indicates the installation of a passive permeable reaction wall at the ES site. The wall caused abiotic reductive dechlorination of solvents by zero valence iron to occur (Gillham & O'Hannesin 1994). This represents the first field trial of this technology and achieved 85–90% removal of solvents and caused the decline in PW2 TCE concentrations observed 150 days after P&T started. A thicker wall with increased residence time may have potentially resulted in 100% solvent removal.

Relevance to UK

In general, ES test conclusions will directly apply to UK aquifers that are similar to the Borden aquifer, e.g. shallow alluvial or drift aquifers of a unconsolidated sandy nature. However, most major UK aquifers (sandstone, limestone, chalk) differ from the Borden aquifer in being consolidated with significant dual porosity nature. Nevertheless, ES test conclusions may still be relevant to such environments and aid understanding of solvent contamination and its remediation. Since most solvent contamination present in UK aquifers has likely entered as a DNAPL, the DNAPL dissolution, plume transport and remediation studied in the ES test are expected to be highly relevant. The relevance of these aspects is indicated below.

DNAPL dissolution

Providing that flowing groundwater can access DNAPL with contact times exceeding perhaps 1 h, then solubility for single component DNAPL, or effective solubility for multi-component DNAPL may be expected in the groundwater that exits from DNAPL residual zones or pools. In practice, however, solubility concentrations are rarely measured in monitoring wells. This may be due to the scale and position of the monitoring well in relation to the DNAPL, or as observed in the ES test, relate to effects that cause reduced groundwater contact with the DNAPL.

At many UK sites DNAPL may have been dissolving for decades with the result that preferential dissolution of DNAPL has occurred in the more conductive horizons or fractures and 'dissolution fingers' developed. Remaining DNAPL may be difficult to access in low permeability horizons or partially isolated pools, such sources potentially resulting in less than solubility concentrations observed a short distance down-gradient, concentration tailing and enhanced source zone longevity. In fractured aquifers, research by Parker *et al.* (1994) suggests that much of the DNAPL originally present in fractures may diffuse into the porous matrix. Back diffusion of matrix solvent to groundwater flowing through the fractures may then represent a long-term, tailing source of dissolved contamination. In many UK aquifers depletion of DNAPL sources may be expected to take decades. Accurate predictions of source lifetimes should not be expected as the mass of DNAPL present is invariably unknown and its distribution and dissolution rate very difficult to establish.

Plume dispersion

Major UK aquifers are generally fracture flow dominated and the ES test dispersion parameters inappropriate. However, many UK contaminated land investigations focus on shallow porous media aquifers for which the measured parameters may be appropriate. Of particular note is the weakness in transverse dispersion that causes plumes to develop of a width little greater than the dimensions of generating DNAPL sources. As DNAPL is often discretely distributed, vertically and horizontally, plumes generated may be easily missed by monitoring wells. The same may also be true of the fractured major aquifers where plumes may often be expected to occupy a relatively narrow zone in relation to the scale of the aquifer. Monitoring of the Sawston incident (Lawrence & Foster 1991) failed to fully track the plume between its potential source and impacted supply borehole.

Groundwater flow field transience resulting from variations in abstraction and seasonal conditions may also cause difficulties in plume delineation and marked changes in monitored concentrations. For example, once borehole supplies are contaminated, abstraction often ceases and the plume may shift laterally in response to the new groundwater flow field. Accurate delineation of the temporal groundwater flow field is a paramount requirement to the effective delineation of plumes.

Plume retardation

Due to the intrinsic low hydrophobicity of chlorinated solvents, dissolved solvent plumes are expected to be amongst the most mobile of organic contaminant plumes present in aquifers. They are considered to be highly mobile compared to many other contaminants, e.g. diesel, PAHs and PCBs. Simple retardation calculations may not give accurate absolute R; however, approximate relative mobilities of organic contaminants may be indicated and useful as a preliminary mobility estimate.

Although the Borden f_{oc} is low, it is not atypical of values encountered in the UK. Foster *et al.* (1991), amongst others, indicate f_{oc} to be typically in the range 0.02–0.2%. The intrinsic sorption potential of many UK aquifers like Borden may be expected to be low, and mineral sorption may dominate over f_{oc} hydrophobic partitioning. R values of 1.5–3 for TCE and 3–5 for PCE obtained during laboratory column experiments on Coventry Carboniferous sandstones (Bourg *et al.* 1993) confirm the high mobility of these dissolved solvents, in spite of a relatively elevated sample f_{oc} of 0.7%. They indicate sorption to both organic f_{oc} phase and mineral phase to be limited, with the latter being dominant. As at Borden, sorption in most UK environments is likely to be a complex process and accurate estimation of R values difficult.

Remediation

The ES test P&T conclusions generally apply to the application of this type of remediation in the UK. Remediations attempted at the ES site and real sites in North America have shown that P&T is capable of removing dissolved plumes and achieving DNAPL source zone containment. Dissolved plume remediation down to typical drinking water standards is, however, onerous, requiring pumping of groundwater volumes that greatly exceed initial plume volumes. Given that many of the UK major aquifers are already fully developed in terms of their water resource potential, employing P&T wells along plume lengths is probably not realistic unless the cleaned groundwater is re-injected. Well head treatment at the contaminated supply borehole with an associated P&T source zone containment well that prevents continued generation of the groundwater plume may represent the most effective and practical remedial option.

P&T is unlikely to achieve rapid removal of the DNAPL source zones; containment wells may be expected to pump for years, if not decades, to deplete DNAPL present. It is thus preferable to develop passive source zone containment technologies (permeable reaction or cut-off walls), or *in situ* technologies that accelerate DNAPL remediation (e.g. chemical oxidation, surfactant or alcohol flushing, steam displacement, air sparging, bioremediation, vapour extraction). Prospects of successfully applying such technologies in deep, consolidated UK aquifers would appear remote at present.

Conclusions

Conclusions from the ES test are shown to be relevant to the development, investigation and remediation of solvent contamination in the UK. DNAPL in aquifers may be expected to generate dissolved plumes that are highly mobile, relatively narrow and difficult to monitor. DNAPL may act as a very long-term contamination source, lasting decades, and although dissolved plumes may be removed by pump-and-treat, albeit slowly, the removal of DNAPL source zones is not presently possible. At present, although novel DNAPL remediation technologies are being developed, most are unproven at the field- or site-scale and their application to deep, consolidated UK aquifers that are often fractured is in doubt. P&T source zone containment wells are the only method presently available that may be anticipated to reliably contain the effects of DNAPL source zones in the UK.

Acknowledgements. The research was supported by the University Consortium Solvents-in-Groundwater Research Program sponsored by Boeing, Ciba Geigy, Eastman Kodak, General Electric, Laidlaw Environmental Services, Ontario Research Incentive Fund and the Natural Sciences & Engineering Research Council of Canada.

References

BALL, W. P. & ROBERTS, P. V. 1991. Long term sorption of halogenated organic chemicals by aquifer MATERIALS, 2. Intraparticle diffusion. *Environmental Science & Technology*, **25**(7), 1237–1249.

BOURG, A. C. M., DEGRANGES, P., MOUVET, C. & SAUTRY, J. P. 1993. Pollution of groundwater in the Coventry region (UK) by chlorinated hydrocarbon solvents. *Journal of Hydrology*, **149**, 183–207.

BURSTON, M. W., NAZARI, M. M., BISHOP, P. K. & LERNER, D. N. 1993. Pollution of groundwater in the Coventry region (UK) by chlorinated hydrocarbon solvents. *Journal of Hydrology*, **149**, 137–162.

GILLHAM, R. W. & O'HANNESIN, S. F. 1994. Enhanced degradation of halogenated aliphatics by zero-valent iron. *Ground Water*, **32**(6), 958–967.

LAWRENCE, A. R. & FOSTER, S. S. D. 1991. The legacy of aquifer pollution by industrial chemicals: technical appraisal and policy implications. *Quarterly Journal of Engineering Geology*, **24**, 231–239.

——, CHILTON, J. P., BARRON, R. J. & THOMAS, W. M. 1990. A method for determining volatile organic solvents in chalk pore waters and its relevance to the evaluation of groundwater contamination. *Journal of Contaminant Hydrogeology*, **6**, 377–386.

LERNER, D. N. (ed.) 1993. Coventry groundwater investigation: sources and movement of chlorinated hydrocarbon solvents in a consolidated sedimentary aquifer system. *Journal of Hydrology*, **149**, 111–272.

PARKER, B. L., GILLHAM, R. W. & CHERRY, J. A. 1994. Diffusive disappearance of immiscible phase organic liquids in fractured geologic media. *Ground Water*, **32**(5), 805–820.

RAJARAM, H. & GELHAR, L. W. 1991. Three dimensional spatial moments analysis of the Borden tracer test site. *Water Resources Research*, **27**(6), 1239–1251.

RIVETT, M. O. 1995. Soil-gas signatures from volatile chlorinated solvents: Borden field experiments. *Ground Water*, **33**(1), 84–98.

——, LERNER, D. N. & LLOYD, J. W. 1990. Chlorinated solvents in UK aquifers. *Journal of the Institution of Water and Environmental Management*, **4**(3), 242–250.

——, FEENSTRA, S. & CHERRY, J. A. 1994. Transport of a dissolved phase plume from a residual solvent source in a sand aquifer. Presented at the European Geophysical Society XVII Assembly, Edinburgh 1993. *Journal of Hydrology*, **159**, 27–41.

——, —— & —— in prep. A natural gradient experiment of solute transport from a residual solvent source. Series of papers in preparation for *Journal of Contaminant Hydrology*.

ROBERTS, P. V., GOLTZ, M. N. & MACKAY, D. M. 1986. A natural gradient experiment on solute transport in a sand AQUIFER, 3. Retardation estimates and mass balances for organic solutes. *Water Resources Research*, **22**(13), 2047–2058.

Index